D1478984

THE DETECTIVE-PHYSICIAN

Miniature which hangs in the Society of Apothercaries of London, painted by Miss Isabel Saul.

The Detective-Physician

The Life and Work of Sir William Willcox,
K.C.I.E., C.B., C.M.G., M.D., F.R.C.P.,
Hon. M.D. Melb., D.P.H., B.Sc., F.I.C.   1870–1941

Physician to St. Mary's Hospital, London, 1907–1935
Scientific Analyst, 1904–1919, and
Honorary Medical Adviser to the Home Office, 1919–1941

by

Philip H. A. Willcox, M.A., M.D., F.R.C.P.

WILLIAM HEINEMANN MEDICAL BOOKS LTD.

First Published 1970

ISBN 0 433 36201 4

Printed and bound in Great Britain by R. J. Acford Ltd., Industrial Estate,
Chichester, Sussex.

CONTENTS

PART 4
CRIMES, CLAIMS AND CAMPAIGNS

PART 5
THE FINAL PHASE

PREFACE

When my father died in 1941 at his London home in Welbeck Street, he bequeathed to my mother and myself an enormous quantity of scientific records carefully stored by successive secretaries throughout his career, "my confidential and scientific documents which are of value for the purpose of research and medical knowledge". One of my first duties was to preserve them safe from wartime damage while the "blitz" on London was in progress, several houses in the close vicinity having already been bombed. Through the kindness of my father-in-law, Professor George Grey Turner, I was encouraged to store them at his home at Taplow in safety while I was abroad on military service. There were many bundles of medico-legal case records, depositions, correspondence, all practice case books and typed copies of all important lectures and addresses collected since 1906.

When I was demobilised in 1946 I gradually studied the medico-legal records and spent many hours fascinated by the inside stories, not only of the Great Trials in which he gave critical evidence, but also of other cases less well known but of equal interest. To what purpose could all these records be put? I could not throw them away. If put together they would obviously make a fascinating story. Scientific progress had become so rapid that there was comparatively little material of value purely for research purposes; such as there was I passed on to others, notably Dr. G. Roche Lynch, senior Home Office Analyst. From the remainder I selected parts which were of historical value and interest, to provide the material for this book. In the writing of it I received encouragement from many people from time to time, some of whom well remembered my father at different stages of his career, in particular Sir Travers Humphreys, Dr. G. Roche Lynch and my former chief Dr. Reginald Miller, all of whom have since passed on. I much regret that I was unable to carry out this task before they died. The stresses and calls of my own practice were until recently too great to allow time for a time-consuming and strenuous mental exercise, but I am pleased to have completed the task in the centenary year of my father's birth. I have attempted to write his life as closely as possible to the way he would have chosen to write his autobiography had he survived the second world war in reasonable health. Compared with such a book most modern political biographies would have seemed dull. It would have contained more personal touches than this humble account. Nevertheless, here is described his professional life based on personal records written as far as possible from his point of view of the events. He never kept diaries in a conventional way but his records were a vast diary of an unusually interesting career. Some of his early experiences as Home Office Analyst were either destroyed or passed on to colleagues. I have myself done some personal research to fill gaps in criminal cases where his notes were incomplete and my occasional comments are written from my memory of his opinion on certain unrecorded matters.

In his periods of relaxation from work I seldom wished to intrude on his leisure by talking "shop", yet when I did he preferred to give helpful advice about my own affairs rather than to discuss his own experiences which were usually strictly confidential. Though a writer of many articles in the medical press and chapters in books he was never the sole author of any book. But it is of interest to recall that as early as 1911 he was approached by Mr. E. Arnold, the publisher, for a book on Toxicology and agreed to dedicate it to the memory of Sir Thomas Stevenson. But the project was abandoned as a result of pressure of work. Again in 1924 with Bernard Spilsbury and Roche Lynch, he planned a book on Toxicology and Forensic Medicine; they actually met at Welbeck Street on October 3rd to discuss the project, but all were too busy to embark on the task.

Throughout the twenty years between the two world wars my father was certainly one of the most popular lecturers and speakers in his profession, judged by the number of addresses and lectures he gave both to medical and lay societies, particularly on subjects of great public and national concern. Though I have studied them all I have referred here only to those considered to be the most important and interesting. His life and work were so interwoven with the affairs of others that this account can best be described as an historical biography. In particular I am thinking of his hospital colleagues and of those who formed that happy fraternity of investigators who developed Home Office pathology from its infancy—Sir Thomas Stevenson, Augustus Pepper, Arthur Luff, John Webster, Bernard Spilsbury and Gerald Roche Lynch; with all of these he had a most friendly and happy association and often paid individual tributes to them. Added together, the work of these investigators on behalf of the Home Office and police extended over a period of eighty-two years. It is worth recording that, though my father was only two years old when Stevenson was appointed Junior Analyst to the Home Office he succeeded him thirty-six years later as Senior Analyst when Sir Thomas died. He therefore was a link in toxicology between its early stages of development and the era of modern technical advances. The same friendly co-operation was maintained with the lawyers of whom the names of Sir Charles Matthews and Sir Archibald Bodkin (Directors of Public Prosecutions), Sir Richard Muir and Sir Travers Humphreys were perhaps the best known. In a somewhat different category was Sir Edward Marshall Hall, the famous defence counsel, whose several appearances in opposition to my father in Courts of Law never interrupted their personal friendship outside. Both Muir and Humphreys had consulted my father as patients on several occasions. He had enjoyed their personal friendship since the days of the Crippen case in 1910. The name of Travers Humphreys as counsel and as a judge for a period of twenty-three years is still too well known to need introduction whereas Richard Muir died too long ago (1924) to be remembered even by the older generation of present-day lawyers. He served as Treasury Counsel for the

greater part of his career, and was regarded by my father and his con-
temporaries as the greatest criminal lawyer of his time. He was appointed
a judge a short time before his death.

By careful study I have selected new material—and hitherto unpublished
—concerning the Great Trials in which my father took part and have
described these cases from a scientific standpoint in contrast to earlier
accounts written by lawyers and professional writers.

I am pleased to be able to throw new light on Sir Bernard Spilsbury's
work by including several cases in which he took part, the records not
having been at hand at the time I loaned material to the writers of his
interesting biography published in 1951.

It is hoped that this work will be of interest to doctors (including
Psychiatrists), lawyers, medical historians, criminologists, analytical
chemists, pharmacists, public health specialists, social workers and all
those interested in poisons, drug toxicity, alcoholism and drug addiction.

In the writing of the book, for the sake of convenience, I have described
my father by his surname and occasional references to members of his
family, including myself, by our first names.

I wish to acknowledge my thanks to the publishers, to the secretaries
who have typed the manuscript, Mrs. Jessie Soons, Mrs. Janet Thompson
and to my sister Mrs. Nancy Young who has also helped in other ways,
and to:—

Sir Norman Skelhorn, Director of Public Prosecutions, and Mr. J.
Wood, Senior Legal Assistant.

The Trustees of the British Museum, the staff of the Newspaper Museum,
Colindale, and of the Royal Society of Medicine.

Dr. W. S. C. Copeman, Chairman of the Arthritis and Rheumatism
Council for Research in Great Britain and the Commonwealth.

The Hon. Sir Eustace Roskill, Sir Zackary Cope, M.S., F.R.C.S.,
Mr. Christmas Humphreys, Q.C.

Mr. Hilary Bodkin, for the loan of a photograph of his father.

Mrs. Y. Bridges, Mrs. I. David (née Roche Lynch), Mr. J. E. Hancock,
Ll.B., Dr. G. Hickie, Mr. Stanley Jackson, Dr. Courtney Lendon, Miss D.
Postle, Mr. Maurice Smith, Ll.B., Mr. C. Sumner, Mr. E. V. Tullett,
Mr. Arthur D. Willcox (Uncle Arthur), Mr. Jack Willcox, Dr. and Mrs.
Richard Willcox and Dr. H. C. Walton.

My wife Inga and my brothers Gerald and John and to Mr. Peter Fiske
for photographic work in connection with the illustrations.

Windsor, 1970.   P.H.A.W.

INTRODUCTION

During recent years there has been a great renewal of interest in medical history and the appreciation of its value as a guide to advance in medical thought. As the medical historian Henry Sigerist wrote: "The creative element in history makes it a powerful instrument of life." Every situation in which we find ourselves is largely determined by historical developments and trends in thought of which we are unaware at the time. The training of the medical student is after all based on the experience of his teachers in relation to the past history of their profession and exerts a profound influence on his education, thought and practice.

This book is rather more than a simple biography. It is a humble contribution to the medical history of the first half of this century, ending while Hitler's war was raging during the blitz on London. Though many others achieved greater heights in their profession, when William Willcox died there ended a career which for its variety of experience was once described as unique, the like of which will certainly never be seen again. Few wielded as great an influence on the profession of medicine for so long a period. His name became a legend in his lifetime. Here was the case of a man who, without outside influence or financial support in his youth, at first earned his living as a schoolmaster, paid for his own medical education at St. Mary's Hospital at a time when there were no state-sponsored scholarships, qualified as a doctor, became a Home Office pathologist and analyst, consultant physician and lecturer in several subjects at his medical school. He became, on the one hand, a vital link in the chain of evidence which brought many a criminal to justice and on the other hand often defended the innocent from injustice at the hands of the Law; he assisted in framing the regulations of death and cremation certification and in controlling the sale of drugs and poisons; he repeatedly prophesied the dangers to the community of hypnotic drugs and drug addiction; he arrested an epidemic of food poisoning at its source in a famous London hotel; he pioneered, with R. G. (later Sir Robert) Archibald, the introduction of the combined "T.A.B." vaccine to replace the typhoid vaccine of Sir Almroth Wright; he arrested epidemics of cholera, typhoid and typhus fevers and controlled dietetic deficiency diseases in an army in Mesopotamia; and traced the cause of an epidemic of jaundice in an aircraft factory to the fumes of tetrachlorethane.

There have been hundreds of excellent doctors but the reason why few biographies are written lies in the fact that most of their daily activities—and probably the most important—are concerned with their patients. The confidential nature of this relationship is such that, in spite of attempts by the public and politicians to disrupt this custom, professional secrecy and integrity is a built-in privilege acquired by a doctor's training which, we hope, will never be surrendered. For this reason the greater part of their work can never be exposed to public knowledge. In Willcox's career, however, there were many notable events which became public news at the time—as a result of inquiries, inquests and law reports. His life seemed to have been lived for the biographer, difficult though the task of the latter may be. It can conveniently be separated into three parts, two of which were separated by his military service in the Great War. In the pre-war period (1904–1915) his medico-legal experience gained for him lasting fame in legal history at a time when, before the creation of special forensic science laboratories, the scientific investigation of crime in England was mainly conducted by a small band of workers who developed the subject from its infancy—Sir Thomas Stevenson, Augustus Pepper, Arthur Luff, John Webster, Willcox, Bernard Spilsbury and Gerald Roche Lynch. Except Pepper and Spilsbury they were all expert chemists and analysts, Willcox and Webster having been trained in Toxicology by Stevenson at Guy's Hospital until his death in 1908.

Luff and Willcox were the only two Home Office Pathologists also in practice as physicians, taking a full share in the teaching of students at St. Mary's Hospital. At this time Pepper planned to retire. Accordingly he and Willcox selected the young pathologist Spilsbury, then lecturer and pathologist at the hospital, to succeed him as Home Office Pathologist to cope with the increasing demands of medico-legal work from the police. Thereafter, relieved of much routine post-mortem work, Willcox became more fully engaged in analytical and other laboratory work in criminal investigations, quite apart from his work as a physician in practice.

Seeking new fields to explore after his military service Willcox resigned his Home Office appointment in 1919, leaving the work in the capable hands of Webster, Spilsbury and Roche Lynch, and subsequently confining his work to that of a consultant physician. But his Home Office connection was retained by his appointment as Honorary Medical Adviser, a self-suggested title which he retained for over twenty years as the one and only holder. In this position he wielded an enduring influence in government departments, and in his own profession in problems of medical and social importance and helped to raise the prestige of the doctor in the eyes of the public and of the law. Before the Great War Willcox gave evidence in twenty-five trials for murder or manslaughter, thirteen at the Old Bailey, and in others of a different kind including criminal abortion cases. Of the Great Trials of the pre-war period were those of Crippen, Broome, Norval, Steine Morrison, Bingham, Seddon and G. J. Smith; in the post-war years were those of Greenwood, Black, Armstrong, Hadwen and Pace. He also at various stages gave critical evidence in numerous cases of private litigation and compensation cases in the King's Bench Division. Regarding British justice as unquestionably the best in the world, he always maintained that to give expert medical evidence in court was a privilege and duty which demands the most careful preparation and meticulous accuracy of presentation. His custom of producing a written report in the witness box and his slowness of speech led to him being described as the most deliberate expert witness who ever stepped into the box. He possessed, as did his colleagues in the same sphere, the ability to present scientific facts in simple language so that it could be understood by any jury. Perhaps the best example of this was in the Seddon trial where it was necessary to describe the complicated technique of analysis for arsenic to the jury.

"The first impression that he gives," wrote a reporter after the Greenwood trial, "is that of an absolutely sound thinker and observer; there is nothing slipshod in his mind, which moves with the precision of a perfect machine. Even the cleverest counsel will fail to disturb his calm and many a barrister who has risen to cross-examine him with high hopes of success has sat down a wiser man."

Certainly his devotion to justice and the Law was absolute and the judges before whom he appeared, with perhaps one exception, all earned his faith and respect. And over and above his own duties in court he was always personally interested in the conduct of the particular case in which he was concerned and where possible would sit through a trial as long as his time would afford. Once, when asked how he achieved success in this field he quickly replied "because I look like a fool and I'm not".

It would be idle to compare Willcox and Spilsbury as expert medical witnesses. Both were closely associated in many cases and were complementary to one another. Spilsbury was a pathologist purely, whose opinion in cases of obscure and violent deaths became unrivalled through sheer experience and knowledge whereas the testimony of Willcox in cases of poisoning and many other kinds of litigation carried greater weight, as Spilsbury admitted, by reason of his experience as a practising physician and his knowledge of chemistry and pharmacology.

Parallel with his scientific work ran his hospital and personal practice covering the wide field of work of a general physician. In assessing a patient, his diagnosis, at any rate later in his life, was intuitive and not based on "rule-of-thumb" methods; in other words each patient was regarded as an individual rather than a "textbook case". To the bedside he brought a spirit of courage and optimism. As a patient once remarked, he seemed to bring the fresh air of Leicestershire into the room, no doubt an allusion to his touch of that county's dialect. No doctor ever claimed infallibility in prognostic skill and one of his mistakes is worth recording. On one occasion he was summoned to the bedside of an old gentleman suffering from heart trouble after a younger consultant had told his family that the condition was hopeless. Willcox gave his opinion that, though he was seriously ill, there was a good chance that he would within a week or two be downstairs with them again. Unfortunately, the first doctor was correct as the patient died the same day. When Willcox was summoned to see the relatives after the funeral, he carefully prepared a humble apology for the mistake but was surprised to be told by the relatives that they were eternally grateful to him as he was the only doctor who had given them "any hope on that dreadful day when father died".

His courtesy to patients and doctors was proverbial and of his kindness his colleague Reginald Miller wrote "the self sacrifice he showed to his patients was an inspiration to all of us". The same spirit was shown to his colleagues and young doctors keen to advance their careers, especially in cases of misfortune. He hated injustice and on one occasion supported a campaign to restore to the Medical Register the name of a doctor—which had been struck off for several years—who, it was considered, had been cruelly and more than adequately punished by the General Medical Council.

He was a man of immense mental capacity and a prodigious worker, yet he never drove others as hard as himself nor expected his children to emulate himself in this respect. Simply by his own example he was able to get the best service from those who worked with him and for him. No one ever described him as conceited, yet he was full of self-assurance and, once his mind was made up, he seldom needed to change his opinion which was quickly formed though he was slow in speech. His enormous output of work was rendered possible by the fact that he seldom travelled abroad except for brief periods (he never travelled by air) and never took long holidays. But a more significant factor was his happy life at home. For his success he owed most to the quality of his wife, Mildred, who devoted herself first to his work and welfare and at the same time created the happy relaxed atmosphere of his home at the time when most London consultants lived and practiced in the same house. She even made all arrangements for the education of the children. In character they were mutually complementary. As would be expected in the daughter of a farmer she had an easy-going gentle nature, her first love being for the peace and quiet of the countryside, but she quickly adapted herself to the irregular life of a busy medical man.

He earned great affection from all who worked for him in any cause—and the same of course applied to his children—by reason of his kindness, generosity, loyalty and sensibility to the feelings of other people, rich and poor alike. He seemed to be a complete extrovert. His secretary, chauffeur and his maid remained in faithful service for very many years, the latter devoting almost her whole life to the family. Despite constant pressure of work he found time to enjoy all forms of entertainment and appreciated art and music but had no aptitude for either. He was never happier than on horseback, preferably with one or other of the family, and loved horses. At the outbreak of war in 1939 one of his first concerns was to remove his two horses from London to the safety of the country, which he did by giving them away to friends. As a man of simplicity and reticence his mind always seemed to be preoccupied with the present and future and he did not readily recall his experiences from the distant past. He hated wasting time but seldom appeared to be hurried except when he had planned to catch a train. Mr. Harold Macmillan recently gave some advice to young politicians embarking on their careers: "Don't jaw, don't gossip, but get on with the job". Willcox would have endorsed this precept for young doctors because he followed it himself.

Chapter 1

Childhood and Education.—1870–1908

Melton Mowbray must have been a quiet and peaceful town during the last century before the days of motor traffic—a centre for the hunting community, where the principal sounds would be the clatter of horses and carriages and the bustle of the weekly markets. Since the turn of the century it had become famous as a hunting centre where visitors from other parts of Leicestershire, and even from London, would gather together in the season for the popular sport of the aristocracy and the farming community. William Henry Willcox was born there in 1870, the son of Mr. William Willcox. William senior was the son of a Whissendine doctor, and was born there in 1844. After leaving school he commenced business in Sherrard Street in 1868, and two years later he purchased the old established Drapery business of George Marriott at 27 Market Place, which was soon to become the leading business of its kind in the town. He was in every respect a remarkable and much loved figure, taking a great interest in public affairs in the town and in the life of the Parish Church where he was Churchwarden from 1879 to 1904.

After his death, a memorial tablet was fixed to the wall of the West end of the South aisle—above the seat which he customarily occupied. The Church at Melton is an attractive cruciform Church with a central tower dating from the 13th century. He was elected to the Town Council in 1872. In 1880–1881 there was a serious outbreak of typhoid fever in the town in which there were over 20 fatal cases. Investigation by the Medical Officer of Health incriminated the water supply, the authorities being advised to search for a new water supply. There was such heavy opposition to the proposed new water-works that Mr. Willcox and two other members of the Council were un-seated at the next election in 1884. In an endeavour to show that the old water supply was of adequate purity for the town, the new Council arranged for bacteriological examination of the water supply in current use. Twenty-three out of twenty-five samples were pronounced unfit for consumption. The sitting members resigned, whereupon strong pressure was put upon the old members, including Mr. Willcox, to seek re-election, which they did, and were again returned to office. This story illustrates the interest in public health affairs shown by the father of a man who was later to gain high medical qualifications and distinction in this speciality. He subsequently became the "Father" of the governing body of the town and Vice-Chairman of the Council for some time before his retirement in 1905, when he left Melton to live at Bottesford until his death in 1906. He played a major part in the erection of the Carnegie Library, securing a gift of £2,000 from Mr. Carnegie, persuading the town to give the site, and, himself a substantial contributor, he was invited to lay the foundation stone on July 21st, 1904. He contributed much effort and generosity to church restorations and charities. He was a Sunday School teacher for 32 years, Manager of the Grammar School, Chairman of the Melton Conservative Association, and Member for Melton of the Conservative and Unionist Association of the Melton Division. He was interested in cricket, and was Vice-President of the Egerton Park Club, attending all the annual re-unions for 25 years.

On his retirement in 1905, Mr. Willcox was presented, at a packed public meeting of townspeople, with a cheque for £290 together with an illuminated address and portrait. In his speech of thanks, Mr. Willcox referred to those who had a desire to have his portrait painted with the idea that it should eventually become the property of the town. "I shall have great pleasure", he said, "in handing over the portrait to the towns-wardens at once, with the desire that they have it hung either in the Town Hall or the Public Free Library". "It is very gratifying", he continued, "to find that several of my Non-Conformist friends have taken an active part in this testimonial, both on the Committee and by subscribing. I attribute this to the fact that I never allowed creed or politics to interfere with my public work in the town".

William Senior married Miss Elizabeth Barnes of Melton, and they had a family of nine sons and one daughter, Minnie, who subsequently took up nursing as a career and became Sister Matron of King's College Hospital in London for 19 years. The sons were William Henry, Charles, Harold, Edgar, Robert, Cecil, Algernon, Octavius and Arthur. They were a happy and united family, not over-endowed with worldly goods, who enjoyed the country around Melton where they were brought up at Brookfield House which still stands as it did. It is at present used as a children's home. Both father and mother were strict churchgoers, with neither particularly high nor low church leanings. Their children were expected to attend Church twice every Sunday. Nevertheless, they other-wise enjoyed every liberty that children in a Victorian middle class household could expect. William senior was interested in the history of the Melton Hunt, by reason of his association and friendship with the hunting folk whom he served in his business. He wrote an article for a local paper on the history of the Hunt from 1810 to 1887 pointing out amongst other things, that the population of Melton in 1801 was only 1,766 (compared with about 17,000 at the present time). The Club in Burton Street, the scene depicted in the painting of the famous Melton Breakfast, was heavily frequented during the season by the aristocracy as well as local gentry from many of the main towns of Leicestershire, and further beyond, who hunted from this centre. During his lifetime Stilton cheese achieved a wide reputation, and was sold in large amounts at an annual market in the town. There has been considerable debate as to the origin of Stilton cheese. It was certainly not first made at Stilton, but probably was made by a housekeeper at Belvoir Castle, the home of the Dukes of

Rutland. Melton became the centre of those hunting with the Belvoir, Quorn and Cottesmore hunts. The latter hunt was the one with which William Junior became associated between the first and second World Wars.

Though the drapery business flourished, William senior was never in a financial position to consider the heavy expenses of University education for all of his nine sons. William, the eldest, attended Wymondham Grammar School from the age of six—a school founded by Sir John Sedley in 1637. Sir John was an important benefactor of many other educational institutions. In 1876, when William junior first entered the school, the scientific and religious teaching was in the able hands of the Reverend E. T. Glasspool, M.A., B.Sc., who became Headmaster in 1880 and retained that position till the closure of the school in 1906. William recounted these details in his speech at the annual prize-giving in 1936 at the County Grammar School of King Edward VII, which he explained was the natural replacement of Wymondham School. This was the only claim he made "to be one of your Old Boys". Of Wymondham he said: "The Foundation was not a rich one and the education could only be carried on along very modest lines as regards school equipment. Also, Wymondham, being over seven miles from Melton and having no railway station within three miles, was geographically unsuitable for being a centre for secondary education. From time to time attempts had been made to move the school to Melton, but these had failed owing to lack of support from the Charity Commissioners. In spite of difficulties, excellent education was provided there. The Reverend Glasspool was a most able headmaster and did splendid work there and I owe a great deal to his teaching and influence. I well remember at the age of twelve learning from him to play quite a good game of chess, and it was he who imbued me with a love of Scott's novels, most of which I read while there".

The only reason for William's transfer to Wyggeston School at Leicester in 1882 seems to have been his difficulty in travelling to Wymondham daily—a problem which was solved by him riding on a pony.

He attended Wyggeston School at Leicester again as a day boy. This school which still sustains its high reputation, was an attractive centre of secondary education for Leicestershire and beyond from 1880 onwards. A considerable number of boys, including his brothers, travelled daily by train from Melton. Canon James Went was headmaster, a great educationalist and administrator, who saw the importance of science in modern education even at that early period. Under his guidance the school became one of the best equipped schools in the country for laboratory and scientific work. A longhand copy of a brief memoir by Willcox of Canon Went written at the time of his death in 1936, was carefully preserved . . . "I was very greatly impressed by the wholehearted and breezy enthusiasm with which he undertook everything in connection with the school, not only the teaching in which he took a share, but also the administrative functions for which he bore full responsibility. Nothing was too small for him to devote his interest. In those days a number of boys came daily to school by train. At the somewhat frugal lunches our headmaster always presided and took a personal interest in all the 'train boys'. His personality predominated at annual speech days and inspired an esprit-de-corps and loyalty to the school in every pupil. He liked to see the school in the front at matriculation and Oxford and Cambridge examinations. We boys knew this, which was an incentive to do our best. It is a satisfaction to us Old Boys that the aspirations of our old school have enlarged, and that all the old traditions and the newer ones in which sports and games are so well exemplified, continue under the leadership of the present headmaster . . ."

Both William and his brother Charles were at the school at the same time. Charles was much handicapped by poor eyesight, but in spite of this he distinguished himself at languages in which he acquired an astonishing aptitude and interest throughout his life, though he went into business and did not use his main ability to earn his living. But William was from the first inclined towards science—particularly chemistry. He left Wyggeston at the age of seventeen and subsequently studied chemistry at Nottingham University, doing the full laboratory course (three years) under the direction of Professor Frank Clowes, and passed the preliminary (1891) and the final B.Sc. of the University of London (1892) with First Class Honours. In order to earn his own living and to ease his father's burden of expenditure in educating his numerous brothers, William worked in a chemist's shop as an assistant at Stratford-on-Avon. No doubt it was at this time that he acquired his love of Shakespeare, his ability to dispense, and his knowledge of pharmacy which later turned out to be almost unrivalled amongst practicing doctors. From 1892 to 1896 he held the post of Lecturer at Queenwood College, near Stockbridge—a private school in Hampshire—where he not only taught chemistry, but pursued his studies and research at the same time, achieving the qualification of F.I.C. (now F.R.I.C.) in 1894.

He retained a great affection for the College, but some years later it was burnt down. In the 1930's he once visited the overgrown site while on holiday in the neighbourhood with his family, and claimed that he could still smell the "stinks" which he had played with nearly forty years before where his "hut" in the grounds had once stood. It was from here that he published his first research project on the Chemistry and Bacteriology of Bran Fermentation, followed by a further paper in 1897 in the Journal of the Society of Chemical Industry on an extension of that study.

While at Queenwood his main recreations were cricket, cycling on a penny-farthing bicycle, and ornithology. The fixture list for 1894 refers to a two mile race on May 2nd between W. H. Willcox on his bicycle and C. Cecil on his mare. Willcox claimed to have won that race, but the result of a longer race on May 14th to the "Rock and Manger" (a distance of nineteen miles) is not known. At cricket his career is obscure, but there is a preserved cutting from a local paper of a match in which Willcox was captain and architect of victory for the College against the local village of Wallop—taking six wickets for thirteen runs and being joint top scorer with fourteen runs in a total of sixty-two against thirty-four for the opposition—described as "a very pleasant and enjoyable game".

At Queenwood, the headmaster H. E. Stewart showed great interest in ornithology, and used to take masters and boys on expeditions to the New Forest and elsewhere for country rambles for the study of birds, and for visits to places of historical interest. At this period Willcox acquired his affection for the New Forest which was the neighbourhood chosen for frequent holidays between the two world wars when riding became his chief recreation. Stewart remained a friend for many years in later life.

St. Mary's Hospital—1895–1904

It can certainly be said that Willcox entered as a student at St. Mary's Medical School with an academic flourish, and at a rather later stage than most of his fellow students. This was at the age of twenty-five in 1895, and four years before Bernard Spilsbury, who was later to be so closely associated with him through their subsequent careers—Willcox being seven years senior in age. He gained the Senior Science Scholarship which was of the value of 100 guineas—a substantial help to a very impecunious student. He often referred in after years to the burden of hard work that fell to him at this time because of the necessity to earn a living while at the same time pursuing strenuous studies for his medical education without any outside help whatever. There were probably few students who received less financial support in this respect than he did at this period. The following year he won the first prize in both Anatomy and Physiology. 1897 was his triumphant examination year, for he not only gained First Class Honours in Anatomy, Materia Medica and Organic Chemistry in the intermediate London M.B., but was Gold Medallist in these three subjects, and won first prizes in Physiology, Anatomy, Histology and Materia Medica at the Medical School.

Of more material value at this stage were extended scholarships worth £30 a year for two years for Materia Medica and Organic Chemistry, and a £20 scholarship for the student showing most proficiency for the year. This latter scholarship was awarded to him in each subsequent year as a student. Though he later claimed that these distinctions were the product of sheer hard work, there is no doubt that his retentive memory, his mental capacity along with his academic maturity were the chief factors gaining him such outstanding success. He was 30 years of age on qualification in the London M.B. in 1900, when he gained First Class Honours in Forensic Medicine, and Honours in Medicine and Obstetrics. He was awarded the University Gold Medal and Scholarship of £60. In 1899 he won other prizes at St. Mary's in Medicine, including Clinical Medicine and Surgery, Hygiene and Public Health, and the coveted Cheadle Gold Medal for original research. In all, it was said that Willcox won over 20 prizes at St. Mary's by the time he qualified.

It might well be thought that these academic achievements necessitated complete dedication to study throughout his student career, but this was not by any means true, for he was an active member of the St. Mary's Medical Society, being Hon. Secretary in 1899 and 1900, and he frequently took part in discussions and showed interesting specimens. At the Annual Hospital Dinner at the Holborn Restaurant in 1897 the Chairman was A. J. Pepper, the surgeon of medico-legal fame with whom he was to be closely associated in later years. Willcox responded to the toast of the Present Students and afterwards recorded and preserved his speech together with the menu of a sumptuous meal of eight courses. In his speech he explained that there was no other medical school he knew in which the same personal interest was taken in the welfare of its students by the members of the Staff; in particular he extended appreciation to the Staff for their kindness and generosity in abolishing the custom of receiving fees in return for special tuition for higher post-graduate qualifications.

Since the second World War, young doctors have been able to earn a reasonable living wage after qualification when appointed resident doctors in hospitals. It is sometimes forgotten that their predecessors appointed to such posts up to that time received no remuneration except board and lodging, and were regarded as apprentices—as indeed in a sense they were. Willcox was not yet free from the anxiety of earning a living when he was appointed House Physician to Dr. David Lees in 1900. Six months later he became Lecturer in Chemistry at the Medical School, holding the position for four years. From 1903 to 1926 he was lecturer in Chemical Pathology, being succeeded by Dr. G. Roche Lynch.

Sir Zachary Cope recalls his first memories of Willcox lecturing in Chemistry: "He drilled into us the most essential points, and if we took down his notes and learnt them well, then one could pass the examination at London University without much difficulty. I remember him well as a Medical Registrar and, of course, later as a colleague on the staff." Though so highly distinguished academically, he always regarded examinations not as an end in themselves, but mainly as hurdles to be crossed.

As Demonstrator in Pathology, he gained substantial post-mortem experience. His diversity of interests and mental capacity enabled him to pass the examination for the Diploma in Public Health in 1900 and the London M.D. the following year. From 1902 to 1919 he was Lecturer in Public Health and in 1907 became Co-Lecturer with Dr. A. P. Luff in Forensic Medicine. In this subject he carried on until his retirement in 1935. There can be few who have held lectureships in so many diverse subjects concurrently, either at St. Mary's or any other teaching hospital. Yet his careful preparation of lectures and his breadth of outlook seemed to bridge the gaps between these specialities. It is quite impossible to envisage any one person mastering so many subjects in the present age of complex specialism.

Willcox soon became friendly and well known to two of the most eminent medico-legal experts of that time. A. J. Pepper, the senior, was a surgeon nicknamed "Professor" Pepper after a well known comedian. He was probably the most brilliant academically qualified doctor who ever worked at St. Mary's, having won three Gold Medals in the finals of the London M.B. He was a great personality, never at a loss for an apt quotation from English literature, and served St. Mary's as a surgeon from 1882–1910. He had frequently been summoned to inquests in Paddington by Danford Thomas, the Coroner of that time, and came to be called by the Director of Public Prosecutions to give evidence in criminal cases involving violent death. Pepper was a brilliant surgeon and teacher who was inclined towards bold surgery when the occasion demanded. Willcox recalled having been one of his dressers at an operation on a young woman who had a circoid aneurysm on her ear. She had been shown at the F.R.C.S. examinations as an example of a case in which operation should be considered too dangerous to contemplate. Pepper not only operated, but achieved complete success; the patient subsequently married and reared a family. His great forensic triumph was his identification of the victim in the Moat Farm Murder. A lady, Miss Holland, lived at an isolated farm in Essex which was managed by a bailiff who was an ex-soldier. Miss Holland mysteriously disappeared. The bailiff remained at the farm and it was remarked that he appeared to have more money to spend than was usual for a man in his position in life. In spite of his statements that Miss Holland had gone abroad, suspicions were aroused and the Police made special search round the farm for any evidence that might serve to unravel the mystery. When the search was on the point of being abandoned, a body was discovered buried in the dried up moat which surrounded the farmhouse. The body was in a state of adipocerous putrefaction and quite unrecognisable from the features. It was that of a female of the age and build of Miss Holland. The jaws and teeth were in a perfect state of preservation and the teeth, which were unusually good for a woman of her age—none having been lost—were identified by her dentist from their number and the special fillings which had been made by him. He pronounced the opinion that the teeth were those of Miss Holland. The skull showed the inlet wound produced by a revolver bullet and the bullet was inside the skull. The bullet was identical with one which would have been fired by a Colt Service revolver and such a weapon was found in the possession of the accused bailiff. He was convicted of murder after a lengthy and careful trial. Pepper's last appearance in Court was at the Crippen trial in 1910. He was the first of the three pathologists who inspected Mrs. Crippen's remains in the cellar at Hilldrop Crescent, the others being Willcox and Spilsbury who had been appointed by the Home Office to succeed Pepper on his retirement.

The other expert was A. P. Luff, slightly junior in age, Physician to St. Mary's from 1890, and Home Office Analyst, and a junior colleague of Sir Thomas Stevenson of Guy's Hospital. Stevenson was Toxicological Adviser and Analyst to the Home Office for over 30 years and the foremost forensic expert of his day. Stevenson and Luff in the course of their careers had investigated the outbreak of arsenical poisoning at Manchester in 1900 arising from the accidental contamination of beer, and gave evidence before the Royal Commission of Inquiry—the result of which was to fix limits on the percentage of arsenic permitted in various food-stuffs. The increase in analytical work arising as a result of that inquiry led to advances in techniques of arsenical detection, and the introduction of the electrolytic Marsh-Berzelius Test by Professor Thorpe in 1903.

When Willcox had completed his resident post as House Physician in 1900, he was at the turning point of his career, with his main interest in Chemical Pathology as applied to medical practice in hospital work, though he had the higher degree (D.P.H.) which would have enabled him to enter the Public Health service as a career. However, he waited for for the chance of becoming Medical Registrar, achieving this position in 1904—a two-year appointment. Before this period however, he had become interested in Toxicology, and became associated with Stevenson in his spare time from his lectureship work at St. Mary's. In 1900, Mr. John Webster was appointed Junior Analyst to the Home Office under Stevenson. Webster, who was highly trained in Chemistry and Toxicology, was not medically qualified but nevertheless subsequently had a most distinguished career in his speciality as an expert analyst.

Willcox would often visit his parents living near Melton Mowbray during this time, and had known his future wife Mildred for several years—"the prettiest girl in Northamptonshire" as he described her to his friends. She was the elder daughter of William Griffin, a yeoman farmer of Crow's Nest farmhouse, at Clapton, near Thrapston, Northamptonshire.

They were married in 1901, and lived at Cricklewood on a somewhat slender income for several years. She was not only a great moral support, but rendered secretarial assistance as is to be seen in his preserved records of her clear handwriting on some of his earlier records and applications for appointments.

Pathologist and Junior Scientific Analyst to the Home Office.— 1904–1908.

Before he became medical registrar at St. Mary's in 1904 Willcox, or "Wilks" as he was affectionately called, had been lecturer in Chemistry since 1900 and in Public Health since 1902. When appointed lecturer in Chemical Pathology in 1904 he resigned the former post but in Public Health he continued until 1919. He had so impressed Stevenson with his ability and enthusiasm while helping in an unpaid spare-time capacity in his laboratory at Guy's Hospital that he had the good fortune to be selected by Stevenson to succeed Luff as Junior Scientific Analyst to the Home Office when the latter's practice became so busy that he could no longer carry on the Home Office work. While in office as Medical Registrar he thus became a part-time junior analyst, and colleague of John Webster. This extra work, a privileged and pleasurable apprenticeship to the foremost toxicologist, became increasingly interesting and fascinating. When he achieved another distinction—that of passing M.R.C.P. London examination in 1905—he held higher qualifications in Medicine, Public Health and Chemistry (B.Sc. and F.I.C.)—qualifications which placed him in the forefront as an all-round expert witness in any Court of Law, as he later became. But the salary of a Medical Registrar was so meagre that a married young doctor had to supplement it as well as he could. In his spare time Willcox coached students, both from St. Mary's and else-where, in various subjects. One doctor later recalled a day in 1906 when he arrived at the laboratory for a session to see a railway carriage door propped against the wall. The Merstham Tunnel Mystery was on but it was never solved. The door had been sent for investigation for blood stains.

On completion of his registrarship Willcox was elected Physician to the Great Northern Central (now the Royal Northern) Hospital in 1906. At a time when junior physicians were not appointed to the care of beds the outpatient duties occupied no more than half a day a week. Willcox was for a time Clinical Assistant to Dr. G. F. Still at the Hospital for Sick Children at Great Ormond Street until 1907, when he was appointed Assistant Physician to St. Mary's Hospital. His new duties, together with his other work, increased so much that he was within four years compelled to resign from the staff of the Great Northern Hospital.

Stevenson (1838–1908) was the foremost toxicologist and analyst in England for over thirty years, an acknowledged master of the technique of poison analysis and public health investigations. Many analysts owed their training in their formative years to his practical tuition at Guy's Hospital, Willcox being one among many. One who became the most renowned was F. G. Hopkins (1861–1947), later Sir Frederick Gowland. Famous for his research in physiology and the discovery of the accessory food factors, later termed vitamins, he became a Nobel Prize winner and President of the Royal Society. He received the Order of Merit in 1935. It was while working in Stevenson's laboratory at Guy's that Hopkins decided to study medicine, qualifying at that hospital at the age of 33 in 1894. It was from Hopkins that Stevenson in 1892 first received news by telegram that specimens were on the way from St. Thomas's Hospital from the bodies of two victims of the poisoner Neil Cream from which he extracted an alkaloid identified as strychnine (Notable British Trials, by W. T. Shaw, Appendix VI).

He was the son of a Yorkshire scientific farmer, an expert on agri-cultural machinery. After leaving school he at first assisted his father before going to study at Guy's in 1859. He had a brilliant academic record, qualified and later became a Medical Officer of Health for several years. At Guy's he became lecturer in Chemistry in 1870 (the year of Willcox's birth), and succeeded Alfred Taylor as lecturer in Forensic Medicine in 1878. He became Junior Analyst to the Home Office in 1872 and Senior Analyst in 1881, a post he held until his rather sudden death from diabetic coma in 1908. He edited Taylor's Medical Jurisprudence in 1883. To the general public his name became famous through his witness in many trials for murders by poison, the most notable being Mrs. Maybrick (arsenic), Dr. Lamson (aconitine), Devereux and Hickman (both morphine), Neil Cream (strychnine), and Chapman and Bell (both antimony).

At the time of his death the *Lancet* biographer wrote: "Stevenson has left his footprints on the sands of time. His name will go down to posterity with those of Orfila, Casper, Tardieu and Brouardel. In his work he was a man of scrupulous exactitude, cool, calm, collected in the witness box, his evidence carried conviction to the jury and inspired opposing Counsel with a dread of challenging his testimony. There was never the slightest difficulty, even to the uninitiated in scientific discussions, to gather the true import of his evidence."

At the time of the Lamson Case (1881) there were no chemical tests known for aconitine, but Stevenson isolated an alkaloid in the organs, vomit and urine, and brilliantly identified the poison by animal experiments.

Through his apprenticeship to Sir Thomas, Willcox acquired his interest both in toxicological technique and in its medico-legal application. From the time Willcox became Junior Analyst (1904) Stevenson gradually delegated a certain amount of Home Office work to his junior colleague.

Scientific Analysts to the Home Office, 1872–1954

	Junior	Senior	Death
Dr. T. Stevenson (Sir Thomas)	1872–1881	1881–1908	1908
Dr. A. P. Luff	1892–1908	—	1938
Mr. J. Webster	1900–1915	1915–1919 (Deputy) 1919–1927	1927
Dr. W. H. Willcox (Sir William) (Hon. Medical Adviser 1919–1941)	1904–1908	1908–1919	1941
Dr. G. Roche Lynch	1920–1927	1927–1954	1957

At the turn of the century, biological tests for human blood, including the precipitin tests, were being developed in Home Office routine work in which Stevenson was assisted mainly by Willcox's researches on the subject—Webster being employed purely in chemical and toxicological analyses. Willcox described the history of this research at a meeting of the Society of Public Analysts in 1927. (Analyst, Jan. 1928, Vol. LIII, No. 622, p. 2.) Mr. Rudd Thompson, the Chairman of the meeting, referred, as one of the early workers upon the subject, to the magnificent work of Willcox, "who was undoubtedly one of the best, if not the best, authority on blood tests, and one whose investigations had done so much to place the precipitin test in the forefront of 'fool-proof' tests, and to make it one of the most valuable aids in forensic cases". He admitted however, that there were many pitfalls if the test was carried out by inexperienced workers. During the subsequent discussion, Willcox stressed the importance of testing standard sera before their use in medico-legal work. In his remarks, he showed the caution which characterized all he did—both in research and clinical work—during his career, explaining the fallacies that might result from inattention to the possibility of errors in all ingredients used for the precipitin test for human blood.

He commenced consulting practice at 43 Queen Anne Street, in September, 1906, while still residing at Cricklewood. Practice was slow to develop until he became better known among London doctors; he saw only three new cases during the last month of that year. During the following year, however, his practice considerably increased.

In 1906, he reported for Middlesex County Council on the limits of boracic acid which should be allowed to be added to preserved ham and brawn, the samples supplied being found to contravene the regulations of the Sale of Food and Drugs Act. On March 21st, he attended Police Court proceedings in the case of *Rex* v. *Harris*—a case of abortion from Apiol. This substance contains an essential oil obtained from the common parsley which had been in use for at least fifty years to induce menstruation in healthy women. For the reason that this could be obtained easily from any chemist, an acquittal resulted following the Recorder's charge to the Jury.

Another sordid case of criminal abortion took Willcox to Lewes Assizes in November; but of greater interest was the case *Rex* v. *Chisholm* at the Middlesex Assize Court in October, in which the parents of a ten-year-old boy were charged with manslaughter and convicted of negligence for their failure—they were Christian Scientists—to call in qualified medical aid to their son during a fatal attack of diphtheria.

In 1907, exhumations of bodies in cases of suspected poisoning were rare enough to attract considerable publicity—as in the case of Mrs. Hancock, the wife of a retired clergyman. Her son by a previous marriage was a barrister named Beech Chester who questioned the validity of her will and the question of natural death, after the doctor in charge had certified the cause of death as heart failure. Willcox considered that death was due to appendicitis and peritonitis, but requested an adjourned inquest pending analysis of organs for poisoning. The negative findings confirmed the original supposition of natural death and solved the Kensington poisoning mystery.

The case of *Rex* v. *Ellis* in 1908 was probably the first occasion on which Willcox appeared at the Old Bailey. This was a case of illegal abortion by the use of large doses of aloes. His opinion given at the West London Police Court had resulted in Ellis being committed for trial on May 1st when he was convicted for supplying a noxious substance with intent to procure abortion. Willcox notes the opinion of the Judge (A. T. Lawrence) that his evidence was given "with precision and great fairness" concerning the danger of the drug in the dose actually given.

Homicidal poisoning with dichromate of potassium must be a rare, if not unique, event. In December 1908, a man named Morger (alias Schlombs) administered this to his wife, and after her death subsequently slashed his own throat with a razor. On being admitted to hospital, he was charged with murder. The case is of special interest because Willcox identified the substance in all the organs submitted to him (although none of the substance was found in the house of the deceased) before he was informed of any details of the case and before the confession of the prisoner in his statement to the police that he had given her this substance along with a draught of chloroform, black coffee and sugar. The amount calculated in the organs was over a hundred times that of a fatal dose.

Between 1904 and 1908 Willcox gained considerable medico-legal experience of fatalities due to revolvers, rifles and shot guns. His records of these cases were later passed on to Spilsbury but his early research in this sphere was discussed in his first paper delivered to the Medico-Legal Society in October 1907—the year after he became a member—on the "Medico-Legal importance of Wounds produced by Firearms". Illustrated by numerous specimens and photographs of accidental, suicidal and homicidal wounds, the paper described the observations necessary for legal purposes on the nature of entrance and exit wounds, the quality of "tatooing" of the skin and the direction of fire. He went on to describe the results of his research designed to estimate the distance at which various types of firearms were fired at the human body. Revolvers and shot-guns were fired at cardboard discs covered with wash leather or actual human skin from varying distances using various types of cartridges and bullets. The paper was followed by an interesting discussion at which several distinguished pathologists took part, among them being Professor Harvey Littlejohn of Edinburgh and Professor John Glaister (Senior) of Glasgow (Trans. of the Medico-Legal Society, Vol. V, p. 5, 1907–1908).

In this paper he referred to the recent sensational murder of William Whiteley on January 24th, 1907 which, though not of great medico-legal importance, was a case of considerable public interest on account of the importance and unusual career of the distinguished victim. Whiteley "the universal provider", was the proprietor of the famous stores which still flourish in Queensway under his name. The business opened in Westbourne Grove in 1863 with a staff of six thousand employees and was so successful that Whiteley soon became the leading shopkeeper in London but perhaps one of the most unpopular on account of the jealousy aroused by his success among smaller tradesmen in the district. Fires broke out at the stores on six occasions between 1882 and 1887 but the perpetrators of these acts of arson were never discovered. Whiteley was murdered in his own shop in full view of several witnesses, the assassin being later identified as Horace Rayner who fired two shots at Whiteley and failed to kill himself in spite of firing a bullet which entered his right orbit and came out at the root of his nose. Though Whiteley died on the spot Rayner was successfully treated by the surgeons at St. Mary's Hospital. He had sufficiently recovered from the injury to face his short trial at the Old Bailey in March 1907, the first murder trial to take place in the new building at the Old Bailey after its opening by King George V and Queen Mary.* There was no chance of an acquittal for there was no doubt of his guilt but he was later reprieved on account of the mitigating circumstances of the crime. Rayner claimed, probably correctly, to be the illegitimate son of Whiteley. Unemployed and impoverished, he had been refused a request for money or employment by his father in the business and had approached Whiteley with threats in the stores, a revolver in his pocket.

*At that time the Prince and Princess of Wales.

The defence counsel were able to argue that the crime might easily have been prevented by the victim himself if he had recognized Rayner as his son. Rayner was a man of evident intelligence and attraction. He composed several poems during his stay in Thistlewaite Ward at St. Mary's; the *Daily Mail* correspondent recorded that there were tears in the eyes of several hospital nurses when he left hospital and likewise, according to the *Daily Telegraph*, among the fashionable ladies who attended his trial. Willcox studied the two bullet wounds with interest and took photographs. "On the left cheek," he recorded, "was an entrance wound with tatooing around it but no burning. The bullet did not penetrate the skull but came out at the back of the neck, being deflected in its course. This wound was not immediately fatal and obviously not suicidal for a right handed person. The distance of the muzzle would be between nine and fifteen inches. The second wound entered the left occiput causing severe brain injury, immediately fatal. The bullet was embedded in the right temporal bone. The distance fired was about the same as the first shot, likewise clearly homicidal."

References

The Trial of Neil Cream. Notable British Trials by W. T. Shore, Appx. 6. 1923.
The Analyst, January 1928, Vol. LIII, No. 622, p. 2.
Transactions of the Medico-Legal Society, Vol. V, p. 5 (1907–1908).

Chapter 2

Consulting Physician and Senior Analyst to the Home Office.—1908–1910

The death of Sir Thomas Stevenson in 1908 was a severe blow to all those closely associated with him though to Willcox, knowing that he was diabetic, it was not a great surprise. Stevenson had intimated that Willcox should succeed him as Senior Analyst. John Webster, the senior of the two, had in fact been a Home Office Analyst since 1900 but he was not medically qualified, expert chemist though he unquestionably was. Webster, a most self-effacing man, bore no resentment at his colleague's preferment and neither expected nor desired the heavy responsibility which Willcox took over. It is significant that their friendly co-operation and mutual esteem and affection played a great part in establishing the great reputation of St. Mary's Hospital in Forensic Medicine founded by Pepper and Luff and maintained for half a century by themselves and by Bernard Spilsbury and Roche Lynch.

One of Willcox's first duties was to complete Stevenson's work on two Public Health problems in which he was engaged at the time of his death while he was still in harness.

In *Leigh* v. *Beauchamp* (father and son) the plaintiff threatened legal action against the defendant for damming up water in the River Eden at Lingfield and flooding his land. The defendant claimed that plaintiff polluted the river water by allowing sewage and refuse from the race-course to be drained into it so that the water had become noxious to cattle to such an extent that not only had abortion been caused, but the purity of the milk endangered. The result of the chemical and microscopical investigations showed that the cattle had not been adversely affected by the water, and the case was amicably settled out of court by the respective parties.

At this stage Willcox, at the age of 38, was officially Senior Analyst and Pathologist to the Home Office. He retained his interest in general pathology and had assisted Pepper in several medico-legal cases as the latter became more busy in his hospital and private practice as a surgeon. But soon after Stevenson's death Pepper retired from the staff of St. Mary's and relinquished Home Office work as well, though he agreed to act in a consulting capacity when required for special cases.

The increasing volume of medico-legal work necessitated the appointment of a new pathologist. Bernard Spilsbury had been appointed Assistant Pathologist at St. Mary's in 1907 at the age of thirty. He was an Oxford graduate who showed a rare flare for post-mortem work, a keen interest in the legal side of pathology and a great sense of devotion and dedication to his subject. He was selected and recommended to the Home Office as a successor to Pepper. So it was that he gradually took over many of the routine and burdensome duties in connection with crimes of violence and post-mortems in other cases of death from obscure causes, while Willcox became gradually relieved of some of his more sordid duties and could spend more time on the increasing laboratory work in the sphere of toxicology and analytical chemistry. But Willcox still retained his interest in medico-legal work of all kinds. His interest in firearm injuries has been mentioned. As early as 1905 he had delivered a lecture on the subject of Infantile Mortality from "Overlaying" (St. Mary's Hospital Gazette 1905). From that time until the First World War his medico-legal work was not confined to laboratory procedures but continued to involve him in cases of the widest variety and interest. The year 1908 marked the setting up of the Department of Public Prosecutions, under Home Office control, with its first Director, Sir Charles Matthews, and Assistant Director and staff. The department relied for medical advice on the Pathologists and Analysts appointed officially by the Home Office.

The year 1909 provided Willcox with work in connection with five cases of criminal abortion and one case of rape, requiring him to spend two days at Swansea Assizes (the first day being completely blank). It is worth noting the small reward he claimed as remuneration—£2 8s. od. as railway fare, 8s. taxi fare, and £9 9s. od. as a fee—an example of the small rewards for medico-legal work carried out on behalf of the police at that time.

Home Office Analysts were commonly thought of—and still are—as white-coated workers confined to a chemical laboratory with its test-tubes and Bunsen burners. Willcox's work at this time was far different from such a conception. He was employed in clinical duties in the out-patient departments of two hospitals and in teaching students as well. He also attended so many inquests and court cases that only the more notable can be mentioned here. His Home Office duties in the laboratory consisted of the examination of clothing, instruments, knives and other weapons used in assaults of violence and criminal abortion—apart from drugs, bottles and other articles brought in by the police. In every case a careful list was made at the head of his notes, and a receipt handed to the bearer. Sometimes material was submitted by coroners, with the agreement of the Home Office, from various parts of the country. His opinion became more and more to be valued in cases of private litigation concerning the manufacture and preparation of food, household remedies in common use, and commercial preparations.

Early in his career, two separate disputes concerned the bleaching process of flour. His research on the growth of young rabbits fed on different kinds of flour, quoted in the Chancery Court in the case of the *Flour Oxidising Company* v. *Hutchinson* (1909) and presided over by Mr. Justice Warrington, was instrumental in winning the case for the plaintiffs supporting the bleaching process in current use at the time. Extension of this research on the nitrite content of flour and its effects on the digestive ferments of rabbits, was brought to court in a similar way in 1912 in the case of *Uddington Co-operative Society* v. *The Medical Officer of Health of Lancashire*.

There was only one example of suspected arson in his career in which his opinion was sought—the case of the Whitechapel Road fire in December 1909. He was asked by Inspector Wensley to report on pieces of glass from a window, and pieces of wood from the staircase of a confectioner's shop. His study of the wood revealed suspicions that some heavy fixed oil had been poured on the wood, rendering it greasy below the surface which was heavily sooted. The evidence, however, was not considered conclusive enough to warrant the Director of Public Prosecutions to prefer a charge of arson—in spite of strong circumstantial evidence. The fire in the shop caused the death of two occupants who lived above the shop—one from the effects of the fire, and the other from the effect of jumping from an upper window. The verdict at the inquest on September 10th was misadventure "in circumtsances of grave suspicion". Lipman's shop was insured heavily, and he had been an undischarged bankrupt. The shop was almost empty of stock and furniture, and two large empty barrels which had contained oil were found in the cellar.

Coroner's Inquiry Committee

Willcox was a regular attender and member of this Committee which met at intervals from February until December 1909 and which had been appointed by the Home Office to revise the regulations which had been in force, with few alterations, since 1887. There had from time to time been criticism and discord between coroners and doctors. In fact, in 1903 the Lord Chancellor (Lord Halsbury) had received a deputation from the B.M.A. and various medical societies, to hear their complaints regarding the practice of a certain London coroner in excluding the doctors in charge of patients from attending their inquests. The Committee of 1909 was designed to straighten out the discord between the various parties by taking extensive evidence from all sides. Sir Victor Horsley, as a representative of the B.M.A., played a prominent part among those who submitted evidence to this Committee. The whole question of the functions of the coroner and the duties of medical practitioners in relation to inquests was thoroughly ventilated. The increasing incidence of burns in children which followed the use of flannelette in children's clothing from 1884 onwards was another item considered at length by the Committee, investigations being directed towards the relative inflammability of flannelette manufactured by different processes and the regulation of its sale by the trade.

Tragedy at the Hairdresser

Accidental poisoning by hair shampoo had been unknown until that tragic day—July 12th, 1909—when Miss Dalrymple, 21 years of age, felt faint and died within about five minutes from the beginning of treatment by an experienced hairdresser at Harrods. The tragedy not only caused widespread publicity in the Press, but was the trigger which focused the attention of lawyers and doctors on the dangers of carbon tetrachloride in hair shampoo. During the next few weeks numerous experiments were conducted, both at St. Mary's by Willcox and at University College by Dr. V. H. Veley, F.R.S., on the toxic and physical properties of carbon tetrachloride compared with chloroform. Carbon tetrachloride was shown to be four times as toxic by volume. But the shampoo in question also contained a proportion of carbon bisulphide—which was more toxic than either. The young lady collapsed over the basin and was helped to the floor by the hairdressers in the room, but died shortly after attempts at artificial respiration had failed to revive her.

The inquest was held by Mr. Luxmore Drew in Kensington. The manager of the hairdressing department explained that the shampoo had been in use for six years, and that occasionally clients had felt faint during the procedure. Dr. Paul Jones said he was summoned as soon as possible, but was unable to revive her by artificial respiration. He noticed the smell of the shampoo in the room. He gave evidence that in February 1907 he had been called to see a lady in a different establishment who had fainted during her shampoo treatment, and was found to have a feeble, rapid pulse. He had also seen another lady who had been rendered unconscious. He had always advised improvement in ventilation, and the installation of fans. Dr. Bernard Spilsbury, who had done the post-mortem, said that he had found signs suggesting Status Lymphaticus and expressed the opinion that the cause of death was syncope due to this cause accentuated by carbon tetrachloride, though she would not have died had she not been subjected to the shampoo.

The verdict at the inquest was Accidental Death caused by the fumes of carbon tetrachloride—with a rider that Harrods Stores "were not justified in employing an unskilled operator in performing this dangerous operation".

On August 25th the Director of Public Prosecutions instituted a prosecution against the manager and the assistant concerned—no doubt promoted by the widespread publicity attached to the case—as similar shampoos were being used throughout the country, no death of this nature having previously been known. The case was conducted at Westminster Police Court by Mr. Horace Smith, and lasted from August 25th to October 11th. Before this, however, Mr. Pepper, Dr. Chaldecott (anaesthetist of St. Mary's Hospital) and Willcox had all visited the hairdressing department and watched carefully the procedure employed in shampooing, during the course of which another client was treated in the usual way under the observation of the three scientists from St. Mary's Hospital.

Mr. Leycester and Mr. Travers Humphreys appeared for the prosecution and Mr. Bodkin for the defence. During the course of the case, Pepper, Chaldecott and Willcox were subjected to extensive questioning and cross examination concerning the chemical and toxic properties of carbon tetrachloride, and Spilsbury's evidence was quickly disposed of. Pepper drew attention to the dangers of the substance by describing the blueness (cyanosis) of the girl shampooed in their presence, and he also spoke of the heavy density of the vapour which was smelt more easily near the floor—owing to its density being greater than air. It was for this reason, he said, that it was quite wrong to have placed the victim on the floor for resuscitation purposes—a fact which the assistants could not have been expected to know. Chaldecott, during his evidence, went back in history to the early days of anaesthesia when chloroform was discovered and first used in anaesthesia by Sir James Simpson and Dr. Sanson, between 1865 and 1867. At that time carbon tetrachloride had been found to be less safe to use in anaesthesia and was therefore discarded—though the substance was used in fire extinguishers and as a solvent in industry.

During the course of the hearing, Willcox had been busy in co-operation with Professor V. H. Veley, F.R.S., of University College, and Professor Augustus Waller of St. Mary's, with experiments on rats and cats—as a result of which it was shown that carbon tetrachloride was four times more toxic, weight for weight, than chloroform. He was subjected to close questioning for two whole sessions of the court, during which he illustrated by using two top hats—presumably Pepper's and his own—instead of bell jars which had contained known percentages of the vapour in his experiments on rats. He considered that five per cent concentration of the vapour in the air of the room would be dangerous, particularly if the window was high up on the wall. The density of the gas was greater than air, so that concentration was greater near the floor level. He aroused laughter in court on two occasions. Cross-examined by Mr. Bodkin, he said he had known of no case of death attributable to the fumes of carbon tetrachloride. A considerable amount of cooling would be produced by the rapid evaporation of this volatile liquid when poured on the scalp. He suggested that a personal experience of this would be more valuable than his opinion.

Mr. Bodkin: "For the benefit of science might I suggest such an experiment on yourself?"

Dr. Willcox: "I would not have one for anything".

Bodkin made a last attempt to confound the analysts. Willcox said that he must admit that Professor Veley's experiment on the cat more nearly reproduced the cubicle conditions at Harrods than his own experiment with the rat, but neither experiment would produce similar results. "You see, the cat was not shampooed". Mr. Bodkin: "Yes. Now turn to another matter. You remember the experiment on Miss Bates—one of the assistants—after Miss Dalrymple's death. Was it not very wrong to put this girl to a risk you would not like to take yourself?"

Dr. Willcox: "At that time we did not know so much about the application of the shampoo as we now know".

Mr. Bodkin: "Oh really. That is the case! I am content with that answer. That is enough".

Mr. Horace Smith: "Assuming the state of knowledge of the medical profession about carbon tetrachloride being what you state it to have been at the time, do you think Harrods could have done any more than they did to prevent the ill effects on its customers?"

Dr. Willcox: "They seem to have taken care—great care—to obviate as far as they know—the dangerous properties of carbon tetrachloride. There were fans and ventilation. But I do not agree that under any conditions it can be safely used".

The prosecution decided on the last day to withdraw the charge of manslaughter as a result of the course of the case, in the absence of evidence of negligence and the steps the management of Harrods had taken in stopping the use of this particular shampoo directly the tragedy had occurred. As counsel for the prosecution explained—the case had been brought up to draw the attention of all hairdressing establishments to the dangers of this substance, and the risk they would run if they continued its use in shampoos.

At the end of the case Willcox was asked to send an annotation to the *Lancet* concerning the dangers of the shampoo, and in this he expressed the need for the Pharmaceutical Society of Great Britain to recommend to the Privy Council that carbon tetrachloride should be added to the Poison Schedule. One doctor quoted in the *Lancet* three cases of ladies taken ill while under the same treatment at their hairdressers, one of whom was resuscitated after being unconscious for a short time.

The directors of the store bore no grievance against him in spite of his evidence in court, because he was asked to inspect the premises and to give advice on the possibility of continuing to use the same substance for cleaning wigs—a process which he decided could thenceforth safely be carried out by personnel carefully trained in the use of the substance with the ventilation requirements needed for the purpose.

Move to Welbeck Street

September 1909 was notable for the move from Cricklewood to 40 Welbeck Street, which was no more than a stone's throw from the consulting room in Queen Anne Street. Though somewhat smaller than most houses in Wimpole and Harley Street, it was pleasant, well built and convenient for a doctor in consulting practice. Not only were patients seen here, but meetings with lawyers, judges, chemists and those of councils of learned societies, in particular the Empire Rheumatism Council. But it was in every sense also a home, where the family lived above the working premises. At that time there were three children. John had been born on February 1st, Gerald was six, and Nancy had come between.

His activities included clinical duties at St. Mary's and Great Northern Hospital, inquests, court cases, and work as examiner at Leeds and Manchester. He was a member of a Masonic Lodge. This year marked the beginning of his custom of an early morning ride each day in Hyde Park. These early morning rides became a regular feature of his life between the two wars, and he also hunted in Leicestershire on Saturdays as often as he could. It was his favourite recreation, and a well earned luxury.

D.P.—2

As a physician Willcox was from time to time consulted to report on the fitness of distinguished prisoners to attend trial. The most notable were Henry Benson of the Feltham's Bank Fraud case in 1909; Mrs. Tugwell, who was charged at Guildford Assizes in July 1910 before the Lord Chief Justice for defamatory libel for sending obscene anonymous letters by post; and Mrs. Pankhurst, the militant suffragette, who had to face her trial in 1912 for smashing windows.

Willcox examined Benson six times in Brixton Prison before his trial commenced. He was a diabetic of mild degree but denied his fitness for trial. The prison doctor supported by Willcox's opinion, considered that he was fit for trial in September. The trial was postponed owing to the illness of the judge, Mr. Justice Coleridge, whose place was taken by Mr. Justice Darling, at the Old Bailey in October 1909. The trial makes amusing reading as the defence was personally conducted by the prisoner to whom judge and counsel allowed considerable latitude and sympathy in his conduct though the judge complained bitterly of the waste of time involved in a case which it was clear to him was hopeless from Benson's point of view. A great amount of abuse was directed at judge, counsel, witnesses and his doctors in turn but all this was treated with exemplary forbearance and judicial courtesy. Benson had already served five years in prison in America for fraud. Returning to Britain he had commenced a career of swindling by inducing innocent people, by clever advertising, to invest their savings in Feltham's Bank and the International Securities Corporation, both bogus companies which went into liquidation. He was sentenced to penal servitude for five years, the first part served under close medical supervision.

The year 1910 was memorable for the death of King Edward VII and the commencement of a new reign which was to last for 25 years. Though the Crippen case came to overshadow the others in notoriety and sensation Willcox also investigated and gave evidence in cases of five murders of violence, three of criminal abortion and a case of rape. In several of these Willcox's evidence was instrumental in securing a conviction or acquittal.

The medical evidence at Cardiff Assizes on March 11th played a predominant part in securing the acquittal of Dr. Arthur Walters at his trial on the charge of murder of a young woman. Following his secret termination of her pregnancy, death followed as a result of septicaemia but there was no evidence that the operation had been done without reasonable care and skill, though in secrecy. At Hertford Assizes on June 22nd, a young man, Beeton, was tried on a charge of infanticide of his own illegitimate child found buried in his allotment in Letchworth Garden City. It was impossible to solve the problem of the cause of death at so long an interval after burial and the proof of murder was not established; Beeton was acquitted.

The death of the 31-year-old third wife of an Army doctor, Surgeon-Major Farmar-Bringhurst, in June, brought Willcox to the Chertsey Police Court. The lady was undoubtedly a morphine addict and both she and her husband were heavy drinkers. The husband had been thought by a Staines doctor to have grossly neglected the care of his wife by encouraging the use of morphine and alcohol, at the same time being unwilling to sanction his wife's admittance to hospital. Her death being reported to the coroner, the inquest verdict was "alcohol poisoning accelerated by lack of proper treatment, her husband being criminally responsible for neglect". Willcox reported at the police court that deceased suffered from kidney and liver disease; but the administration of morphine in such a case would be dangerous. No morphine had been found on analysis but this did not surprise him as morphine is quickly destroyed in the body after death. The husband was committed for trial at Guildford Assizes in July but the Grand Jury did not proceed with the charge of manslaughter.

Willcox was an expert witness in 1910 at three trials for crimes of violence in two of which the prisoners were acquitted. The brutal Gorse Hall murder of a wealthy contractor, G. H. Storrs, in his lonely mansion on the Yorkshire moors had attracted widespread interest in September 1909. One suspect was tried and acquitted. The trial of the second suspect, Mark Wilde, took place at Chester Assizes before Mr. Justice Horridge on October 24th at which Willcox gave evidence on the bloodstains found on Wilde's clothing after a lapse of nearly a year. Wilde was an ex-soldier found to possess a revolver exactly resembling the weapon used for the crime. But the case seemed to be one of mere suspicion and he was acquitted. The case remained an unsolved mystery. Two days later Willcox appeared at Reigate County Court to give similar evidence in the case of *Rex* v. *Dwayne*. Dwayne was a farmer charged with the murder of a man described as a travelling showman found murdered in a field at Horley in March; there were severe head injuries. Again the prisoner was discharged owing to insufficient evidence to prefer a charge.

In the third murder of violence Willcox gave evidence which was perhaps the main factor leading to a conviction. It was an example of detection in the Sherlock Holmes manner. The Slough murder of a 69-year-old woman, described as big and strong, in her secondhand clothes shop at 22 High Street, Slough, on July 15th, 1910, was described as one of the cruellest murders in the history of the town, though of course there have been other brutal murders in the town since that time. The crime was committed in daytime in the back sitting room of her shop. She had evidently died from suffocation, as a local doctor confirmed at the port-mortem. Her hands were tied together and a cushion lay over her face. The prisoner, William Brooks, alias Broome, a motor mechanic, lived nearby. He was arrested within three days. In his room were found nineteen gold sovereigns and two half-sovereigns. The deceased woman had been known by her friends and relatives to carry on her person sovereigns wrapped in brown paper inside her purse. On the table in the room where she was found lay the purse and brown paper. The latter was sent to Willcox together with clothing and finger nails of the victim. The brown paper showed clear signs of the pressure of 19 coins the size of sovereigns and two the size of half-sovereigns. Examining with a lens he saw particles of gold. He went on to demonstrate how gold can leave particles on brown paper by pressure. Obtaining several gold coins, he kept them in his pocket wrapped in similar paper for several days. He could in a like manner demonstrate particles of gold on the paper with a lens.

The prisoner had been found with a scratch on his face on arrest; there were some bloodstains on his shoes, signs of bleeding around the thumb nail, and another nail was split. The coroner was much impressed by the evidence of the gold coins as expressed in his summing-up of the case. At the adjourned inquest a verdict of wilful murder against William Brooks was returned.

The trial of Brooks took place at Aylesbury Assizes on October 21st and 22nd before Mr. Justice Bucknill, whom Willcox was destined to meet again two years later in the case of *Rex* v. *Seddon*. There was other circumstantial evidence incriminating Brooks but Willcox clearly demonstrated to the judge the impression of the coins on the brown paper and the particles of gold visible with a lens. The prisoner was duly convicted. This case was once quoted by a judge as a classical example of a conviction for murder based entirely on circumstantial evidence.

Chapter 3

The Hilldrop Crescent Mystery.—1910

(*Rex* v. *Crippen*)

In the history of crime in Britain probably no other mystery has attracted more profound fascination than the disappearance of Mrs. Cora Crippen on January 31st, 1910. This, and the events which followed, notably the trial and conviction of Dr. Crippen on a charge of wife-murder, have provided useful and profitable material for plays and articles in the press. Certainly no other crime has been more frequently discussed or debated for so long a period, and the name of Crippen has become almost a household word. Even when the case was finished, the secret of the true course of events surrounding his wife's death was never revealed but died with Crippen at Pentonville. The police investigations, and the inquiries at the inquest and at Bow Street and the Old Bailey were headline news in the press for almost the whole period from July until the end of that year.

In the trial of Crippen, so fully described in Filson Young's book (Notable English Trials) written ten years later, the medical evidence was of paramount importance; that of Willcox was second only to that of Augustus Pepper in length and authority. At no stage in his career did Willcox describe in any kind of detail the role he played in the corroborative evidence of identification of the remains, and the cause of death.

Hawley Harvey Crippen was born in Michigan in 1862. He was reasonably well educated and studied medicine at Cleveland Homeopathic Hospital, becoming a doctor of medicine there in 1885. This qualification did not enable him to practice in this country on the medical register. He was interested in the ear, nose and throat speciality. He first married at the age of twenty-five, and had one son. After his wife died in 1891 his son was brought up by his grandmother. Dr. Crippen worked in New York for a time and the following year married an attractive blonde Russian Pole, by whom he had no children. For a time they lived in St. Louis, but came to London in 1900 when Crippen became manager of Munyon's advertising business for homeopathic remedies, established in Shaftesbury Avenue. According to Crippen and other witnesses at the trial, Mrs. Crippen had had an abdominal operation for the removal of an ovary. In 1892 Crippen returned to New York on business for his firm. During this period of six months, Mrs. Crippen was said to have become friendly with Bruce Miller, but he had returned to America before Crippen's return to London and he never met Cora Crippen again. At this stage, according to Crippen, their marriage began to disintegrate and she became irritable, bad tempered and impossible to live with as a wife. In 1905 they took up residence at 39 Hilldrop Crescent off the Camden

Road and near Holloway prison—a rented semi-detached house which was too large for them and gave them the opportunity to supplement his income by taking in paying guests. In 1909 Munyon's offices were in Albion House, New Oxford Street, but Crippen resigned his position in order to join a dental surgeon in a business known as the Yale Tooth Specialists in the same building as Munyon's. His position as medical adviser to several other firms dealing with drugs and an aural clinic ceased when they were shut down in 1909.

Mrs. Crippen was apparently a vain, flamboyant and selfish woman who lost her affection for her husband several years before her mysterious "disappearance". She was also extravagant and resented her duties as a lodging-house keeper, fancying herself as an actress, with an ambition for operatic work. Styling herself Belle Elmore, she was scarcely a success even as a music hall actress with a moderately good singing voice, though she did acquire periodic engagements in this role. Mixing with the stage fraternity, she became treasurer of the Music Hall Ladies' Guild whose meetings were held at Albion House.

In 1909 Crippen's affections had drifted towards a young typist, Ethel Le Neve, who was in his employment. His finances were in a precarious state, maybe on account of his wife's extravagance rather than his own. At the time of Mrs. Crippen's disappearance his current banking account was overdrawn.

Their friends Mr. and Mrs. Martinetti dined at Hilldrop Crescent on January 31st—"quite a nice evening" as Mrs. Martinetti described it at the trial. But they had accepted the invitation under pressure from Crippen. They left the house at 1.30 a.m. Mrs. Crippen was never seen alive again. Crippen's explanation of her disappearance, which he later confessed was false, was that she had been summoned to go immediately to America to care for a sick relative. The secretary of the Music Hall Guild received this news and notification of her resignation as treasurer in a letter written by hand, but not by Mrs. Crippen's.

On February 9th Crippen pawned her brooch and rings for £115 and on the same day visited the Martinetti's to let them know that Cora had preferred to go to America herself rather than let him go. Had Crippen played his cards well he would probably have succeeded in evading undue suspicion. He had merely to play the part of a lonely husband awaiting the return of his wife, but like so many criminals he blundered on several occasions, no doubt losing his head.

On February 20th in company with Miss Le Neve wearing several pieces of his wife's jewellery, Crippen attended a dinner and ball of the Ladies' Music Hall Guild, meeting several of his wife's friends. By March 12th Ethel Le Neve was openly living at Hilldrop Crescent, and about this time he gave three months' notice to terminate the lease of his house. Before Easter he told the Martinetti's that Cora had developed pneumonia. Two days later he departed with Ethel to Dieppe for an Easter holiday but sent a telegram to the Martinetti's informing them of Cora's death at Los Angeles. Unfortunately for Crippen, it so happened that a Mr. Nash, whose wife was one of Cora's friends, was on business in California in May. While visiting Los Angeles he had been unable to obtain any news of Cora's illness or any record of her death. Returning to England, he visited Scotland Yard without delay on June 30th, being dissatisfied with Crippen's explanation of his wife's disappearance and death.

Chief Inspector Dew was detailed to launch an inquiry into the disappearance of Mrs. Crippen. When he visited Hilldrop Crescent on July 6th, he found Ethel le Neve already running the house with the help of a French maid. Crippen gladly conducted him over the house, displaying his wife's furs, clothes, and the unpawned jewellery. But by then his nerve began to fail him. Confessing that his story of her death was a complete fabrication he explained that he had said this in order to cover up the "scandal" of her sudden departure to rejoin her ex-lover Bruce Miller; for all he knew his wife was still alive and well in America, but he did not know where. Crippen promised Dew that he would write a description of his wife to be published in the American press in order to solve the mystery of her disappearance—a step that was never fulfilled. When Dew returned the next day, he found that Crippen and Ethel le Neve had gone. Crippen had notified Albion House of his resignation as assistant to his employer, the dental surgeon. Dew and his assistants then made a most exhaustive search of the house. Noticing several loose bricks on the floor of the coal cellar he explored further and found human remains caked with soil and lime, wrapped in a pyjama jacket corresponding in pattern to Crippen's pyjama trousers found in the bedroom. The police then circulated descriptions of the missing couple and issued a warrant for their arrest.

On Friday, July 29th, the missing couple became headline news when their identity by the Captain of S.S. Montrose was first made known. Captain Randall had been given details of the missing couple. After the departure of his ship from Antwerp bound for Quebec on July 20th he kept his passengers under close observation. Being himself interested in crime, he used his powers of detection with unusual effect. He noticed that "Mr. Robinson" and his son were an unusually devoted couple. Not only so, but "Master" Robinson was a girl disguised as a boy, wearing trousers with hair cut short. Two days after sailing, he ordered his wireless operator to tap out a message to Scotland Yard—the first time wireless telegraphy was used to assist in the arrest of a criminal at sea.

Dew wasted no time. Leaving Liverpool the next day on the Laurentic, which was a faster ship, they overtook the Montrose on the river St. Lawrence at Father Point on July 31st. The Robinsons were arrested, taken into custody and, after extradition formalities at Quebec, were brought back to England, arriving at Liverpool on August 28th.

The Investigation of the Human Remains

Pepper was the first scientific expert summoned by the police to inspect the remains *in situ* in the excavated cellar. Piece by piece he conveyed them to Islington mortuary for detailed inspection on July 14th. It was on July 22nd at the end of the day's work that Willcox himself received specimens at his laboratory at St. Mary's Hospital from the coroner's officer of

Holloway. His extensive examination and description was made on the following day, a Saturday afternoon.

Five stoppered glass jars were properly sealed but not labelled as usual, for Pepper had already told him the news. He first labelled the jars and systematically examined the contents of each in turn. The first jar contained the stomach, heart, one kidney and part of the liver. No organ showed signs of disease, but there was some putrefaction. The second contained a pair of combinations coated with lime, blood-stained in places; the third, brown human hair in a hair curler with the name of the maker inscribed, a tattered handkerchief, a cotton camisole with six pearl buttons; the fourth, the armpiece of a flannelette pyjama jacket with brown and green stripes, caked with blood and lime; the fifth contained another piece of the same bloodstained jacket labelled Jones Bros. Ltd. Holloway, Shirt Makers.

Willcox was eager to obtain as much as was possible of the human remains from the grave for analysis for poisons in order to be able to calculate as accurately as possible the amount of any discoverable poison in the body as a whole. He requested further supplies, preferably whole organs if possible. Further samples of human hair varying from 2 ins. to 6 ins. in length, a hair curler and another piece of liver were brought by the police surgeon, Dr. Marshall, on July 25th. On August 8th Pepper himself delivered the piece of skin which was to supply the chief evidence of identification at the trial in October. At the end of the portion of skin human hairs were growing, resembling pubic hair. After writing a careful description of it he put the skin in a special fluid designed to prevent further changes of putrefaction and handed it to Dr. Bernard Spilsbury on the same day for pathological study.

On August 2nd Pepper informed Willcox that the police had discovered that Crippen had purchased five grains of hyoscine on January 1st, 1910, from a chemist in Oxford Street. By that time the analysis was well under way. On August 13th Pepper witnessed Willcox's experiments on the alkaloid extracted from the liver and stomach contents. The effect on the cat's eye of a few drops of the extract was to dilate widely the pupils, thus showing the presence of a mydriatic alkaloid, one of a group of drugs of which hyoscine was a member.

Further specimens were brought to him by Marshall on August 14th, another hair curler, the lungs, intestines, portions of muscle and more hair. Soil from the grave in a separate jar was found to contain traces of an alkaloid.

When Willcox visited Hilldrop Crescent on August 23rd with Inspector Cornish, his purpose was not merely idle curiosity. He wanted to satisfy himself that all possible contents were investigated, and also to take samples of soil. He took three separate specimens away. Not content with his discovery of a mydriatic alkaloid, he was intent on investigating for arsenic as well. But his analysis showed that the soil was free of all poison and could not have been the source of the alkaloid already found in the remains.

Analysis of the Alkaloid

He next set out to identify the individual alkaloids by chemical tests and microscopical examination of the crystals, the brown spheres characteristic of hyoscine.

By the time-honoured method of extraction devised by Stas, the pure alkaloid obtained from all the organs amounted to ·43 of a grain. But it must be remembered that the head, neck and limbs with their muscles were never recovered from the cellar. Willcox's calculation that there was probably half a grain in the whole body was perhaps an understatement clearly on the cautious side, as the content in the brain and muscles must have been considerable. In his final report of September 2nd he commented that the relatively large amount found in the stomach (1/30 grain) and intestines (1/7 grain) showed that the poison was taken by mouth. The liver (1/10 grain) and kidney (1/40 grain) content suggested that the deceased probably lived for an hour or more after the poison was taken.

The Inquest

Earlier the inquest had opened on July 18th at Holloway. But the unexpected death of Mr. Danford Thomas, the Coroner, rendered it invalid. It was accordingly re-opened by Mr. (later Sir) Walter Schroder, on August 16th when formal evidence was submitted. On September 12th Willcox presented the results of his investigations and his opinion on the cause of death. The Crippen case was unusual in that the inquest proceedings terminated several days after the end of the Magistrates' Court inquiry at Bow Street, the former proceedings being held up by the prolonged police inquiries and the necessity to call many witnesses. The opinion of Pepper and Willcox was that the remains had been buried for a period between four and eight months. The jury returned a verdict of wilful murder against Crippen. But on the coroner's advice the jury made no reference to Miss le Neve as an "accessory after the fact".

Bow Street

Crippen and Ethel le Neve appeared before the Magistrates on August 29th the former charged with the wilful murder of his wife, and the latter with being an accessory after the fact. Presided over by Sir Albert de Rutzen the hearing was attended by many notable people connected with the stage, including Sir W. S. Gilbert and H. B. Irving on all six days. The court was fully packed.

Travers Humphreys appeared for the prosecution and Arthur Newton for the two prisoners. The evidence of Pepper lasted for most of the morning of the fourth day, and was supported by that of Spilsbury for a period of forty minutes on the fifth day. Their evidence was mainly concerned with the skin of the abdominal wall and the scars on it—the most important part of the remains used for identification.

Willcox was in the box for three hours. He agreed with the previous experts that the piece of skin was from the abdominal wall and that the scar was identifiable.

He had never before given evidence in a case of alleged murder by hyoscine, this being the first case of its kind in Britain. The isolation of a mydriatic alkaloid meant that it was either hyoscine, atropine or hyoscyamine, confirmed by Vitali's test. The differentiation by the bromine test and the nature of the residue—a gummy mass—pointed to hyoscine, the typical brown spheres being seen under the microscope. His evidence was of great technical interest as it illustrated the difficulty that faces the analyst working on contaminated specimens sent for analysis. He had been puzzled by finding traces of cresol in the stomach, and arsenic in the intestines and liver, but not in other organs. On inquiry, he found that the mortuary attendant had sprinkled liberal amounts of cresol on the specimens in the mortuary. The solution and powders at the mortuary were also analysed and found to contain a small percentage of arsenic. The presence of arsenic in some organs, and none in others, indicated that it was due to contamination in this way, as he had informed Travers Humphreys three days earlier. He regarded a fatal dose of hyoscine to be half a grain, the medicinal dose being 1/100th of a grain or less. The poison could have been taken in a drink such as sweetened tea or coffee without altering the flavour. Putrefaction of the remains would be delayed by the presence of lime in the grave—but adipocere formation would be accelerated by it. The remains had been buried for less than a year; in that period some of the hyoscine would have been destroyed. In cross-examination he denied the possibility that alkaloids produced by the changes of putrefaction could have been confused with hyoscine.

The Trial of Crippen

It was said that there were over four thousand applications for seats at the Old Bailey, so great was the interest attached to the case. Half-day tickets were accordingly issued. At Crippen's entry into a packed court on October 18th, a hushed silence suddenly prevailed. The case was tried before the Lord Chief Justice, Lord Alverstone, and lasted five days. Counsel for the Crown were Mr. Richard Muir and Mr. Travers Humphreys and Mr. Ingleby Oddie, later well known as a London coroner. Appearing for Crippen were Mr. A. Tobin, K.C., Mr. Huntly Jenkins and Mr. H. D. Roome. Thirty-six witnesses gave evidence, two of whom came specially from America—Mr. Bruce Miller who had been friendly with Mrs. Crippen several years previously, and Mrs. Hunn, Mrs. Crippen's sister.

The evidence of the scientific experts occupied close on half the time taken up by all thirty-six witnesses; the testimony of Augustus Pepper lasted nearly twice as long as that of Willcox and was heard for the greater part of the second day.

The main scientific evidence expected from the experts concerned the identification of the remains, the approximate time of their burial and the cause of death. All were interrogated about the all important exhibit of skin and muscle, but for Pepper and his young colleague Spilsbury, then aged thirty-seven, this was the main object of their attention in their evidence concerning the identification of the remains. Willcox's main concern was the cause of death—poisoning by hyoscine, as he had already indicated at Bow Street.

Muir and Humphreys had been coached in the subject of the chemical and medical properties of hyoscine before they appeared at Bow Street; and Willcox had loaned them a well-known text book of Toxicology.

When Willcox entered the box on October 20th, it was almost a repetition of his evidence at Bow Street, but the audience was a new one. By the Stas technique of extraction he had obtained a gummy substance, the mydriatic alkaloid which dilated the cat's pupil. Applying the bromine test he had found typical brown spheres of hyoscine under the microscope; the first occasion in which this drug had been used in alleged criminal poisoning. The well-established Vitali test yielded the typical change of colour to violet, thus confirming that it was a vegetable alkaloid distinct from certain alkaloids sometimes produced by bacteria in putrefaction of animal flesh.

Willcox had been disappointed to be unable to estimate the melting point of his alkaloid. It was a method which served to differentiate not only alkaloids from one another but the individual members of the mydriatic group, hyoscine, hyoscyamine and atropine. Cross-examined by Tobin, he explained that the melting point of hyoscine treated with gold chloride was 190 °C, at least thirty degrees higher than the other two. In the Crippen case he had less than half a grain at his disposal, whereas he needed at least two grains to carry out this test along with the other investigations; and he had failed to find any further supplies in his personal search of the soil from the grave. Nevertheless, the fact remained that the method offered a new line of advance in the identification of alkaloids in courts of law. Recent technical advances have now enabled scientists to estimate the melting point of alkaloids by micro-physical methods whereby minute amounts can be melted under the microscope while a special thermometer is read. Not only so, but many new techniques of analysis can now be used, such as paper chromatography and ultra-violet and infra-red spectroscopy. But the Stas process of extraction, though further elaborated, still remains in use today. Police inquiries revealed that Crippen had purchased five grains of hyoscine from an Oxford Street chemist on January 1st. It was perhaps unfortunate that Pepper communicated the information to Willcox about two weeks before the analysis was completed. Willcox was thus exposed to the suggestion by defence counsel that hyoscine was discovered as an afterthought—a cruel and unkind inference which was not used by Tobin in the later stages of the trial to his own advantage in view of the fact that Willcox claimed a period of three weeks to complete extraction and analysis of the alkaloid.

Willcox's evidence was supported by that of A. P. Luff who had been Junior Home Office analyst until succeeded by Willcox in 1904. Luff's experience of cadaveric alkaloids had been greater than his successor's, and his reliance on Vitali's test was equally firmly held.

The scientific experts for the Crown were all from St. Mary's Hospital; Pepper supported by Spilsbury, and Willcox by Luff. It seemed that the case might lead to a battle between teams from two London hospitals, for the three experts for the defence were G. M. Turnbull (pathologist), R. C. Wall (physician and pathologist) and A. W. Blyth, all from the London Hospital. But try as they did, their evidence lent feeble support to the defence counsel. Turnbull and Wall had previously formed the opinion that the exhibited piece of skin had come from the thigh and that the supposed scar was merely a fold in the skin. But during their testimony in the box they were forced to change their minds and agree that it was more probably part of the abdominal wall. Blyth was equally unable to counter the firmly held view of Willcox and Luff about the nature of the alkaloid. He had to admit comparative ignorance of cadaveric alkaloids in putrefaction and was merely able to quote from an obscure Italian text-book which was critical of the value of the Vitali test.

The jury was left in little doubt that the Crown experts were right; death had been caused by hyoscine, the remains had been buried for a period between two and four months, and the exhibited skin with its scar of the old operation was in fact from the abdominal wall of Mrs. Crippen.

Richard Muir enhanced his reputation by his masterly conduct of the case as prosecuting counsel.

After retiring for half an hour the jury found the prisoner guilty at 2.45 p.m. on the fifth day of the trial, after a strictly impartial summing-up by the Lord Chief Justice.

The trial of Ethel le Neve at the Old Bailey on October 25th was completed in one day. The same three counsel appeared for the Crown. She was defended by F. E. Smith (later Lord Birkenhead), who had earlier refused the more difficult brief for the defence of Crippen, supported by Mr. Barrington Ward. Only nine witnesses were called; Pepper and Willcox gave formal evidence each for only a few minutes. She was found not guilty and acquitted.

Crippen appealed against his verdict. The case came before the Court of Criminal Appeal on November 5th, before Mr. Justice Darling, Mr. Justice Channell and Mr. Justice Pickford, but was unsuccessful. Crippen was executed at Pentonville on November 23rd, 1910.

As a criminal, Crippen was notable for his strangely attractive qualities of character, his courtesy and unselfishness, and the calmness with which he faced up to his succession of misfortunes. He certainly faced his trial and death with courage, and earned the sympathy of a wide circle of people who appreciate the horrors of a selfish, nagging and overbearing wife. Even Inspector Dew liked him, and enjoyed his company at lunch at the Holborn Restaurant after the first unproductive search of his house. None of the witnesses at the three court inquiries described him as other than a pleasant man; and one described him as one of the nicest men she had ever met. His affection for Ethel never wavered and in his last letters he did his best to protect her from any accusation of guilt.

For close on sixty years, the case has been the subject of frequent debate. Having poisoned his wife with hyoscine, why did Crippen need to dispose of her remains in the way he did? Why did he not call a doctor and claim that she had poisoned herself with the drug he had left lying about the house? Doubtless the ruse would have been successful and would have saved him the need for the hasty flight and the ghastly task of disposal. And how did he dispose of the head and limbs? Only Crippen knew the answers and the secrets died with him.

Willcox resented being referred to as "the man who hanged Crippen", and rightly so. He would have been far happier if it had been shown that Mrs. Crippen had committed suicide. In spite of his acute sense of right and wrong, he felt sorrow and compassion for Crippen as did many people. Nevertheless, the case established certain records. It was the first case of alleged murder by hyoscine in British legal history and the first case in which wireless telegraphy was used to arrest a criminal on ship at sea.

Willcox alluded to the case in various lectures on toxicology in later years, and a quotation from his Harveian Lecture to the Harveian Society on March 15th, 1928, refers to Crippen's purchase of poison in relation to the Poisons Register.

"The numerous Acts and Regulations governing the sale of poisons in this country have served as a great protection to the public. In many noted trials the purchase of poison by the accused has been revealed by the record of the register of the sale kept by the vendors. This happened in the Crippen case, where the purchase of hyoscine had been recorded in the poison register of the chemist."

The liberal sprinkling of quicklime on the remains in the cellar was a fatal mistake referred to in a lecture to the Society of Dyers, and to the Literary and Philosophical Society of Manchester in 1924:

"Before the Crippen case it had been stated that hyoscine was a very decomposable alkaloid that no one could detect a few days or weeks after death . . . To make assurance doubly sure Crippen buried the viscera in quicklime which was just what the expert wanted, for it helped to preserve the viscera, and without it I doubt whether the hyoscine would ever have been discovered. Crippen possessed the little knowledge that is dangerous."

Willcox was asked by a barrister interested in forensic chemistry about the mode of action of quicklime as a preservative, as it had been understood that executed criminals had customarily been buried in quicklime to destroy the body rapidly. The answer lay in the rapid hydration of quicklime yielding calcium hydrate, a fairly efficient alkaline antiseptic, but in addition calcium hydrate combines with the fat of viscera to form a calcium soap called adipocere, which forms a protective covering round buried remains.

The cat used in his experiment at the laboratory was subsequently named "Crippen" and was cared for by one of the students. It lived for several years, produced a family of kittens. But the name of Crippen must have carried a curse, for it was later unfortunately killed by a dog.

Miss Ethel le Neve escaped the publicity that often pursues acquitted prisoners by emigrating to Canada soon after the trial. There she married and had children. She returned to Britain after many years and lived to a ripe old age, dying in obscurity in 1965.

References

"The Trial of H. H. Crippen"—Notable British Trials by Filson Young, 1920.

"Sir Travers Humphreys—A Biography" by Douglas G. Browne, Harrap 1960.

"Bernard Spilsbury—His Life and Cases" by Douglas G. Browne and E. V. Tullett, Harrap 1951.

Harveian Lecture to Harveian Society, March 15th 1928. Postgraduate Medical Journal, July 1928.

Lecture at Manchester to the Society of Dyers and to the Literary and Philosophical Society 1924. B.M.J. January 17th 1925.

Chapter 4

From Crippen to Seddon.—1910–1912

The Carlisle Murder

On the same day as Willcox appeared at the Court of Appeal in the Crippen case, November 5th, there occurred at Carlisle the brutal murder of a local leather merchant of repute, Alexander Norval, in his warehouse at West Walls.

It was one of the most brutal murders in the records of the city at that time, a city that was noted for its comparative freedom from crimes of that nature. The brutality of the murder, coupled with the fact that it was a case of suspected patricide by the son of the deceased, attracted enormous interest throughout the North of England.

The circumstantial evidence was strongly against the son Archibald who was employed in his father's business and had been known to have quarrelled with his father over financial matters on several occasions, and was said to have forged a cheque in his father's name. Death had been caused by multiple fractures of the skull by an axe found at the site of the crime, and parts of the warehouse, including the walls and floor and stair-case, were bespattered with blood.

In this case Willcox was required to carry out so many investigations on the spot that he spent three days at Carlisle in early December in order to help collect sufficient evidence for the police to justify the charge of murder against the son at the Magistrate's Court. The trial commenced at Carlisle Assizes on January 26th before Mr. Justice Grantham, and lasted for three days. It resulted in a popular acquittal, in spite of the circumstantial evidence against the prisoner. The father was known to be a somewhat hard and domineering man; the son also ran a bookmaker's business—"a mischievous trade, of the worst type as he took money from people at the corners of streets" as the learned judge explained when charging the Grand Jury at the beginning of the case.

Willcox's evidence resembled that of a detective rather than of a doctor, the sort of evidence that in later years would usually be given by Spilsbury and other forensic pathologists. He had carefully examined clothing worn by the deceased and by the prisoner, also the bespattered walls and stair-case of the warehouse, discovering human blood stains. He gave evidence concerning the multiple fractures of the skull, consistent with multiple blows from the axe corresponding to indentations on the cap worn at the time of the crime. All the blood stains on the clothing and in the warehouse were those of human blood. He went further than this, by stating the opinion that deceased was probably assaulted on the staircase, receiving further injuries in falling to the floor at the foot of the stairs, where a pool of blood collected.

In spite of strong circumstantial evidence, the prosecution were unable to expose sufficient motive or direct evidence of witnesses near the scene of the crime to influence judge or jury in favour of the prisoner's guilt. The prisoner was acquitted after the jury's absence for only eighteen minutes. It was a popular verdict, received with cheers inside and outside the court, but the perpetrator of the crime was never discovered.

If Willcox had kept all the articles of clothing, weapons of offence, and other specimens sent to the laboratory, he could soon have created a museum to interest doctors, police and criminologists alike. Probably the restriction of space at St. Mary's, and the financial stringencies of those times, prevented this. It certainly could not be said that he was not "museum-minded". He even had the skull of poor Norval there, for a police officer called in January to collect it. It was handed over by Webster, to be returned to Carlisle in readiness for the trial. Other interesting objects investigated were the clothes worn on arrest by Steinie Morrison, the Clapham Common murderer, and the metal bar with which he struck the fatal blows on his victim, about which Willcox gave evidence at the Old Bailey in March 1911; and within a few weeks, the clothing worn by one of the gang of Houndsditch assassins named Garstein, found dead by Inspector Wensley in a flat in Grove Street, accidentally shot by another of the gang who murdered three policemen but escaped to be besieged in a house in Sidney Street.

Poison in Tea

The depositions of the case *Rex* v. *Ansdell* make amusing reading, revealing a fascinating story of crime detection in a case of less importance than murder by poison. By a curious coincidence the intended victims were the entire household of a man named Arthur Willcox. The father of seven children, he lived in a house in Camberwell which must have been incredibly crowded for so many occupants, at any rate according to present day standards. Arthur was a boot and shoe repairer. He could have claimed no relationship to W. H. Willcox, though by chance he shared the name of Arthur with the doctor's youngest brother. The case was otherwise of special interest as one of intentional poisoning without intent to kill, an offence falling into the provisions of the Malicious Injuries Act of 1861 under which the accused, Ernest Ansdell, was charged.

On March 21st, Inspector Duggan brought to St. Mary's Laboratory a teapot, a kettle and cup which had been taken by Mrs. Arthur Willcox to the police station, acting on her doctor's advice.

For a long time Ernest Ansdell had been regarded as the fiancé of the eldest daughter, Anne. A young man without a home, he had for some time been a lodger in the house, sleeping in the living room on a chair-bedstead. He was employed in a local brewery. The father, Anne and Ernest commenced work early in the morning. It had been the practice of Mrs. Willcox or Anne to fill the kettle with water at night to be ready in the living room to prepare tea for breakfast. The kettle would be placed on the gas-ring in the living room where there was presumably no water tap.

Early in March Anne had had a quarrel with her sweetheart, as a result of which he had left the house on several mornings without taking tea.

On March 11th, Anne made the tea and washed her hands and face with the remaining hot water. Her face smarted and burned; the soap would not lather. The tea tasted sharp and acid, as her father agreed. The same episode recurred on March 16th. The tea was noticed to be black, tasting acid and unpleasant.

When the police surgeon inspected the tea in the pot he suspected it contained oxalic acid, yet it could hardly have been such a lethal poison to cause such little harm to the family.

Willcox's notes of the analysis were scribbled on twelve sheets of foolscap paper. He soon discovered that the kettle water contained sulphurous acid and bisulphite of lime, substances which Ansdell had evidently acquired from the brewery. The analysis of the tea was more tricky owing to the chemical content of tannic acid in the infusion of tea, but it was success-fully carried out. In the concentration in the tea and water, the amounts of poison consumed would not be dangerous, yet how was Ansdell to know this? His intention to do nothing more than make his victims ill had failed. Certainly none of them were affected, except on a psychological level. Yet the case was of sufficient importance to bring Willcox to the Central Criminal Court on April 25th and 26th to the trial of Ansdell before the Recorder. The teapot, kettle and cup were passed round the Court as exhibits. As Richard Muir could produce no evidence that the accused put the poison in the kettle, the case was quickly terminated, the prisoner being acquitted. It is tempting to reflect that, had one of the family died after drinking the tea, the trial would have been one of sensational interest in the history of toxicology.

Strychnine Poisoning in Margate

Early in 1911 a doctor practising in Margate had under his care the wife of the leading solicitor and coroner of that town. He had for several months prescribed a harmless medicine containing calcium lactate and syrup of orange to flavour. But on the night of June 8th her usual dose tasted bitter; she had severe cramps and convulsions affecting her legs and jaws. When he tasted the medicine the following morning the doctor found it bitter and his patient writhing with convulsions which he was forced to control with chloroform. A clear case of strychnine poisoning. Yet two other patients had had calcium lactate from the same stock bottle at the local chemist but had suffered no ill effects. Yet to Willcox the identification of strych-nine was easy; probably the easiest alkaloid to identify. He found 3·8 per cent in the stock bottle of calcium lactate, bearing the name of the manu-facturer. In the medicine he found over half a grain of strychnine in a fluid ounce, equivalent to over four poisonous doses in a half ounce dose. Willcox could at first offer no suggestion as to how the poison gained access to the stock bottle from which the lady's medicine had been dis-pensed. But probably the managing director of the manufacturing firm was right. The dispenser, if he had bottles of strychnine and calcium lactate on his bench, in a moment of aberration during weighings must have returned some strychnine solution to the wrong bottle. The accident must have happened immediately before the new bottle of medicine was dispensed for this particular patient. The chemist was lucky to escape prosecution for negligence.

Carbolic Acid Poisoning

The death on March 31st of a ten-day-old infant led to lengthy correspondence between the coroner and the Privy Council whereby the sale of carbolic acid products became more strictly controlled by law. The post-mortem showed all the signs of corrosive poisoning of the gullet and part of the stomach. Carbolic acid was used for scrubbing the floors and was the only corrosive poison found in the house. The inquest was held at Greenwich by Mr. H. R. Oswald. In her evidence, the mother said that she never fed her baby on the breast. It began to vomit dark brown fluid about three days after birth. A cup and spoon were used for feeding until a bottle was brought into use a week after birth. The carbolic was bought by the infant's sister aged thirteen. Willcox's examination of the organs clearly established from the appearances of the throat, the gullet and the stomach that the baby had swallowed a small quantity of a corrosive poison such as carbolic acid (phenol). The coroner stated that this was another instance to show how easily poison could be purchased. "It amounted to a scandal that a girl of thirteen should be able to purchase enough to kill numbers of people without the slightest restriction." The verdict was "death from exhaustion following the administration of a corrosive acid (carbolic) but by whom and how it was administered there is not enough evidence to show."

This important and tragic case led to necessary changes in the Poisons Law. After correspondence between the coroner, Willcox and the Pharmaceutical Society with the Privy Council, an order in Council on October 11th enacted that from May 1st, 1913, all liquid preparations of carbolic acid sold as disinfectants, carbolic or carbolic substitutes, must be restricted to the provisions of Section 5 of the Poisons Act of 1908, in other words, they had to be labelled "poison" and bear the name and address of the vendor.

Murder in North Finchley

Murders of young women, if there is no sexual motive, are usually crimes of jealousy. That of a young housemaid of twenty-two, Alice Linfold, at North Finchley on April 27th was a particularly brutal affair. Her fiancé George Pateman, aged thirty-three, had threatened suicide a few days before, having said his farewells to Alice. Nevertheless, his father was lodging at the home of the girl's parents. On the fatal Sunday the girl went to her home from her house of employment. Late in the evening Pateman's father escorted her back. He saw someone meet her, but he could not identify the person in the darkness. Shortly after, she rushed into the kitchen bleeding profusely with her throat savagely cut and died without speaking. Pateman was arrested early the next morning. His clothing showed extensive blood stains which Willcox showed had been shed from an anaemic person, as the girl was known by her doctor to be.

Bernard Spilsbury, who had carried out the post-mortem, made his second appearance at the Old Bailey to give evidence with Willcox at the trial of Pateman before Mr. Justice Darling on July 3rd. In summing up, the judge first alluded to Willcox's work, pointing to evidence of the girl's blood on the prisoner's clothes, as graphically described by Richard Muir: "The science of evidence with regard to blood stains has taken a step further in this case than any other in my (Muir's) experience. It appears that this was an anaemic girl and the skilled analyst is able by modern methods to say that the stains on this man's clothes are of human blood. Further, they are of anaemic blood as were also the stains on the girl's clothes."*

Deaths resulting from criminal abortion in London alone formed a sordid and time-consuming though necessary part of medico-legal practice from which Willcox and Spilsbury found no escape. Later in the year a case of incest demanded Willcox's report and evidence at the Old Bailey. From April to November he gave evidence in six separate cases of criminal abortion in the Central Criminal Courts. Five resulted in convictions including that of a doctor charged with manslaughter. In these cases the medical evidence concerned the use of instruments and drugs, or the detailed examination of post-mortem specimens. In each case the expert's attendance at the inquest and police court preceded the trials.

Notwithstanding his association with crime, Willcox's authority was such that he was repeatedly involved in public health matters. We find him, towards the end of 1911, reporting on the purity of samples of drinking water sent from Aden and the sewerage disposal technique in use at Hertford, for local authorities. His last experience in litigation for that year was as an expert witness for the defence at the West London Police Court where Mr. A. H. Bodkin, who later became D.P.P., was acting for the Excel Meat Company of Hammersmith in an action brought by the Hammersmith Borough Council. The case would probably never have arisen had it not been that a barrister living next door to the company claimed that a nuisance in the form of obnoxious smells emanated from the meat factory which prepared cooked meats and hams ready for consumption. He claimed that these smells were so unpleasant that they upset members of his family by making them feel ill. Willcox inspected the factory and found everything efficient and satisfactory from a public health point of view. The defence was supported by a police inspector who found the smells appetising. But what is one man's meat is another man's poison. The chief magistrate also inspected the house and neighbourhood. He decided that nuisance did in fact exist, but imposed a fine of only £10 with costs.

* At that time the technique for the detection of blood groups from blood stains on clothes and other objects had not been discovered.

The Poison Mysteries of Lancaster Castle

The ancient Norman Castle of Lancaster was besieged at various times in its history, lastly by the Cromwellian forces during the Civil War. Part of it was modernised and in recent times has contained the Assize Court and an Art Museum.

From November 1910 to the end of 1911 it was the scene of several tragedies befalling the family of William Bingham who had for thirty years been the official custodian and guide. The post was a resident one and Bingham, a widower at the time, was the father of several children. During the period mentioned no less than four deaths in this family occurred in succession in the Castle residence. Suspicion of poisoning became news following the death of the fourth victim in August 1911. To superstitious folk it seemed that some ancient curse of the castle had struck the family and some evil hand had been at work.

Several pathologists and analysts investigated, and established the cause of death in this victim, and two of the three earlier cases, as acute arsenical poisoning. Though Willcox played no part in the investigation his help in a consulting capacity was sought by the Director of Public Prosecutions, Sir Charles Matthews, in early October 1911, when the Inquest and Magistrates' Court depositions were submitted to him with a request to report his opinion to submit as evidence at the trial to be held at the end of the month. He was present for two days at the trial. The mystery of the case and the romantic scene of the tragedies justify a brief account here.

The death at the age of thirty of William's daughter Annie did not arouse undue surprise, though Willcox, had he been asked in court, would have been critical of the death certificate recorded as "Hysteria and cerebral congestion", on November 12th, 1910.

William, the father, died on January 23rd, 1911, at the age of seventy-three after an illness lasting about thirty-six hours in which vomiting and diarrhoea was followed by collapse and death. Likewise the certificate of gastro-enteritis was exposed to criticism in the light of later events.

His son, James Henry Bingham, succeeded him as custodian. Being a bachelor he arranged for his sister, Margaret, to take up residence as his housekeeper. She had previously been the matron of a home for mental defectives in Hull, and within a few days she died following a similar illness lasting four days, certified as dying from a brain tumour on July 23rd, 1911.

She was replaced by her half-sister, Edith, but matters did not run smoothly in the house. She was known to have quarrelled with her brother several times, was frequently out with her boy friend till late at night. She was, it seemed, slightly subnormal mentally and only partially literate. Early in August her brother decided to replace her as housekeeper by engaging a Mrs. Cox Walker to look after his house though he never threatened to turn Edith out of his house.

On Saturday, August 12th, shortly before the new housekeeper arrived, James was taken ill and died three days later. The illness commenced half an hour after his lunch at which he ate some beef steak purchased by himself in the town, cooked by his sister Edith, and eaten by himself only. He was violently sick while showing visitors round the Castle and was seen by his doctor. Dr. J. McIntosh immediately suspected arsenical poisoning and took urgent steps to investigate by arranging to collect all fluids vomited over Saturday night. The city analyst, Mr. Martin, found a high arsenical content but wisely saved the bulk of the material for Mr. W. H. Roberts, the County Analyst. More than $4\frac{1}{2}$ grains of arsenic per pint was found in the vomit, which meant that the total volume of six pints contained over thirty grains of arsenic. The patient was very ill the next day but had improved on the Monday morning. Following the doctor's visit he relapsed however. So sure was the doctor of his diagnosis that he moved the patient to another house in the town but death occurred on the Tuesday evening.

At the inquest Roberts reported a relatively large amount of arsenic in the organs. There was no evidence to show how the poison had been taken, but suspicion naturally fell on the sister of the deceased, Edith, who had cooked the steak. An arsenical weed killer and the watering can used to spray the Castle grounds were found in a cupboard in the house. The weed killer was shown to be a highly concentrated arsenical preparation containing ninety-five grains per fluid ounce, equivalent to a fatal dose in ten drops.

Had Edith poisoned her brother in retaliation for being displaced as housekeeper by another woman outside the family circle? This appeared to be the probable motive.

The Coroner not only adjourned the inquest but obtained Home Office permission for exhumation of the three members of the family who had died earlier. Dr. McIntosh and Dr. Edmundson, who carried out the post-mortems, found the organs relatively well preserved and no cause of death. They sent the important organs to the County Analyst along with samples of soil lying above the coffins.

The organs of Annie, the first member of the family who had died, were free of arsenic. The organs of William, Margaret and James were found to contain large amounts of arsenic, the details being as follows:

Victim	Age	Duration of Illness	Death	Arsenic content in grains				
				Stomach	Small Intestine	Liver	Kidney	Spleen
William	73	36 hrs.	24 Jan. 1911	1/12	1/40	1	1/250	1/500
Margaret	48	Over 4 days	23 July 1911	1/250	1/90	1·1	1/130	a trace
James	37	Over 3 days	15 Aug. 1911	1/400	—	1/2	1/95	1/600

At the close of the adjourned inquest on August 30th, Edith Bingham was arrested on the Coroner's warrant and committed to the Assizes on a charge of wilful murder of her brother.

In his report Willcox stated that the result of the analyses of the organs from the three deceased persons were respectively consistent with the history of the three illnesses. The absence of arsenic in the remains of Annie Bingham though unexplained, was useful confirmatory evidence that the finding of arsenic in the other three bodies could not be attributed to analytical error by contamination of materials used in the technique of the Marsh and Reinsch tests; in other words, the remains of Annie served as useful "control" specimens in the analytical investigations. The water supply of the house had already been investigated and found free of poison. Matthews had suggested that arsenic might have been present in the animal which provided the beef steak. Willcox firmly contradicted this theory by stating that in death from arsenical poisoning the concentration of arsenic in muscle is extremely low, far too low to yield quantities comparable to those found in these cases or to cause death.

The trial at Lancaster Assizes before Mr. Justice Avory took place on October 27th, 28th and 30th when Edith Bingham was charged with the murders of her father, her half-sister and her brother.

Willcox was present at the opening and consulted Mr. Langdon, K.C., and Mr. Gordon Hewart, counsel for the Crown, shortly beforehand. Mr. Wingate Saul and Mr. Sellers defended the prisoner.

It was admitted that the three victims had died from arsenical poisoning and that in all probability James had died as the result of eating the beef steak or some substance taken with it. But a charwoman had witnessed the cooking of the steak and saw no reason to suspect that poison had been added. Though the circumstantial evidence pointed to the prisoner the motive was too inadequate to convince the jury. Edith did not stand to profit financially by her brother's death to any appreciable extent; indeed she lost a comfortable home by the tragedy. Though untruthful she was probably too simple-minded to realise the potential poisonous properties of weed killer available in the house.

W. H. Roberts, the County Analyst, testified that death in each case was due to arsenical poisoning. The weed killer was so powerful that 10 drops might have caused death, being a fatal dose of 2 grains. The poison would have been undetected if eaten in the steak. The wallpaper and distemper of the rooms of the house were free of arsenic.

Willcox considered that William, the father, had probably had more than one dose of arsenic because, having been ill for three days, a quantity of arsenic still remained in the stomach after death and burial. Margaret was taken ill soon after breakfast on July 19th though she had at that meal eaten of the same food as others of the household. Here, only a trace was found in the stomach, indicating that she had most likely been killed by a single dose. In the case of James, his improvement on the third day by no means disproved that death was due to a single dose of arsenic.

Toward the end of the proceedings on the first day the judge felt compelled to adjourn early, owing to the prisoner's fits of weeping and moaning and her hysterical behaviour bordering on a collapsed state. Witnesses had testified to her distressed state on the occasions of the deaths of her close relatives.

After retiring for only twenty minutes the jury returned a verdict of "Not guilty" on all counts. The case seemed to have rested mainly on suspicion. There was no evidence that the accused had arsenic in her possession or had been seen to administer it. But for unpleasant discord with her brother and the appointment of the new housekeeper she would in all probability never have been suspected. Yet the fact remains that someone unknown had poisoned three people within nine months and the clever hand that had administered the poison was never discovered. Yet another mystery had been added to the history of Lancaster Castle.

Chapter 5

The Poison Mystery of Tollington Park.—1912
(*Rex* v. *Seddon*)

Napoleon was said to have described England as a nation of shop-keepers, a sarcastic comment on their supposedly businesslike attitude to life. Had he lived at the time when Frederick Seddon and his wife were on trial for murder, he might have claimed justification for his contempt for the British people. For the alleged murder of Miss Eliza Barrow by poison was cleverly carried out for financial gain and the acquisition of her property. In the solution of the mystery of this crime, Willcox and Webster played so conspicuous a part that their names became permanently linked with this memorable case.

Frederick Seddon was a conceited, thrifty and avaricious man from Lancashire, who enjoyed the acquisition of property for its own sake, yet spending little money either on himself or others. In 1910 he was aged 40, living at 63 Tollington Park in Finsbury, with his wife aged thirty-seven, five children and his seventy-three-year-old father on the ground and first floor of their respectable three-storeyed house, his business as an Insurance Company Superintendent being conducted in the basement. The house still stands unaltered today.

To the outside world they might have been regarded as typical residents of the neighbourhood, yet Seddon and his wife were revealed by several witnesses at the trial as an unusual and unostentatious couple who probably had few friends in the district. Seddon's meanness is illustrated in the police depositions taken from his father who went to live with the family in February 1911. The house, adequate enough for the family, was scarcely large enough to accommodate Miss Barrow and her ten-year-old son as lodgers in the three top floor rooms, an arrangement which commenced in July 1910. Seddon and his wife occupied the first floor bedroom, five children (the eldest a boy of seventeen) and their grandfather the back bedroom on the same floor, a partition dividing the grandfather and boys from the girls. Yet at the time of Miss Barrow's fatal illness Seddon's sister and her daughter came to stay; the visit caused the boys and their grandfather to move to one of Miss Barrow's rooms on the top floor, the room next to the invalid lodger.

Miss Barrow was described as eccentric, deaf and elderly, yet she was no more than forty-nine at the time of her death. She was quick tempered and prone to moods of silence, rather like Edward Black who figured in a later poison drama of 1922. Possessed with private means sufficient in those days to enable her to live in a crude, simple fashion without the need to work for her living, she shared with Seddon a character trait of thrift and meanness which may have accounted for the confidence she came to acquire in Seddon as a financial adviser.

Of the fifty-two witnesses at the trial only two need detain us here: Mr. and Mrs. Frank Vonderahe who lived less than a quarter of a mile away. Frank was a cousin of Miss Barrow and her only relative, except for his brother. Before 1909 Miss Barrow had lived with a Mrs. Grant and her son. After Mrs. Grant's death Miss Barrow had adopted her orphaned boy Ernest, caring for him with affection as her son. In 1909 she came with Ernest to live with the Vonderahes, but the arrangement did not work out as had been hoped, quarrelling started and she decided to leave. Being a confiding woman Miss Barrow discussed her worldly possessions with the Vonderahes, and later with the Seddons, no doubt seeking their advice from time to time. At the time she moved to Tollington Park she was the owner of £1,600 of India Stock, £200 invested in the Finsbury Savings Bank, a public house, and the barber's shop next door. In a cash box she kept considerable sums of money in cash, and jewellery. From all accounts she appears as a woman of little intelligence, a fact which perhaps explains her confidence in Seddon as a clever business adviser, as he probably was.

Miss Barrow's illness commenced on September 1st, 1911, taking the form of gastro-enteritis, which never cleared up. Her death came as a surprise to Dr. Sworn when Seddon reported it at his surgery in the early morning of September 14th, his patient having died in the night. He had visited his patient several times during the illness and had prescribed pills and medicines. The death certificate, notified as epidemic diarrhoea, was handed to Seddon. No doubt the doctor had been led to believe Miss Barrow had no surviving relatives.

Seddon hastily arranged the funeral with an undertaker at the cost of £4, of which sum it was mutually agreed that Seddon should retain 12s. 6d. and it took place two days after her death. She was buried in a common grave. But the Vonderahes were not even informed of the death of their cousin. By chance they learnt of it two days later from their son, who attended the same school as Ernest Grant. The Seddons, it seemed, were not at home when the Vonderahes called at the house, but when Mrs. Vonderahe with a friend was granted an interview the next day she was handed copies of the Will, and of a letter supposed to have been posted at the time of Miss Barrow's death, informing them of the sad news and plans for the funeral. The cousins now learned that the deceased had sold all her property and investments in return for an annuity of £3 per week, but they still were unaware that Seddon had himself been the purchaser. Seddon was the sole executor of Miss Barrow's Will, signed by Seddon's father. Her few remaining possessions were bequeathed to Ernest Grant and his sister, consisting of clothing, furniture and jewellery.

Frank Vonderahe was refused an interview that evening, Seddon having informed his wife that he was going on holiday to the seaside. When Frank Vonderahe confronted Seddon two weeks later, his suspicion was confirmed but his reaction was also one of anger. Suspicion, because Miss Barrow's death and the handling of her Will had been personally conducted by Seddon without his rightful knowledge as a relative, and anger because he had been prevented from making the arrangements for the burial of his cousin in the family vault at Highgate cemetery, which he had known of since his boyhood. At this stage he communicated with the Director of Public Prosecutions, Sir Charles Matthews, and the police.

The Exhumation

When Willcox was consulted by George Cohen, the coroner, at Welbeck Street on November 9th, he advised him that in the light of the legal and medical evidence so far at hand an exhumation was fully justified. On instruction by the Home Office Spilsbury and Willcox carried this out at Finchley Mortuary on November 15th, nine weeks after burial, in the presence of Frank Vonderahe and his brother Albert, who identified the body.

Spilsbury found no sign of any gross disease in any of her organs, except in the stomach and intestines which showed signs of inflammation, due either to an irritant poison or to gastro-enteritis. Suspicion of the former diagnosis was suggested by the remarkable preservation of most of the organs characteristic of arsenical poisoning.

The Analyses

The problem of the cause of death was now in the domain of Willcox and Webster. Their work in the Seddon case was one of the most exhaustive and intricate of scientific investigations hitherto carried out in crime detection. They were engaged on a search for poison, the amount in the body and evidence as to the probable time at which the fatal dose was given, and in what way it was given. Time was important and speed necessary to allow the inquest and other legal procedures to commence as soon as possible. As it finally emerged, these investigations in the Seddon case were afterwards regarded as the standard against which later similar investigations in cases of arsenical poisoning were required for legal purposes.

Willcox and Webster had already conceived the idea of employing a new modified method of analysis of unprecedented accuracy and speed. Here was a wonderful opportunity to introduce it.

Hitherto the most delicate test for arsenic was the Marsh test discovered in 1836. The suspected extract of the material is placed in the apparatus generating hydrogen, and arsenic, if present, passes off through a tube as arsenuretted hydrogen. The tube is heated to allow the arsenic to be deposited as a black "mirror" just beyond the heated area. The hydrogen is produced by the interaction of zinc and sulphuric acid. A dangerous source of possible error is the possibility of the zinc containing arsenic as an impurity. The notorious case of 1859 was the classical example; the toxicologist Taylor had made such an error in calculating arsenic using the Reinsch test in the Smethurst case of 1859. Again, Willcox had encountered the same problem in 1909 in a case in which he was consulted.

A man of fifty-nine died after an illness of three weeks' duration, in which vomiting and diarrhoea were prominent symptoms; analysis of the urine by a local pharmacist before death showed by the Marsh test a large amount of arsenic. The coroner adjourned the inquest pending further analysis by Willcox, who found no trace of arsenic. The arsenical mirror was due to impurities in the zinc used. The liver of deceased showed changes consistent with the history of chronic alcoholism, the undoubted cause of death. This fear of impurities had lurked in the minds of toxicologists and analysts for many years until Professor (later Sir Thomas) Thorpe (1845–1925), Professor of Chemistry at the Royal College of Science, invented the electrolytic method for producing hydrogen from platinum electrodes known to be absolutely free from any trace of arsenic. The method must have been used by Sir Thomas Stevenson before his death in 1908 because he must have known Thorpe as a contemporary expert in chemistry. But there had been no suspected murders by arsenic in recent years until the Bingham cases at Lancaster in 1911. In the case of *Rex* v. *Bingham* the method had been used as a qualitative test, but not as a quantitative test as in the Seddon investigations. The new method of quantitative analysis based on Thorpe's test was by the use of standard "mirrors" with which to compare mirrors obtained from extracts containing unknown amounts of arsenic. Though minor modifications may have been introduced, the new method of quantitative analysis for arsenic became the recognised procedure for many years, at any rate until the second world war. This is no place to describe the technique in detail, but at the trial of the Seddons the members of the jury were taught the theory of the method and were shown the mirrors obtained from the organs of Miss Barrow. The method obviated the necessity of weighing minute amounts of arsenic from innumerable tested specimens.

First, they passed hundreds of different known quantities of pure arsenic in solution through the apparatus, in each case obtaining the mirror to be preserved as a "standard mirror". Next, with the unknown extract of the organ to be tested the mirror obtained was compared with the standards of a known amount of arsenic. Probably it was a natural consequence of this research that led to the idea of quantitative analysis of chemical substances by colorimetry.

On November 29th Willcox returned to the mortuary. He had wisely ordered that the body should not be re-interred. With the utmost care he weighed the whole body—67 lbs. 2 ozs. He took away further samples of hair, muscle and several nails. Each organ had already been weighed with precision. Small quantities of each organ were analysed, the stomach, intestines, liver, kidneys, spleen, lungs, heart, brain, muscle, skin, nails and bone. In each case the mirror was compared with the standards ranging from one milligram down to 1/200th of a milligram. By arithmetic the amount of arsenic in each organ was obtained by multiplication. Traces found in the hair, nails, skin and bone were ignored in calculating the total amount of arsenic in the whole body. Yet the procedure was not one of absolute scientific accuracy. To obtain this it would be necessary to disintegrate and use the whole body, a procedure too lengthy and im-

practicable to be used for legal purposes, quite apart from ethical considerations. How could the total weight of all the muscles of the human body be
calculated? In this estimate they were forced to use scientific knowledge
possessed by the foremost authorities in anatomy. The total weight of the
muscles of the human body is equal to 2/5ths of the total body weight.
In the case of Miss Barrow 6 grms. of muscle contained 1/30th milligram of
arsenic, which meant that in all her muscles there were 67·2 milligrams
(1·03) grains equivalent to half a fatal dose of arsenic. And in other organs
analysis yielded a similar total quantity, the greater part being found in
the intestines (41 mgs.) liver (11·13 mgs.) stomach (7·3 mgs.), kidneys
(1·91 mgs.) and smaller fractions of a milligram in the remaining organs.

Now Willcox was well aware that Marshall Hall, the defence counsel,
was well acquainted with scientific evidence in relation to the law. Being
the son of a doctor he possessed, perhaps, more medical and scientific
knowledge than any other advocate of his time. Knowing that he would
have to face a lengthy cross-examination, Willcox took the precaution of
not relying entirely on the new method of analysis. Taking the organs with
the highest arsenical content, in this case the liver and intestines, he
estimated the arsenic by the old and well-established Reinsch quantitative
test, in which the extracts were treated with sulphuretted hydrogen, the
arsenic being precipitated as sulphides, and weighed. From these two
organs he obtained by weighing 0·8 grain (52·13 mgs.) of arsenic equivalent
to nearly half a fatal dose.

On December 4th he reported to Sir Charles Matthews that he had no
doubt that death was due to arsenical poisoning and that a poisonous
dose had been taken in the last two days of life of deceased, judging by
the arsenic in the intestines and liver. The same day Matthews' orders to
arrest Seddon were carried out. On December 11th Willcox reported that
the total amount of arsenic in all the organs examined was 131·57 mgs.
(2·01 grains). Allowing for other organs not examined, the total content in
the body would have been well over this estimate. The presence of minute
amounts in the skin, hair and nails indicated that arsenic had been
administered for two weeks or more before death, a period corresponding
to the duration of Miss Barrow's illness.

Having informed Richard Muir of the trend of events in the laboratory,
Willcox produced his results at the adjourned inquest on December 14th.
The verdict was "death due to arsenical poisoning administered by some
person or persons unknown."

The Source of Arsenic

The first stage of the investigations was by now completed, except for
further analysis of the hair samples. Willcox and Webster next turned their
attention to the investigation of materials taken from the house by the
police; medicines, pills and flypapers. The latter were the only substances
recovered from the house which were known to contain arsenic; at the
trial it was inferred that arsenic had been extracted from the flypapers by
the Seddons, though no direct evidence was ever produced. Mrs. Maybrick,

at her trial in 1889 on a charge of poisoning her husband, had admitted her habit of obtaining arsenic from this source for (so she said) use as a cosmetic for her skin. In August and September the weather was fine and hot; flies must have been abundant in London and flypapers were evidently in great demand.

Analyses were carried out of flypapers obtained from the house, four chemists shops in the neighbourhood, and from samples from Mather's factory. In each case arsenic was extracted (a) by boiling in water, (b) by pouring boiling water on papers torn up into small pieces and soaking overnight, (c) soaking small pieces in cold water overnight and (d) boiling the flypaper in water for five minutes only. By method (a) the highest content of arsenic was obtained in each case. The arsenic content of each flypaper varied between 3·8–6 grains, more than a fatal dose in each.

On March 4th, the day the trial of the Seddons commenced, Willcox issued a further report expressing his opinion on the possible sources of the poison. Arsenic is relatively tasteless and soluble in cold water in a strength of one grain per ounce. It could be obtained from a laboratory, or chemist, by signature in the Poisons Register, by a doctor's prescription in the form of tablets each containing 1/20th grain, or as weed killer and vermin killer. Careful study of the depositions was of little help. During her illness Miss Barrow had been known to take fluids in many forms. Valentine's meat juice was recovered from the house, a concentrated extract to be diluted with water, one teaspoonful to one tablespoonful. If the arsenic from a flypaper was added in reasonable dilution no alteration in colour, smell or taste was detected. Likewise with brandy, half a fatal dose could be added without detection in two ounces; and it was known that Miss Barrow had taken brandy frequently during her illness.

The Trial of the Seddons

The trial, which commenced on March 4th at the Old Bailey before Mr. Justice Bucknill, was to last ten days, being one of the two longest trials in which Willcox ever took part, the other being the Armstrong trial of 1922. It was remarkable in many other respects. Seven counsel took part. As was usual in cases of charges of murder by poison, the Attorney-General led for the Crown—in this case Sir Rufus Isaacs, later Lord Reading. He was assisted by Mr. Richard Muir, Mr. S. A. Rowlatt, and Mr. Travers Humphreys. Seddon was defended by Mr. Marshall Hall assisted by Mr. Dunstan and Mr. Orr. Mr. Gervais Rentoul defended Mrs. Seddon. There was no precedent for a capital case where two persons were indicted for the same offence, and confronted by the same evidence; where the jury were required to make a choice of four verdicts. The net which entrapped the accused was one of circumstantial evidence woven so closely that the defence had little chance of extricating them; evidence of motive, opportunity and behaviour which was fully explored. Neither Seddon nor his wife were ever seen to handle arsenic by any witness, though they had sent their daughter to purchase flypapers containing it.

Nor were they known to possess any knowledge of poisons by reason of their occupation or education.

Probably in no other trial had the technical details of scientific investigation been so exhaustively exposed and so many investigations in the laboratory been carried out, as was the case here. Willcox calculated that Webster and he had conducted 148 scientific tests. In the only recent comparable trial, *Rex* v. *Bingham* (1911), details of technical analysis for arsenic had scarcely been discussed in court at all, the quantities analysed by the experts being accepted without question. But in the Seddon case Marshall Hall sought every avenue of escape through the net. As the trial proceeded it seemed that the scientific evidence was the only avenue of escape still left to him to explore with any hope of success. The Attorney-General dealt exhaustively with the business side of Seddon's life and the financial aspects of the case which took up a great part of the evidence in the first three days of the trial. No attempt can be made here to probe into the details. It forms no real part of this story, but it is nevertheless of great interest as revealed in Filson Young's account in the Notable Trials series.

No less than fifty-two witnesses gave evidence, including the five doctors. Dr. J. F. Paul and Dr. J. A. Francis had attended Miss Barrow before her final illness, Dr. H. J. Sworn during its course; on the 4th day Spilsbury, then Willcox, appeared in the witness-box, the latter completing his evidence on the 5th day. He was in the witness box for nearly four hours.

Spilsbury's evidence was corroborative of that of Willcox. The exhumed body was unexpectedly well preserved, showing no signs of any gross disease except those of inflammation of the stomach and intestines as would be expected in arsenical poisoning. There were no features to indicate that arsenic had been given over a prolonged period, for weeks or months. He agreed that two grains had been administered within three days of death and a like amount perhaps before that.

In his evidence Willcox described how the analysis had been carried out using the new electrolytic Marsh-Berzelius test which had eliminated the possibility of impurities in the apparatus. The arsenic content of the liver and intestines had been estimated, however, by the well recognised Reinsch method, the arsenic in these two organs being weighed. He had carefully used a quarter of the whole liver and a fifth part of the whole intestine in this way, allowing the remainder to be preserved either for confirmatory analysis or for investigation by an independent analyst chosen if desired by the defence. From the liver and intestines 0·8 grain of arsenic was actually weighed—an amount approaching a fatal dose and nearly half the total arsenic analysed. Willcox was thus exposed to criticism of the new method in respect of the remaining part of the total arsenic analysed in the body (2·01 grains).

His opinion was that a dose of about five grains had been taken within three days of the death of deceased, allowing for three grains likely to have been eliminated by purging, vomiting and excretion in the urine. He was frankly surprised to find that the jury quickly understood his simple description of the Marsh test and took keen interest in the five specimens of mirrors containing arsenic alongside the blank mirror obtained from the liver of a normal healthy sheep. Other exhibits from the laboratory were bottles containing extracts of flypapers diluted with water to form brownish coloured liquid and a bottle of Valentine's diluted meat juice containing a grain of arsenic. He went on to explain the presence of traces of bismuth and mercury in the stomach and intestines being due to the pills and medicine known to have been prescribed previous to Miss Barrow's final illness. The bismuth mixture had itself been analysed and found free of any trace of arsenic.

But the climax of the trial came during Marshall Hall's cross-examination of Willcox. The whole subject of arsenical poisoning was explored in the greatest detail and the case of Miss Barrow's illness and death in particular; the flypapers and Valentine's meat juice as possible vehicles of administration and the possible idiosyncrasy of the deceased to arsenic.

Marshall Hall made three desperate attempts to discredit Willcox's estimations of minute amounts of arsenic by comparing the mirrors with known standards. He studied several of the mirrors and passed them to the jury, selecting that from the lungs.

"Take, for instance, the lungs. The mirror you have got shows 1/50th of a milligram?—Yes.—That is what you get from a sample which weighs six grams, is it not?—Quite so, the multiplying factor is large.

"I dare say you will tell me the multiplying factor in order to arrive at the amount of arsenic which that organ contained?—Roughly fifty.

"Therefore an error in the diagnosis of the mirror is multiplied 50 times in the calculation of the amount of arsenic?—Exactly.

"Would you mind telling me what was the multiplying factor in the case of the stomach?—About two hundred.—In the kidneys?—Sixty.

"So that in every one of these cases a very minute error in the measurement of the mirror would make a great difference in the ultimate calculation?—That is so.

"And it is only fair to ask you, have you taken the greatest possible care in your examination of the mirrors to examine them to the best of your ability? Yes, I have done my very best."

Willcox had indeed taken the greatest pains to be accurate, for his work had been checked first by Webster at St. Mary's Hospital and now by the jury in court.

Next, Marshall Hall raised the subject of the weight of the body of Miss Barrow. No one knew what she had weighed when alive, and Willcox, two weeks after the exhumation, weighed her precisely—67 lbs. 2 ounces. Her height was 5 feet and 4 inches.

"Would you accept that the body may have weighed ten stone at the time of death?—I should say that it was less than that.

"Do you think that ten stone would be an unfair weight to take as probable?—Not when she was in health.

"In the case of muscle examination, the sample that you took weighed six grams?—Yes.

"And you produce a mirror which you diagnose as 1/30th of a milligram?—Yes.

"The multiplying factor in that case is something enormous, is it not?—It is very big.

"It is nearly 2,000 as I work it out?—It would be approaching that.

"In the case of the muscles you have no absolute weight by which you multiply your sample, have you?—No.

"I find that the result of your calculation was no less than 1·03 grains (67·2 mgs.) of arsenic?—Yes.

"That is to say, slightly more than half the total calculated weight of arsenic in the body?—About half.

"Now you have worked upon the assumption that the weight of the muscle in the body is equivalent to about two-fifths of the weight of the body. That is an accepted dictum, is it not?—Yes.—But this is the relative calculated weight of muscle in the living body, is it not?—Yes, or in the dead body.

"And the weight of all component parts is to some extent dependent upon the weight of water in those parts?—Yes.

"Now, in this case you have got a drying up of the whole body, have you?—Yes, some drying.

"The ratio of the drying is quicker in the muscle than it is in other parts of the body?—Not necessarily.

"But I suggest to you that muscle contains 77 per cent of water?—Yes. "Bone contains only 50 per cent so that you see the muscles would lose water, assuming that they lose at the same rate, in a greater proportion, 77 to 50, compared with bone?—I agree with you as regards bone but not as regards other organs.

"And I am sure it was an oversight, but in making this calculation you have made no allowance whatever for the loss of water?—No, I have not.

"Do you think you ought to have made some allowance?—Well, the calculation of the weight of muscle can only be approximate.

"If you make the allowance that I suggest ought to be made, the effect would be slightly to reduce it?—Yes, slightly to reduce it.

"Using it honestly to the best of your ability, it is only an approximate calculation that you arrived at in regard to the amount of arsenic in the body?—That is so."

Marshall Hall had made his points well. The total body weight must have decreased between burial and exhumation, but this period was only nine weeks. During that period the weight of muscle in proportion to the whole body, two to five, would not have changed to any great extent though had the period of burial been a year or more Marshall Hall's clever hypothesis would have carried more weight in the eyes of the jury than it actually did.

Lastly, Marshall Hall played his last card again with clever ingenuity. This time he dealt with the hair.

"You are convinced that this is a case of acute arsenical poisoning?—I have no doubt about it.

"In the proximal hair you found 1/80th milligram?—Yes. I took 3 inches of hair from both the proximal and distal ends.

"In the distal hair (at the extremities) what did you find?—1/300th mg.

"The distribution of arsenic in the hair would not alter after death?—No.

"The metabolic changes cease: you get no alteration in the amount of arsenic?—No.

"Is the finding of arsenic in the hair corroborative of acute or of chronic arsenical poisoning?—If arsenic is found in the hair, it indicates that arsenic has probably been taken over some period, something like three months, but there would be traces in the proximal hair earlier than that.

"The amount you have got here in the distal hair is a comparatively large amount?—This amount might possibly mean some arsenic had been taken perhaps a year or more ago. The taking of arsenic could have been intermittent."

Marshall Hall then changed the line of his enquiry to the question of accumulation of arsenic in the body and its excretion by the kidneys. Meanwhile Willcox was in deep thought about the explanation of arsenic in the distal hair. Had he been right in saying that it does not alter after death? By the time Marshall Hall reverted to the hair, he had a possible explanation.

"Dr. Mann is a great authority on arsenic in hair?—Yes, the greatest authority.

"His view is that arsenic does not move with the metabolic changes, and you agree with me that the changes in the tips of the hair would be practically nothing?—Yes, but there is one point which I have not mentioned, which I should mention now, which rather affects these results. That is, that when I took the hair for analysis it was at the second examination; the hair had been lying in the coffin and the ends of the hair (about 10 inches long) had been soaked in the fluid exuding from the body."

Willcox had solved the problem in his own mind while answering other questions in the witness box. Poor Marshall Hall was now disconcerted.

"Yes, but you washed the hair carefully?—Yes, I washed off anything on the surface, but it is possible that absorption had occurred, so that the results are higher than the results would have been if the hair had been taken dry. This opinion is borne out by the analysis of the hair from the undertaker, which showed an infinitesimal amount of arsenic."

By a curious chance Seddon had arranged with the undertaker to cut some hair from Miss Barrow's scalp to give as sentimental souvenirs to Ernest Grant and his sister. The absorption of arsenic by hair soaked in arsenical solutions after death was a new discovery in toxicology, later to be verified by several research workers.

But Willcox was not content to let matters rest there. While the cross-examination was proceeding, he decided he must prove to the court, if he could, the truth of his hypothesis that hair could absorb arsenic after death from immersion in fluids containing arsenic. But first he had to complete his lengthy cross-examination. Marshall Hall reverted to the hair problem a third time.

"Does the finding of arsenic in the distal hair in any way affect your view that death was due to acute arsenical poisoning?—Not in the very slightest.

D.P.—3

"Why?—Because there was a considerable amount of arsenic in the stomach: 1/10 grain; 2/3rd grain in the intestines, and that arsenic must have got in within two days of death; and the amount in the liver."

Marshall Hall could not dispute these findings. He produced no expert witness for the defence to contradict the scientific evidence; here was the main weakness of his case. He had, however, obtained the services of a physiological chemist, Dr. Rosenheim, to check on the methods and results of the analyses. This was brought out in Willcox's evidence in re-examination by the Attorney-General at the end of the fourth day's hearing:

"Can you tell me whether a gentleman skilled in medicine came to you from the defence during the course of the case?—Yes, Dr. Rosenheim.

"And did you show him the mirrors you had made?—Yes.

"Did you show him the results?—I showed him everything. We went together through all the mirrors from every organ and matched them together with the standard mirrors.

"Had you any part of the organs left at that time?—Yes.

"Was the apparatus set up?—Yes.

"Was it in a position to be used there and then if necessary?—Yes."

Thus it was made apparent to the court that Dr. Rosenheim had no wish to go into court to criticise the analytical work.

During the early part of the trial Willcox had carried out tests by mixing extracts of flypaper with brandy, a drink which Seddon had been seen administering to Miss Barrow. By mixing three parts of an extract containing one grain of arsenic with one part of brandy, the mixture was slightly darker brown than brandy similarly diluted with water. The taste was not apparently altered. These specimens were produced as exhibits by Willcox in court on the following morning, the fifth day of the trial. But it was late on the eighth day that Willcox was recalled to court for the third time to present his crucial experiments on the riddle of arsenic in the distal hair.

"The hair which is the subject of this experiment was normal and free from any trace of arsenic. I soaked this hair for twenty-four hours in the bloodstained fluid obtained from the coffin. I washed it as thoroughly as possible. I then broke it up to destroy the organic matter and submitted the hair to the Marsh test. I found the hair had absorbed an appreciable quantity of arsenic. I have the mirror here as an exhibit (passing it to the jury). The result is that hair soaked in body fluids containing arsenic will absorb arsenic throughout its entire length. The constituent in hair called keratin will absorb arsenic . . . This deposition of arsenic in the hair would occur after death. Fourteen days elapsed between my first and my second examination of the body . . There is no difference in arsenical content between the distal and proximal hair except that the proximal ends, being thicker, absorbed slightly more."

So it was that a new discovery was made by a curious chance—the cross-examination by a clever lawyer of an experienced analyst—that arsenic could be absorbed into hair by soaking in fluids containing arsenic; a new and obviously important observation in forensic science. Marshall Hall had failed in his battle to destroy the value of the scientific evidence in the eyes of judge or jury, but nevertheless made the most of his brilliant oratory in his final speech for the defence, ending up with an allusion to the limitation of scientific investigation:

"There is one thing the scientists have never yet been able to find, never been able to discover, with all their research and their study, and that is how to replace the little vital spark that we call life. Upon your (the jury's) verdict here depends the life of this man."

Sir Rufus Isaacs, early in his final speech, referred thus to the testimony of Willcox and Spilsbury:

"Whatever else may be said of science, whatever criticism may be directed to medical testimony, this is at least established in this case—that the evidence of Dr. Willcox and Dr. Spilsbury examined, closely scrutinised, as it quite properly was by my learned friend, stands quite uncontradicted and unchallenged. My learned friend paid a very high compliment to Dr. Willcox, and I would like in passing to say this, that in the course of a very long experience at the Bar I never remember hearing witnesses give evidence as Dr. Willcox and Dr. Spilsbury did, with more impartiality and more honesty in every word they uttered. This, however, is not in controversy in this case. I am not uttering one word with which my learned friend would disagree. On the contrary, Mr. Marshall Hall has emphatically stated he is in complete agreement with the views I have just stated to you . . . Dr. Rosenheim, my learned friend's expert witness who was expected to go into the box to contradict, has not been called to do so in this case. He was here during the whole of the evidence given by Dr. Spilsbury and Dr. Willcox . . . and he has not been called for the simple reason that he could not contradict anything that they had said."

Turning to the question of possible inaccuracy in the reading of the mirrors, he claimed that this was more than compensated by the omission of the arsenic in the hair, skin and bone in the final calculation of the arsenic content of the whole body.

But the greater part of this lengthy speech was taken up with the business and financial affairs of the Seddons, and Rufus Isaacs was himself an expert in this department. While these transactions are of great general interest they are inappropriate in this account though several points must be referred to in order to indicate the insuperable strength of the circumstantial evidence which weighed the balance against the accused.

Seddon had arranged the annuity with Miss Barrow without the employment of a lawyer; he himself made the contract and document of the transaction. He got possession of £1,600 India Stock without any written agreement at all. Miss Barrow was known to have had in her possession in the house gold sovereigns to the value of £316 and bank notes to the value of about £165, all of which disappeared after her death. Most of these notes had been changed by Mrs. Seddon for gold sovereigns at various shops, and at the post office where she gave a false name and address on a date in August 1911. Then there was the evidence of the purchase of fly-papers by the daughter Maggie at Thorley's the chemist shop, on August 26th and of the identification of the girl by Mr. T. Thorley who remembered her well coming to his shop to make the purchase. The second attempted purchase of flypaper from a different chemist on December 6th, two days after her father's arrest, was even more puzzling. It was not a season for flies. This chemist refused the sale because he had heard of Seddon's arrest! Presumably she had been sent by her mother, perhaps on legal advice to obtain flypapers for analysis on behalf of Seddon's legal advisers. The prosecution had irrefutable proof that Seddon had consulted a jeweller on the day after Miss Barrow's death. He had ordered her ring to be enlarged to fit his own finger and the engraving of her name and initials on her watch to be erased.

Approaching the close of his speech, Sir Rufus Isaacs referred to the value of circumstantial evidence:

"It is right that you should scrutinise, examine and investigate it most carefully. It is utterly wrong to suggest, as has been suggested in this case, that you should not convict on circumstantial evidence. If criminals can only be convicted on direct evidence, the result would be that a vast number of crimes would never be discovered. But I entirely agree with my learned friend that you must be slow to convict on circumstantial evidence."

In summing up, the speech of Mr. Justice Bucknill was a little less lengthy, and though unbiased, inclined towards a conviction but, as Willcox said afterwards, both judge and jury had no doubt whatever in their minds of the cause of death and the reliability of the tests on which the case to a great extent depended. One or two allusions to Willcox's work and opinion must be quoted here, though the legal arguments were also thoroughly brought out.

"The Crown says that the direct cause of death was a fatal dose of arsenic given to her, though previous doses may have been administered, within three days of death or even within four or five hours. That is the evidence of Dr. Willcox to which I now call your attention. Dr. Willcox's evidence is of expressed certainty—'I am sure that she died of acute arsenical poisoning; I have no doubt about it. . . .' But the reason why he says this is because of the amount of arsenic which he found in the stomach and intestines." And again,

"Now, gentlemen, it has been said very often that, however high the authority of a scientific witness may be, the jury are to be distinctly independent because the evidence is of opinion only. Well, that has its limitations. In this particular case Dr. Willcox stands at the very top of his profession in regard to scientific analyses. That is admitted; Mr. Marshall Hall has said that. He has also said of Dr. Willcox what, of course, he is entitled to say for all who know him as a public man, that he is an absolutely honest, straightforward man who would not go one hair's breadth out of his way to hurt anybody. He has a reputation which entitles him to have that said of him. I should think you will agree with me from the way he gave evidence—the modest and quiet, but at the same time the clear and firm manner he gave his evidence."

This final speech of the judge and the closing scenes were the most dramatic part of the trial. The jury were absent for exactly an hour before announcing their verdict. Frederick Seddon was found guilty and his wife not guilty. Seddon had evidently prepared himself for this verdict for, when asked by the Clerk of the Court whether he had anything to say, he proceeded to deliver quite a long speech, seeming to be suddenly relieved from his inhibitions. In perfect command of himself, as Filson Young describes the scene, he went through an intricate yet lurid array of facts and figures, and finally, raising his hand to take the Mason's oath, he swore by the Great Architect of the Universe that he was innocent of the crime. His composure both before and after his sentence was fully maintained while the judge was so emotionally upset that he was only able to pronounce sentence between sobs, and he finished it in tears.

The Appeal was heard before Mr. Justice Darling, Mr. Justice Channel and Mr. Justice Coleridge on April 1st. Marshall Hall's speech lasted two days but was unsuccessful. Likewise the Appeal to the Home Secretary, Mr. McKenna, which had been supported by three hundred thousand signatures. Seddon went the same way as Crippen and at the same prison, Pentonville, on April 18th, 1912.

There were some who thought that Mrs. Seddon was as guilty as her husband, or even more so, yet she was acquitted and discharged. But the evidence at the trial went to show that Frederick Seddon was the dominant partner of the two, and the household was conducted on patriarchal lines. Perhaps it was for these reasons she got off or perhaps because she was the mother of five children. She married again in the same year and emigrated to California.

The historical importance of the Seddon case lay in its legal ramifications, the brilliant conduct of the case both by the Crown and the Defence Counsel, and the scientific evidence which was a landmark in the history of toxicology in relation to the Law.

References

The Trial of the Seddons, Notable British Trials by Filson Young, 1914. (William Hodge & Co.).

Bernard Spilsbury—His Life and Cases by Dennis Browne and E. V. Tullett, 1951. (Harrap).

Famous trials for Murder by Arsenic.
With the exception of the Maybrick Case Willcox gave critical evidence in each Trial.

Case	Year	Length of final illness of Deceased	Analysts	Arsenic analysis of main Organs in milligrams						Total analysed	Period of Burial before Exhumation	Result of Trial
				Stomach	Intestine	Liver	Kidneys	Lungs	Muscle			
Maybrick	1889	13 days	Thomas Stevenson	0	6	21	Trace	—	—	27	20 days	Conviction Reprieve
Bingham, Margaret	1911	3–4 days	W. H. Roberts	·26	·72	71·28	·5	—	—	72·7	7 weeks	Lancaster Castle Cases
Bingham, J. H.	1911	3½ days	W. H. Roberts	·16	—	32·4	·7	—	—	33·3	—	Acquittal of Ethel Bingham
Bingham, Wm.	1911	36 hours	W. H. Roberts	54	1·62	64·8	·32	—	—	72·14	8 months	
Seddon	1912	2 weeks	W. H. Willcox and J. Webster	7·3	41·0	11·13	1·91	·94	67·2	131·57	9 weeks	Conviction
Greenwood	1920	12 hours	J. Webster and G. Roche Lynch	·6	4·88	8·5	1·2	·79	—	18·07	10 months	Acquittal
Armstrong	1922	4 weeks approx.	J. Webster and G. Roche Lynch	4·5	48·3	138	13·2	1·0	—	208·2	10 months and 3 weeks	Conviction
Black	1922	12 days	J. Webster and G. Roche Lynch	·17	1·22	1·55	·5	—	—	3·73		Conviction
Pace	1928	16 days	R. Ellis	Trace	304·6	233·3	64·8	—	—	602·7		Acquittal

Chapter 6

The Scientific Witness—1912-13

For Willcox, as Home Office Pathologist, it was not unusual to have two murder cases under investigation concurrently. The death of Miss Barrow was still sub-judice when the year 1912 opened, though Seddon had been under arrest since December 4th. On the morning of January 3rd the body of a forty-nine-year-old woman, considered to be a prostitute, was found naked bar shoes and stockings on the bedroom floor of her two-bedroom house in Leicester. To natives of Leicestershire and Rutland this was a particularly rare and horrible crime as they were proud of the fact that their crime rate was lower than that for any other part of the country. Examination of the body indicated that she had bled to death; her bed was soaked with blood no doubt caused by an extensively cut throat. Police investigation led to the arrest of her suspected assailant on the evening of the day the crime was discovered. The deceased had been seen in the "Crown and Cushion" on the previous day in the company of two men, one of whom had been seen off from Leicester on a train at 3.30 p.m., thus having a successful alibi. The other man, Archie Johnson, aged 28, was therefore under the strongest suspicion. The police delivered most of his clothing to Willcox at St. Mary's Hospital on January 8th. Meanwhile, the police surgeon had found signs of extensive injuries likely to have contributed to death; but in addition tooth marks on the skin of the neck became an important part of the scientific evidence in the enquiries. The skin from the neck was carefully removed; the tooth marks corresponded roughly with the indentations made on blotting paper by the prisoner on arrest. The specimens became important exhibits at the trial. At the resumed inquest and police court hearing on January 16th Willcox described recent extensive smears of human blood on the lining of the trousers but there were very few stains on the outside of the jacket and trousers. Moreover these stains on the lining of the trousers were smears which he thought were caused by a man putting on the trousers over blood smeared legs; the inference being that the murder was committed by a man in a state of undress. The jury's verdict was one of wilful murder against Johnson. The evidence had suggested murder following a sexual assault.

The trial of Archie Johnson opened on January 29th at Leicester Assizes before the Commissioner of Assize Mr. H. F. (later Sir Henry) Dickens, the Crown Counsel being Sir Ronald Atkins. At the commencement the Commissioner ordered all women present to vacate the Court, a step which even at that time seemed somewhat prudish in the light of the extensive press publicity accorded to the sordid details of the murder revealed at the trial. In his evidence Willcox supported the evidence regarding the significance of the tooth marks made on the skin of the neck in relation to the identification of the prisoner. Nevertheless in spite of the strong circumstantial evidence and perhaps on account of the complete absence of any clear motive for the crime the jury acquitted the prisoner after retiring for thirty-five minutes toward the end of the third day of the trial.

The condition known as Status Lymphaticus as a rare cause of death has always been a subject of controversy among pathologists, some of whom have denied that the disorder is ever the sole cause of death. The thymus gland, situated in the chest, is relatively large at birth but becomes smaller in size from the age of two onwards; it may disappear almost entirely in adult life or remain as a small gland weighing less than five grams, according to Spilsbury. From 1870 onwards it came to be realised that in cases of sudden death, post-mortem examination might reveal no other cause of death than an enlarged thymus; in certain circumstances the enlarged gland could obstruct the air passages. Not unnaturally in law the thymus became a gland of great importance.

The death of another woman prostitute, Molly Balsdon, who lived alone with her Pomeranian dog in a flat in Shroton Street, London, was such a case. On February 28th, 1912, she was found dead in bed. The post-mortem, carried out by Pepper and Spilsbury, revealed pressure marks on the neck, some probably caused by nails, at the angle of the jaw, on the chin and on the left shoulder. There was bruising of the neck muscles. The signs pointed to strangulation, yet the thymus gland weighed twenty-one grams, four times what would be expected in an adult.

Suspicion was focused on a man named Alabaster, heard in her flat in the early hours of the morning of the tragedy. He had fled to Paris where he was arrested and charged with the murder. Willcox was requested by Sir Charles ("Willie") Matthews, the Director of Public Prosecutions, to report on the case and to join in the discussions with Pepper, Spilsbury and Richard Muir, the Crown Counsel. Maurice Alabaster was tried at the Old Bailey on June 14th and 15th before Mr. Justice Bankes; he was defended by Marshall Hall. The joint opinion of the doctors was that, though the thymus was not large enough to cause death from natural causes, external pressure on the neck by throttling had caused sudden asphyxia or heart failure, the fright being probably a contributory factor in causing death. The prisoner had pleaded not guilty of murder, but guilty of manslaughter. On the direction of the judge the Jury's verdict was manslaughter and the sentence was nine months in the second division.

In the summer of 1912 the police in Shropshire were concerned with an outbreak of horse maiming which was traced to a suspect later certified as insane by the Medical Superintendent at Shropshire Asylum. Willcox's scientific detection, as in the case of *Rex* v. *Brooks*, was seen at its best here. His affection for horses and his interest in their welfare fully justified his unremunerated visits to Shropshire. He carried out a thorough investigation of the clothes of the prisoner and the contents of the jacket pockets of a man whom witnesses had seen in the field where the horse was found injured.

The jacket, shirt and a piece of sponge were sent to St. Mary's laboratory for investigation. On the jacket were small bloodstains, horse hairs four inches long were found in the right pocket and a handkerchief stained with human blood was found in the left pocket. Again using the precipitin test he found that the stain on the outer aspect of the right shirt sleeve was horse's blood. With a lens he found short bay hairs and a few black hairs on the jacket which exactly resembled those taken from the horse a few days later. At Wenlock Quarter Sessions held in October before the Recorder, Willcox submitted evidence that the wearer of the jacket had maimed a bay horse with black points and had cut his finger in the process. The prisoner pleaded guilty and the jury recorded a verdict of guilty but insane in the light of psychiatric evidence of obsessional insanity. "I was not quite correct," Willcox stated many years later, "because the animal was not a horse but a mare."

Home Office authority for carrying out exhumations of deceased persons could be obtained without much difficulty in cases where it appeared that there was reasonable suspicion that death had resulted from unnatural causes; such suspicion was conveyed to the police and to the coroner by relatives or friends of the deceased person for reasons of a legal nature. Authority for an exhumation would seldom be refused in spite of the fact that death had been medically certified in the normal way. The death of fifty-year-old Fanny Poffley at West Shefford, near Newbury, had caused little surprise to her doctor as she was a known sufferer from asthma and a fat, heavy woman as well. She had been nursed by her husband and two teen-aged children shortly before death. Unfortunately for Mr. Poffley he was known by the local chemist to have purchased on May 8th an ounce of strychnine for the purpose of killing rats. Several friends saw her shortly before death when convulsions were noticed; as one witness put it, "she was stretched out stiff, clutching at everything, fighting for breath for half an hour before death," not a very good description of strychnine convulsions; nevertheless the exhumation was carried out on July 12th by the local doctors, the organs being sent to Willcox for analysis. But the results were entirely negative for strychnine and other poisons. The heart showed considerable disease and dilatation consistent with death due to asthma. The case rested entirely on suspicion which would never have arisen had not Mr. Poffley purchased the strychnine when he did. The verdict of death from natural causes was undoubtedly correct. As Willcox stated, strychnine is a poison which does not decompose for a very long time in the organs after death and its detection by an experienced analyst was a comparatively simple matter.

The shooting at Edmonton of Charles Mansfield in bed on September 15th was a case of suspected fratricide in which the medical evidence tipped the scales of justice against his brother John at Tottenham Police Court in October and at his trial at the Old Bailey in November. The brothers had served together in the Rifle Brigade until John, on retiring from the service came to live with his brother earlier in the year 1912.

They had had a quarrel on the night of the tragedy. The accused claimed that the fatal shot was fired accidentally in his struggle to gain possession of the revolver with which his brother threatened him. On September 27th the coroner's jury had returned a verdict of wilful murder against John.

Willcox had made a careful study of the body post-mortem, of the six-chambered revolver, the bullet recovered from the body, of the clothing worn by deceased and the bed clothing through which the fatal bullet had passed. The fact that the bullet had traversed several layers of bed clothes was regarded as evidence against the theory of suicide. Experiments made with a similar revolver indicated that the distance from which the fatal shot was fired was not more than six inches. In his evidence at the police court Willcox illustrated by means of a white mark on his waistcoat the exact spot at which the bullet entered the body and, with a revolver, the angle at which the weapon was fired. The fatal shot, if self inflicted, must have been fired with the left hand as it would have been impossible for a right-handed person to inflict such an injury on himself unless the trigger had been pressed by the thumb. John Mansfield was found guilty at the Old Bailey on November 6th, 1912 and sentenced by Mr. Justice Phillimore with a strong recommendation to mercy.

The murder of Mrs. Catherine Hall on the night of November 23rd at Thornton Heath must have been the most brutal example of wife-murder ever investigated by Willcox. Mr. and Mrs. Hall earned their living by selling flowers in Croydon, were both habitual heavy drinkers, and were the parents of five children living in a neighbourhood of coster-mongers and hawkers. Hall had already served various terms of hard labour for larceny on six occasions. At the local public house near their home they had become intoxicated on the night of the tragedy, but before then quarrelling had been frequent, no doubt due to Hall's jealousy of an ex-soldier who had been lodging in their house. Police enquiries revealed that in February the man had sold Harry Hall a pony and cart. Part of the cost was paid in cash, the remainder being paid in the form of a weekly rental of half-a-crown in return for accommodation in the house. Before long Mrs. Hall began to go out on drinking bouts in company with the lodger with whom she engaged in an illicit friendship. On the night of the murder Hall was seen to assault his wife outside the public house and to drag her home where he renewed his attacks with the utmost brutality. The following morning he reported to the police that he had found his wife dead in bed. The body showed horrible signs of severe multiple injuries, a fractured skull, broken nose, extensive wounds and bruising of the face, the chest, abdomen and limbs.

Willcox received articles of clothing from the victim and the prisoner on arrest. Numerous bloodstains were found on all the clothes and on the shirt it appeared that the stains had resulted from actual spurting of blood from an artery. On the jacket and trousers there were long brown hairs exactly corresponding to hair cut from the head of the deceased woman. Similar hairs were found on a poker, broom handle and on the waistcoat bespattered with blood. At Croydon Police Court and at Guildford Assizes there was overwhelming evidence of guilt. Hall was convicted for manslaughter and received a sentence of twelve years' penal servitude. It would seem he was lucky to escape a capital sentence.

Two Exhumations

Exhumations, whether or not they are followed by trials for murder, are so unusual that they always attract the morbid curiosity of those interested in unnatural causes of death, though very often they serve merely to allay suspicion of foul play.

In the first three months of 1913 Willcox and Spilsbury conducted two exhumations by order of the Director of Public Prosecutions, Sir Charles Matthews. In both cases proceedings progressed no further than the inquest stage; in both the deceased were persons of wealth whose deaths led to legal repercussions concerning the disposal of their estates; both cases were of medico-legal and general interest.

Hugh Trevanion, a young bachelor of twenty-eight, was an example of a young man of inherited wealth who unfortunately was never trained for any occupation—his wealth being inherited from his grandfather who had made a large fortune in Australia during the gold rush. From his investments Hugh had an income of about £1,400 per annum when the value of money was nearly ten times that of today, and income tax was almost negligible. A Veronal addict known to have possessed morphine at various times, he died of Veronal poisoning on September 9th, 1912, in his flat at Hove where he lived with his friend and companion Albert Roe.

At the inquest held in the deceased's sumptuously furnished flat, the emotions of the coroner, jury and witnesses were aroused by the distress of the bereaved mother, and the painful disclosures of the deceased's drug habits. The cause of death being obvious, the coroner did not order a post-mortem. The verdict of the jury was death by misadventure from Veronal poisoning. Trevanion was buried in the family vault at Norwood Cemetery. It was through representations to the police by Trevanion's mother that the circumstances of the death were investigated and application for exhumation was made to the Home Office. The family of Trevanion and the police were aware of the peculiar relations of the two young men, no doubt homosexual, though this term, if not taboo in 1913, was at any rate not yet fashionable. There was certainly a possible motive for murder by poisoning even though grounds of suspicion were not very strong. Roe was not only the sole beneficiary of the will of his friend, but had received about £10,000 from Trevanion during his lifetime in return for his companionship and the abandonment of his career in the Merchant Navy.

Willcox and Spilsbury carried out the exhumation in the presence of Mrs. Trevanion on October 8th, 1912. She identified the body of her son dressed in a silk nightgown, pinned by a brooch in the shape of an umbrella and set with diamonds, formerly her own property. There were two bangles on the right wrist.

At the post-mortem they found no sign of physical disease in a well-preserved body, but analysis of the main organs alone showed over $8\frac{1}{2}$

grains of Veronal. No morphine was found, but Trevanion had been known to be in possession of it, though not a morphine addict.

The verdict of the first inquest being quashed by the High Court, Mr. Vere Benson opened the second inquest on January 24th, 1913. Held in the Magistrates' Court at Hove, barely large enough to accommodate the large crowd of press reporters and members of the public, it was probably the longest inquest Willcox ever attended. The greater part of seven days was taken up by the case. Willcox was so interested that he was present on six days in Court, the case being spread over three weeks and finishing on February 14th.

The evidence of Spilsbury and Willcox was readily accepted. Both agreed that the body was well-preserved and showed no sign of physical disease. Willcox estimated that the fatal dose was about 150 grains allowing for the large amount of the drug distributed throughout the body, and that it had been administered within thirty-six hours of death. His estimate of a fatal dose of Veronal was about 50 grains. In the last three months he had seen six cases of Veronal poisoning including a case who recovered following a dose of 45 grains, thanks to energetic treatment. In the case of Trevanion, it would have been difficult to dissolve such a large fatal dose in half a bottle of wine which he was known to have taken at dinner on the evening of his death, and if given in a cup of hot coffee the taste of Veronal would have been detectable.

Trevanion, according to the evidence of his medical attendants in Hove and in London, had taken overdoses on at least two previous occasions; first in July 1912, when he had regained consciousness after artificial respiration, and more recently he had recovered from a dose of Veronal admitted by Trevanion to have been over 100 grains. He had been taking Veronal for several years and seemed to have revelled in his addiction, having boasted of his capacity to tolerate large doses of the drug and of alcohol. The London doctor described him as an amusing and brilliantly clever young man, quick at repartee but effeminate in manner and appearance, and very much under the influence of Roe whom he considered had done his best to wean him from drugs and alcohol.

Roe impressed the court by his honesty and candour and interested those present in the account of his career. He had joined the Merchant Navy after school and obtained a Master Mariner's Certificate. He first met Trevanion when he was first officer on the Oratava on a trip to Australia in 1906. A close friendship then began. He found Trevanion depressed by his family quarrels in which his mother was involved. On a second cruise to Australia Trevanion was accompanied by his brother and was noticed to take Veronal and alcohol to excess. Roe did his best to interest the young man in other activities. His help and friendship were so much appreciated that Trevanion implored him to resign his career at sea and become his permanent companion, as he later agreed to do in 1909. A few weeks before the tragedy Roe informed Trevanion that he contemplated marriage, which would have involved leaving the deceased's service and the disruption of their friendship.

The coroner's final speech lasted an hour and three quarters but was in favour of suicide. How, he asked, had deceased come to take a dose of Veronal in the region of 150 grains? Did he take it himself, or was it administered by another? By exclusion Roe was the only person with a possible motive and opportunity, but there was no evidence of administration by him. Though he stood to benefit by deceased's will he had sacrificed his career to be Trevanion's companion and had already been well rewarded financially. After 25 minutes deliberation the jury recorded a verdict of "Death by an overdose of Veronal but how and by whom administered there was no evidence to show". Their rider was "we consider that Veronal and drugs of a similar nature (barbiturates) should be forthwith placed on the poisons schedule and it should be made illegal to procure the drug unless prescribed by a medical man". The jury thus acted on Willcox's opinion as expressed in his evidence. The case was the only one in his career in which Willcox was photographed while giving evidence in a Court of Law, and it was reported as headline news by most of the daily papers of that time. It was clearly a case of suicide, more likely accidental than intentional, and an example, often quoted by Willcox in later years, of barbiturate addiction the existence of which was for long denied by several eminent authorities.

The scene of the second exhumation by Willcox and Spilsbury was the village churchyard of Iver in Buckinghamshire in the early hours of the cold morning of March 19th. In the company of Scotland Yard detectives they left London by car at 5 o'clock in the morning, the early hour being chosen to escape unwanted publicity. The tombstones of Colonel Charles Meeking and his family may be seen against the hedge on the far side of the parish churchyard in Iver. The interest of the case lies not so much in the scientific evidence as in the attitude taken up by the executors of the deceased's estate no doubt due to ill feeling which arose among the deceased's family after the colonel's death the previous year at the age of seventy-two.

Again the deceased was a man of inherited wealth, a millionaire whose father was the founder of a large drapery business. He had a town house in Belgrave Square and a country house at Iver, having been High Sheriff of Buckinghamshire. As a widower he had married a young French woman no older than his grown-up children, among whom circulated doubts as to whether their father's death was natural or not. Through their solicitors the permission for exhumation was granted by the Home Office but only as a "private" transaction and Willcox was approached accordingly. He wisely insisted on having Spilsbury to co-operate and stated their proposed fees which were readily acceded to. It was the most remunerative post-mortem ever carried out by the two pathologists, each receiving a fee of £125.

The body was conveyed to a mortuary which formerly existed behind the High Street in Eton. They found a dilated heart and a valvular defect considered to be an adequate cause of natural death, Willcox's intensive search for evidence of poisons being negative. When one of the executors argued that the colonel had never suffered from heart trouble Willcox affirmed that it was not unusual for elderly people to develop fatal heart trouble within a few hours of death. Unfortunately a dispute arose subsequently between the solicitors acting for Mrs. Meeking and those acting for the other relatives. The former, in order to allay the cruel rumours and publicity circulating concerning the colonel's death, published a letter in the *Daily Telegraph* of May 8th quoting the post-mortem report signed by Willcox and Spilsbury and mentioning that the exhumation had been carried out with Mrs. Meeking's willing consent. One of the Colonel's medical attendants, Dr. E. Cautley, published a letter in the same paper at the same time, protesting at the action of the Home Office in granting an exhumation order without any reference to the doctors who had attended the deceased. Stating that there was nothing unusual in the cause of death and the fatal course of the last illness, he went on to deplore that such action should be possible without full preliminary enquiries to obtain sufficient evidence to justify it, enquiries which would have avoided all the unpleasant publicity connected with the case.

Suspected Poisoning

Quite often Willcox would be consulted by the Home Office or coroners in cases of death from obscure causes where suspicion of poisoning arose purely as a result of local gossip. The death of thirty-one-year-old Mrs. Astbury at Southbourne on January 17th occurred after an illness lasting four days which neither her doctor nor a local specialist could diagnose. Two of her children suffered from similar symptoms—fever and headache —but made a quick recovery. Yet from the description of the illness supplied by the coroner to Willcox it seemed likely that the illness here was either cerebrospinal fever or septicaemia. Routine analysis of the organs of deceased showed no signs of poisons as he expected, nor did the post-mortem help in diagnosis. But Willcox carefully assessed all the features of the illness in the family as recorded by the doctor and came to the conclusion that they all suffered from septicaemia (no doubt due to the meningococcus, judging from the nature of the rash as described). But the inquest had been postponed till February 24th partly, as the coroner wrote, because of extravagant rumours in the district as a result of the husband's "hasty and jealous temper"; the verdict was death due to septicaemia due to bacterial invasion. In contrast to the generous fee in the Meeking case Willcox noted his modest fee of one guinea for attending the inquest at Southbourne and travelling expenses of half a guinea for the train journey, supported by five shillings for taxi fares at both ends of the journey.

The Tottenham Shooting Mystery

The circumstances surrounding the death of Alice Conely, a thirty-four-year-old widow, on April 24th, 1913, from a gunshot wound were so bizarre that Willcox was requested by Sir Charles Matthews, Director of Public Prosecutions, to attend the post-mortem at Tottenham Hospital and the inquest. The case was clearly an unprecedented accident, probably a unique case of its kind. Deceased had been nursing her brother-in-law, Frank Smith, confined to bed, under the care of his doctor, for heart trouble. She was found dead at the doorway of the bedroom. At post-mortem there was found an entrance bullet wound in the upper part of the right thigh, the bullet being found at the back of the thigh, the trajectory almost horizontal in an upward direction. It had penetrated the main artery of the limb. The bullet had traversed the bedclothes and a curtain at the bottom end of the bed. It was found to correspond with the rifle found in Smith's bed.

At the time of the tragedy Smith was seriously ill and was placed under police custody in hospital while under arrest for suspected murder. He had been employed as an engineer's fitter at a cartridge factory. At the inquest on April 29th the landlady gave evidence that Smith had been depressed enough to threaten suicide in her presence. There was no suggestion of a quarrel. Willcox, who had carefully studied the bedclothes, the wound and the clothing worn by deceased, gave evidence that the direction of fire was almost horizontal; that deceased who had entered the room just before the fatal shot was fired, must have been partially concealed from the view of Smith lying in bed. Willcox's theory fitted almost exactly with the statement made by Smith to the police: "I had the miniature rifle in bed intending to shoot myself, for I am sick of it all (the illness) but feeling better in the afternoon I tried to unload it. Hearing Mrs. Conely coming back to my room I hurriedly put the gun under the bedclothes to conceal it, when it went off." The verdict was death by misadventure.

Anti-Semitism in Russia

Seldom has a crime produced such political repercussions or inter-national publicity as that of the murder in March 1911 of a thirteen-year-old boy name Yuschinski whose mutilated body was found in a cave near the town of Kieff in Russia. So rife was anti-semitism in Russia at that time that, aided and abetted by the Russian Orthodox Church, the magistrates at Kieff seized upon a Jewish worker employed at a factory where the boy was last seen alive, and imprisoned him for two years on a charge of ritual murder of the boy.

The notorious psychiatrist, Professor Sikorski, along with several pathologists of doubtful integrity and political bias, supported the absurd theory that the boy had been tortured and ritually murdered, by the accused man Beilis. Though there was nothing in the post-mortem to support the theory from the beginning the judicial authorities set out to stamp the case with this repulsively outrageous charge in order to stir up anti-semitism throughout Russia. For many months the haunting night-mare of this extraordinary case hypnotised Russian public attention by filling whole pages in the Russian press.

The German government was so outraged by the case that diplomatic contact about it was made with the British and French governments. Their respective protestations and sense of outrage were communicated to the Russians and no doubt were a factor in delaying the trial for more than two years. The medico-legal experts of the three countries were called upon to report on the medico-legal evidence obtained from confidential official reports on the post-mortems carried out by the Russian pathologists. Pepper, Willcox and Charles Mercier, the Charing Cross Hospital psychiatrist, produced a joint report in May 1913. They considered that it was an ordinary murder of violence committed with a chisel or probably an awl such as is used by shoemakers, the wounds on the head and trunk being the cause of death. They entirely refuted the absurd hypothesis of Sikorski that there was any evidence of blood-letting, of torture, or any indication of the race and nationality of the assassin. The French and German experts were in entire agreement with their views.

Although anti-semitic feeling was common at Kieff at that time, at the end of the trial lasting for thirty days Beilis was acquitted by the jury. Nevertheless, all enlightened Russians were shamed and disgusted by the exhibition of ignorance and superstition that the proceedings at Kieff disclosed to the world. Though the acquittal was hailed with satisfaction the astonishing attempts of the prosecution to re-establish one of the myths of the Dark Ages were almost universally deplored.

Sikorski's reputation for professional integrity was so damaged by his false evidence and interpretations of the post-mortem reports, politically inspired, that a special meeting of the St. Petersburg Psychiatry Society was called to consider the case. A resolution was passed condemning his evidence as "pseudo-scientific, in disagreement with the facts recorded in the post-mortem reports and contrary to the provisions of the Statute of Criminal Procedure".

The politically inspired trial not only caused great press publicity in all European countries but caused a protestation in the medical profession in Britain. The report of Pepper, Willcox and Mercier was discussed at a meeting of the sections of Forensic Medicine and Psychiatry at the Royal Society of Medicine in August which was addressed by medico-legal experts from France and Germany. Sir James Crichton-Browne, the famous psychiatrist, expressed the feeling of the doctors present about the case "as one in which racial antipathy amounted to a criminal conspiracy and seized upon a mere independent criminal act and distorted and perverted it for its own purpose."

Unsuccessful Claims

Willcox was a man of such integrity and kindness that he often supported the cause of a bereaved relative, usually an impoverished widow, in an effort to obtain just and reasonable compensation in a just cause where there was any hope of success but he was not necessarily successful even in the later stages of his career. In the case of Mrs. Wheeler v. the London Omnibus Company he fought unsuccessfully in a claim that he considered should never have been allowed to go to court and showed up the meanness of certain of the company officials.

Wheeler was a booking clerk, aged fifty-two, in the St. Pancras parcels office of the Midland Railway who was severely injured by being knocked down by a bus in October 1912, sustaining two fractured ribs and a fractured wrist. After treatment at the Royal Free Hospital he was fit to resume work on December 2nd. But on the previous day, the very day he received notification of £50 compensation, he sustained a brain haemorrhage and died on the day he was due back at work. This was obviously a stroke and not an injury. Medical opinion at the inquest at Southend was that death was in no way attributable to the accident, the verdict being given accordingly.

In April Willcox was approached by the widow's solicitors in support of a claim for damages, the company having withdrawn their offer of £50 compensation in view of the inquest verdict.

The case came up in the King's Bench Division on May 22nd before Mr. Justice Rowlatt. The company was defended by Mr. E. Marshall Hall, and Willcox was the sole "medical" witness for the plaintiff, Mrs. Wheeler. Admitting that Wheeler was shown at post-mortem to have excessive degeneration of his arteries—more than normal for his age—Willcox firmly claimed that this condition had been accelerated by the shock and the resulting depression and anxiety caused by the accident. In court he quoted chapter and verse from Osler's famous textbook to show that these factors were recognised to predispose a patient to the chance of rupture of a small artery in the brain, as in the case of Wheeler. But the verdict was for the defendants and his case was lost. But he noted that compensation should have been reasonably and fairly met by the Omnibus Company and considered it a disgrace that they should have allowed the case to go to court. He was so incensed by the meanness of the officials that he immediately decided to return the cheque for his fee of £25 paid to him by Mrs. Wheeler, at the same time informing the solicitors for both parties of his reason for doing so, a gesture which was met by a highly appreciative letter of gratitude from Mrs. Wheeler.

The unexpected death of a dockyard worker named McVittie brought Willcox to an inquest at Portsmouth in June and to Winchester Assizes the following year. The sudden attack of gastro-enteritis having proved fatal on the seventh day of the illness the doctors suspected food poisoning from eating a pork pie a few hours before the illness began. At the inquest Willcox gave evidence that it was likely that the pork pie was the source of the infection; his colleague, the St. Mary's bacteriologist John Freeman, had recovered food poisoning bacteria from the blood at the post-mortem carried out by Spilsbury who found evidence of kidney disease. But there were no witnesses to show evidence of inefficiency in the making or baking of the pies or infection in the meat used or of contamination in the baker's shop. Willcox together with the medical witness representing the firm had earlier investigated the public health aspects of the case. Likewise, analysis by Willcox for poisons gave negative results. The jury's verdict was death from food poisoning from a pork pie as the result of an accident, there being insufficient evidence to show how the infection had got into the pie.

The widow unsuccessfully pursued her claim for damages at Winchester Assizes in February 1914. It was doomed to failure because not only did Spilsbury show there were signs of kidney disease but there was sufficient evidence to suggest that, owing to the unhygienic conditions at the dock-yard where McVittie had taken the pork pie for his lunch, contamination had much more likely occurred after purchase of the pork pie than before.

The Hatton Garden Pearl Robbery

During the years before the Great War when Willcox was senior scientific Analyst to the Home Office his opposite number on the legal side was Mr. (later Sir Richard) Muir, Senior Treasury Counsel, who came to be regarded as the most feared prosecuting lawyer of his time, with a reputation for hard work, a phenomenal memory and his meticulous attention to detail—qualities which Willcox may well have acquired from him by example. The solution of the mystery of the Hatton Garden Pearl Robbery of 1913, so brilliantly ending with the arrest, trial and conviction of the four thieves was one of Muir's greatest successes. It was one of those non-medical problems in which the help of Willcox was sought in the sphere of medical detection and though he played a minor part at a late stage in the investigations it was considered by Muir to be a link in the chain of incriminating evidence of sufficient importance to merit a two-hour interview between these two experts on September 22nd, following the arrest of the criminals. In spite of their cleverly executed coup they were caught in attempting to dispose of their plunder.

The robbery was most carefully planned, beginning with one of the gang cultivating the friendship of a postman, watching and waiting for the opportunity of stealing a consignment of jewellery consisting of a pearl necklace, valued at and insured by Lloyd's for £130,000, and two other precious pearls in the same parcel. The thieves were disappointed to discover that the parcel contained pearls and not diamonds which they really preferred for the simple reason that pearls were more difficult to exchange for money.

The famous diamond and pearl merchant Max Mayer with an establishment at 88 Hatton Garden dealt with some of the finest jewels on earth. This necklace consisted of sixty-one perfectly matched pearls which had taken ten years to collect. His agent in Paris, Henri Salomon, did not succeed in finding a buyer and at the request of Mayer sent the necklace together with three drop pearls by registered post from Paris on July 10th in a parcel sealed with Max Mayer's monogram "M.M." It was their practice to send parcels in this way as it was considered safer than by messenger. The next morning the parcel arrived at his office together with Salomon's letter advising him that the parcel was on its way. On opening the parcel, instead of the pearls he found it contained sugar cubes wrapped in newspaper. He almost fainted with consternation. Scotland Yard detectives considered it would be almost impossible to convert the pearls into cash for they were too well known wherever pearls were bought and sold; and their loss would soon be widely advertised.

The detective work which led to the arrest of these arch-thieves was complicated and brilliant. The Lloyd's underwriters offered a reward of £10,000 for information leading to the recovery of the pearls. In August two French pearl brokers were approached by a man named Gutwirth who was in possession of the necklace. The underwriters, in co-operation with the detectives, employed another French jeweller to purchase the odd pearls (not the necklace) for 100,000 francs (valued at £4,000) to be paid for in bank notes supplied by themselves, the numbers on the notes being carefully recorded. The gang of four thieves were arrested on September 2nd but the necklace was not recovered either on their persons or in their houses. The necklace was eventually discovered in the Lost Property Office at Scotland Yard, where it had been regarded as consisting merely of imitation pearls. It had been thrown away in a box in the street at Finsbury by the wife of one of the gang, Locket, when she heard of the arrest of her husband. The finder had fortunately delivered the parcel to the police station.

Earlier, a die maker named Gordon had informed the police that he had been engaged by Silverman to make a seal from a wax impression consisting of the letters "M.M.". He identified Silverman before the arrests took place while the suspects were under constant police surveillance.

The leader of the gang and the brains behind the theft was a man named Grizard with an established reputation as a jewel thief who had twice previously been unsuccessfully prosecuted by Muir and escaped the net of the law. Knowing that Mayer frequently received parcels of jewels by post he planted his confederate Silverman in an office at 101 Hatton Garden close by Mayer's establishment. Cultivating the friendship of the postman, Silverman achieved the opportunity, whether by bribery or not was never discovered, to take a wax impression of the seals which were on all the parcels sent to Mayer from his Paris agent. On the morning of the robbery the postman entrusted with the delivery of the blue parcel called first at Silverman's office and while there, through negligence, allowed one of the members of the gang to open the parcel and substitute the pieces of sugar while Silverman engaged the postman in interesting conversation.

In a case of this kind it was an achievement to arrest the suspect thieves but an equally formidable and challenging task fell to Muir of drafting the indictment in such a comprehensive way that no loop-hole of escape should be possible. He left no stone unturned to achieve this object. Willcox recorded their meeting as lasting for two hours. An analysis was required of the sealing wax used by Salomon on the original parcel, a critical examination of the wax on the package as delivered and of the wax recovered from Silverman's office. They also wanted to estimate the shortest time necessary for performing the task of undoing the parcel, substituting the sugar cubes and re-sealing as it had been done on the day of the robbery, a simple experiment in manual dexterity.

At the laboratory at St. Mary's Hospital there were delivered separate specimens of sealing wax, the seal recovered from Silverman's office, together with the wax, ladle and pliers found there.

While Webster was away on holiday Willcox was assisted by a young newly qualified doctor, Gerald Roche Lynch, who in later years was to succeed Willcox in so many appointments and co-operate so often in investigations in the field of chemical pathology. They were able to show that the sealing wax originally used by Salomon was of quite a different chemical composition from that found on the fresher seals on the parcel at delivery, that sealing wax sold in France was quite different in chemical composition from varieties sold in Britain and that the red dye differed. But finding that there were no less than seven inorganic chemical ingredients of sealing wax Willcox decided that the laboratory was too much pre-occupied with routine medical investigations to proceed further with the detailed and lengthy analyses. He procured the services of an expert consulting chemist of his acquaintance, Mr. A. Chaston Chapman, who was more expert than himself in this type of analysis. Chapman found that the wax originally used to seal the parcel in Paris, while differing from that used by Silverman in resealing, exactly corresponded with traces of wax still detectable on parts of the paper of the parcel.

Willcox himself compared sealing wax impressions using different waxes to show their close resemblance and estimated by practising on "dummy" parcels that the minimum time necessary for opening, stealing the jewels and resealing would be slightly more than two minutes.

In due course the four prisoners were charged at the Old Bailey with stealing and receiving pearls, Grizard did not escape from the clutches of the law the third time. He and his three confederates had all been previously convicted for some form of theft or larceny. Grizard and Locket were sentenced to seven years' penal servitude, Silverman to five years and Gutwirth to eighteen months. As Muir said afterwards, how tragic it was that Grizard's undoubted ability could not be devoted to some more worthy and useful speciality.

On the same day that the pearl robbers were arrested Muir and Willcox had appeared at the Old Bailey in a clearcut case of criminal abortion for which Dr. Lang and his associate McCarthy were tried before Mr. Justice Rowlatt; Muir prosecuted for the Director of Public Prosecutions. The evidence of Willcox and others was so conclusively in favour of a conviction for criminal abortion by drugs and instruments that even the powerful defence counsel—Marshall Hall, Humphrey Jenkins and Curtis Bennett— were of no avail. The patient had recovered from septicaemia after a serious illness. Lang was awarded one year and McCarthy four months' imprisonment.

Child Murders

Child murder is the most harrowing form of crime imaginable, and it is curious that Willcox was concerned with two such cases in the last few months of the year 1913 in which he gave evidence at the inquests and at the trials at the Old Bailey. Both cases were murders of children by parents, in one case by the father and in the other by the mother.

The three-day trial of Frederick Robertson commencing on October 22nd on a charge of murder of his three children while his wife was in hospital, revived memories of the Crippen case, for he disposed of the bodies of his three children under the cellar floor of the house where his family were living until June 1913. The bodies were discovered by the next tenant of the apartments on July 20th, about a month after the crime was said to have been committed. Neither the police surgeon nor Pepper and Willcox, who examined the bodies at Hackney Mortuary on July 29th, could ascertain the cause of death owing to advanced putrefaction. Willcox found no trace of poison in the bodies of the children or in the soil in the cellar and there were no blood stains on the accused's clothing; his opinion of the cause of death was admittedly a matter of conjecture, probably strangulation or smothering, though chloroform or cyanide poisoning could not be excluded. Robertson was convicted and sentenced by Mr. Justice Lush.

The tragic and heartrending story of the eleven-year-old Blue Coat schoolboy Alexander Cowe and his mother was revealed at the inquest on the death of the boy held at St. Pancras by Mr. (later Sir) Walter Schroder on November 5th.

On September 29th the boy was found dead in bed in a locked room of a London hotel, the door being forced open by the staff. Lying beside the boy was his mother, deeply unconscious. Stuffed in the boy's mouth was a pocket handkerchief. Tabloids of morphine, a hypodermic syringe and an empty chloroform bottle were found in the room. Though Spilsbury considered that death was most likely caused by asphyxia he sent the main organs to Willcox for routine analysis. While Mrs. Cowe was recovering in the Royal Free Hospital Willcox found in the main organs of the boy over three grains of morphine corresponding to an estimated fatal dose of five grains taken by mouth, an appreciable amount being found in the stomach and liver. Willcox deduced that death was accelerated by asphyxia induced while the boy was unconscious and presented the opinion at the adjourned inquest on November 5th. The verdict was wilful murder by morphine accelerated by suffocation.

Mrs. Cowe's husband had committed suicide by drowning himself in his bath eleven years previously, having failed in business as a draper and speculator. She had been rendered penniless, barely able to support her two boys by her earnings as a midwife and general nurse. The elder boy, also a pupil at the Blue Coat School, had committed suicide at the age of seventeen as a result of overwork and strain at his scientific studies, the cause of death being coal gas poisoning. His mother had excusably become depressed. In her evidence at the trial at the Old Bailey before Mr. Justice Ridley on December 12th, she described how she had been robbed of the sum of £12 while looking in a shop window and had not enough money to meet her hotel bill; her whole married life had been a long struggle against poverty and misfortune. The verdict of the jury at the trial was "guilty but insane and not responsible for her actions". She was detained at His Majesty's pleasure.

Poisoning by Morphine and Veronal

The barbiturate drug Veronal again appeared in the news in 1913 as a cause of death which drew Willcox to two inquests. That at Margate held on August 26th concerning the death of a young lady presented no special features except that death was probably due to accidental suicide. The death of Dr. Horace Dimock of Wisbech in October attracted greater publicity because it occurred within a few days of his arrest on a charge of criminal libel for sending anonymous and objectionable postcards and letters to various people; no doubt it was a case of some form of dementia. The day after arriving to stay at his mother's house at Stretham, a Cambridgeshire village, he was found dead in bed. Post-mortem revealed no cause of death. Willcox investigated for poisons and gave evidence for the Home Office at the adjourned inquest at Stretham on December 3rd. In the organs examined he found 2·67 grains of morphine and 6·7 grains of veronal. He estimated that the whole body would have contained at least five grains of morphine, one grain being a likely fatal dose, and a possible fatal dose of veronal. He considered that death was directly due to morphine accelerated by the effect of a large dose of veronal taken the night before death. The verdict was "death from morphine and veronal poisoning, self-administered whilst temporarily insane from mental depression", in other words, suicidal poisoning.

References to the Hatton Garden Pearl Robbery

Sir Travers Humphreys—A Biography by Douglas G. Browne, Harrap, 1960.
Sir Richard Muir—A Memoir of a Public Prosecutor by Sidney Felstead, John Lane, the Bodley Head Ltd., 1927.

Chapter 7

Strychnine and Hyoscine as Poisons—1914

In January 1914 Willcox was introduced unexpectedly to the subject of veterinary toxicology after the mysterious and tragic death of two valuable circus horses and a zebra at the Olympia Circus which had opened on Boxing Day. To the distinguished surgeons of the Royal Veterinary College the cause of the small epidemic of gastroenteritis was quite obscure. No doubt it was on the recommendation of Lord Lonsdale who, as a Leicestershire man, knew Willcox and of his interest in horses and poisons, that the three veterinary surgeons—among them Professor Frederick Hobday—consulted Willcox at Welbeck Street on January 21st, three weeks after the animals had died. Though the Professor of Chemistry at the College Laboratory investigated the post-mortem material for poisons with negative results, Willcox extended the search but failed to find any chemical poison. Two valuable horses in adjoining stables and a zebra, stabled apart, had died on December 31st while two other horses separately stabled, were seriously ill but recovered. No one was able to track down the origin of the epidemic to contamination of the fodder with poisonous plants, a theory which Willcox thought highly unlikely as many other horses had been given the same food. It was admittedly a rare disease in horses but he concluded that the illness must have been of bacterial origin, a theory impossible to prove so long after the event.

The alkaloid strychnine is obtained from the seeds of the plant Strychnos nux vomica, a tree indigenous in many parts of the Far East, such as India, China, Burma, Malaysia and northern Australia. Discovered in 1819, it has been used from time to time as a homicidal poison but the characteristic symptoms of its poisonous effects and the difficulty in obtaining the drug have been factors in limiting its use in criminal poisoning in Britain. Two of the most famous poisoners to use strychnine were doctors; both were tried and convicted at the Old Bailey—Palmer, the country practitioner of Rugely, in 1855 and Neil Cream, the Lambeth murderer, who was brought to justice in 1892 as a result of Sir Thomas Stevenson's masterly identification of strychnine in the remains of his victim.

In the first three months of 1914 Willcox became involved in a case of strychnine poisoning which by a narrow margin escaped becoming a cause célèbre. It was the case of a semi-retired farmer, aged 48, named Thomas Roberts living in the remote village of Carno in Montgomeryshire, whose death led to investigations by the Home Office and police which never solved the mystery from a legal angle though the scientific evidence left no doubt as to the cause of death.

On January 3rd Willcox received orders from the Home Secretary to investigate the remains obtained at the post-mortem of the body of Thomas Roberts to be exhumed at Carno on January 6th. When the specimens arrived at the laboratory the next day with a letter from the pathologist, Dr. A. Shearer, he knew nothing about the history of the case but Shearer's second letter described how Roberts had died five weeks earlier, having been found a few minutes before death shouting and groaning, lying in the orchard adjacent to his garden, with his back arched, lying on his back and his heels according to the witnesses who discovered him. It seemed to be a case of strychnine poisoning. Yet the deceased's doctor, Dr. David Edwards, was summoned to the house shortly after death and from his knowledge of his past health considered the likely cause of death was heart disease of long standing; nevertheless he notified the Coroner, an inquest was held on December 3rd and the verdict pronounced accordingly. There was no post-mortem.

The post-mortem on the exhumed body buried for five weeks showed no sign of heart disease or indeed of death from any natural cause; the body was in a good state of preservation. All four limbs were very rigid and the hands tightly clenched.

Willcox found ·72 grain of pure strychnine, corresponding to ·87 grain of strychnine hydrochloride, in all the main organs examined. His opinion that the whole body must have contained at least one grain—double a fatal dose—was probably an understatement. In the liver alone there was ·44 of a grain and a smaller amount in the stomach, indicating that the fatal dose had been taken by mouth and caused death rapidly as there were only minute traces in the intestines. Directly Willcox's report reached the Home Office extensive police enquiries were planned in preparation for the re-opening of the inquest, but before taking this step Sir Charles Matthews, the Director of Public Prosecutions, in whose hands the decision lay, again consulted Willcox for his advice on the medical and scientific aspects of the depositions. There was no doubt of the cause of death judging by the reports of the illness of the deceased and the analytical findings. Moreover Matthews considered quite rightly that there was ample circumstantial evidence likely to incriminate a man named Evan Morgan on whom suspicion had rested when the solicitor of the deceased's sister had communicated with the police.

Thomas Roberts was a simple man of little education who, according to his brother-in-law, was barely able to speak English. Perhaps for this reason and also because he was a bachelor, he leant heavily on his close family friend and financial adviser Evan Morgan, aged 60. Following his father's death in 1910 Roberts inherited an estate which, at a time when farming in England and Wales was an unremunerative occupation, must have seemed enviable to the small poor community of a remote part of North Wales. The old man had made a Will when scarcely in a fit state to do so, shortly before his death. It was witnessed by Morgan and Dr. Edwards, the local doctor. His only daughter, and sister of the deceased, Mrs. Watkins, received no mention or benefit from her father's estate, but at the time took no legal action beyond consulting her solicitor. Thomas

Roberts Jnr. inherited three small farms, one of which he sold for £672 after his father's death. On April 4th, 1912, he had opened a joint banking account with Morgan in recognition of his help and valued friendship. Soon after this he made his own Will by which he bequeathed £100 to the Congregational Church, £39 yearly to his sister, Mrs. Watkin, and the remainder of his estate to Morgan. In terms of cash—according to Morgan's evidence at the inquest—the estate was valued at no more than £800, of which a debt of £200 was owed to his uncle. Not only did suspicion of unnatural death arise in the minds of Mrs. Watkin and her husband after her brother's death on December 1st, but several other discoveries were made by the police. Roberts had purchased strychnine two days before his death from a chemist at Newtown. He had proposed marriage, made plans for his wedding a few weeks before his death and had decided to alter his Will accordingly. He had been visited at his house on two occasions by Morgan on the day of his death and had taken whisky with him at about 5.30 p.m. Morgan had been the last person to see Roberts alive and in excellent health at that time.

The inquest was reopened by the same Coroner who conducted the first, Mr. J. T. Gittens, on March 25th at the market town of Newtown. The examination-in-chief was conducted by Mr. F. Sims representing the Director of Public Prosecutions, and Mr. Martin Woosman represented Mr. Evan Morgan against whom, as the Coroner observed, the possibility of a charge of murder had to be borne in mind. So great was the public interest in the case throughout North Wales that not only was the Court filled to capacity but the demands for the *Montgomeryshire Express* and *Radnor Times* were such that special ½d. editions providing verbatim reports of the case were issued day by day. The enquiry had most of the ingredients of a trial except for the absence of long speeches of distinguished learned Counsel for prosecution and defence. The inability of several of the twenty-nine witnesses to speak English necessitated the use of an interpreter and accounted for the lengthy enquiry spread over seven days. The day-to-day affairs of the small farming community were so interwoven that the case was of more than ordinary interest and complexity. The witnesses included the two doctors who carried out the post-mortem, the local practitioner, Dr. David Edwards, and Willcox who paid two visits to Newtown to give evidence on the third and last days. Though the deceased was known to have purchased strychnine within two days of his death, no evidence was produced to show that Morgan or anyone else handled it except Roberts himself, who had spoken of using it to exterminate moles on his farm. Morgan denied that he knew details of the Will of the deceased. The police failed to find any trace of poison in Roberts's house but the search was not conducted until five weeks after the tragedy.

Dr. Edwards had attended Roberts for several illnesses in the past and had known him well. He was well aware that Roberts had an enlarged thyroid gland (goitre) but also considered he had valvular disease of the heart. He must have felt embarrassed when at the second enquiry he was forced to eat his words in the light of the post-mortem and analytical findings, for no sign of valvular disease was found by the pathologists. But to give him his due he had not examined his patient until a few minutes after death and obtained no useful information about Roberts's symptoms preceding it.

Willcox stated that there was no doubt a fatal dose had been taken within one-and-a-half hours of death, judging by the amount of strychnine found in the stomach and intestines. Strychnine being rapidly eliminated from the body, none of that found on analysis could be attributed to its use in a medicine given many weeks previously. The symptoms of deceased were absolutely consistent with strychnine poisoning. Though pure strychnine is insoluble the hydrochloride of strychnine could be readily dissolved in small amounts of whisky and water. It was in common use at that time in vermin killers which by law had to be artificially coloured when sold. He had found no discolouration of the stomach contents as would be expected if such a substance had been taken. There was no doubt, therefore, that the poison had been taken either in the pure form or as the hydrochloride of strychnine.

The Coroner: "What is the possible explanation of the failure of Dr. Edwards to detect on Roberts's clothes, lips, or in the whisky in the glasses any indication that death was due to some irritant poison?"

"Strychnine is not an irritant poison. Dr. Edwards did not see Roberts before death. There would be no sign at all about his clothes or lips to indicate strychnine poisoning nor would there be indication of the cause of death except by analysis."

Mr. Sims: "Were the symptoms consistent with heart disease or any other natural cause?"

"Considering the symptoms, the condition of deceased in the morning and the rapidity with which death supervened, in my opinion the symptoms were not consistent with death from heart disease or any other cause."

"Within what time would a dose of one grain be likely to cause death?"

"If taken in a soluble form on an empty stomach, as seems probable from the evidence, death would occur within two hours of the taking of the poison, probably between one and two hours."

"Would the addition of half a grain to a glass of whisky and water have been apparent and, if so, would not the addition of a whole grain have been much more obvious?"

"One grain is a very small amount. It could easily be dissolved unnoticeable to the eye, but strychnine has a bitter taste and dissolved in whisky and water would cause it to taste so, but the taste would be disguised if the whisky were only very slightly diluted."

A chemist of Newtown described how he had sold sixty grains of strychnine hydrochloride to Roberts for the price of one shilling on November 29th, two days before the tragedy. The envelope had a red label marked "strychnine poison". The purchase was correctly recorded in his Poisons Register. He had never previously sold poison to Roberts.

Willcox was summoned from London to give supplementary evidence on the seventh and last day. Meanwhile it had been seriously suggested that strychnine might have lodged under Roberts's finger nails while engaged in laying the poison at his farm, a point the Coroner was anxious to clear up.

The Coroner: "Would one grain be likely to get under the finger nails and cause death by accidental contamination?"

"No. One grain is an appreciable amount. Unless the nails were very long and the poison purposely packed there I should think it would be extremely unlikely. Moreover, Dr. Shearer had said that the nails were not abnormally long."

Willcox had anticipated that question and had brought with him from London a stoppered bottle containing one grain of strychnine. He passed it to the Coroner and Jury to inspect.

"Could deceased's goitre have in any way caused death?"

"No. Goitre is a common complaint and rarely disturbs health unless it becomes toxic. No evidence of that condition had been mentioned in this case nor would a goitre be likely to cause mental depression."

Willcox finally described his tests of the solubility of strychnine hydrochloride, showing that as much as two grains could quickly be dissolved in two tablespoonsful of whisky diluted with variable amounts of cold water without stirring.

The Coroner's summing-up lasted for an hour and a half, an indication of the thoroughness of the enquiry. He dealt with each possible theory of the cause of death one by one. There was no doubt, he stated, that death was due to strychnine poisoning. Suicide was unlikely, if not impossible. Morgan's evidence had been frank and consistent. The deceased had been a nervous man, his hands often tremulous, and had found his business responsibilities a heavy burden which Morgan shared with him in an apparently friendly and helpful way. If murder, Morgan was the only possible murderer. There was no motive unless it was assumed that Morgan knew the contents of the Will of deceased, which he denied. Could he have known more about the Will than he admitted? There was no evidence that Morgan had had the poison in his possession or had handled it, but he had had ample opportunity to remove all traces from the house before the police search commenced. Finally, the Coroner suggested that the jury should consider that death was due to strychnine and leave it at that.

The jury of seventeen men retired for an hour-and-a-quarter and returned their verdict, according to the Coroner's advice, at the late hour of 8.30 p.m., "Death due to strychnine poisoning but the evidence is insufficient to prove how or by whom it was administered".

Loud cheering broke out outside the Court. But in a way the end of the case was unsatisfactory. Police investigations had failed to construct a case to entitle a jury to return a verdict equivalent to a "true bill" against Morgan and it was barely credible that he would have risked the consequences of murder in order to frustrate the alteration of Roberts's Will in view of the comparatively small benefit he stood to gain by his death, for Roberts was in no way a man of great wealth. The result of the case raised interesting possibilities. Suicide and accidental death could be excluded on firm grounds. If the jury's verdict had been that of murder, how would the trial have ended had Richard Muir conducted the case for the prosecution? Somehow this unfortunate Welsh farmer had died from strychnine poisoning from some unknown hand and his death was added to the records of unsolved poisoning mysteries.

In cases of private litigation Willcox's appearances in court before the Great War were comparatively infrequent. Usually these were claims for damages for alleged food poisoning brought against restaurants and vendors of foods. Though less sensational they were the most remunerative side of medico-legal work. During the spring and summer of 1914 the stage was being prepared for a libel action brought by the firm of Sutton, Bendle & Co., the proprietors of Bendle's Meat and Port Nutrient, against the United Kingdom Alliance and the secretary of its Hull branch—a Temperance Society which had published a pamphlet charging the Company with fraud, in that their nutrient port wines were not being sold by honest representations and were in fact dangerous. The substance of the published statement had appeared in the British Medical Journal in 1908. This Society had as its main object the suppression of the liquor trade. Among other additions the two port wine preparations contained somatose—a meat preparation added for nutritional and "tonic" purposes during illness and convalescence.

The case was heard in the King's Bench Division before Mr. Justice Bray in June and July. Sir Frederick Low, K.C., appeared as leading Counsel for the plaintiffs against Mr. Gordon Hewart (who became Lord Chief Justice in 1922).

The case was primarily a conflict of scientific evidence and opinion between both sides. If the case for the nutritive and beneficial purposes of the wine were proved, the libel would be no matter of legal argument. Willcox and a consulting analytical chemist gave evidence for the plaintiffs, claiming that somatose was "a true nutrient meat preparation with restorative and stimulating properties", a teaspoonful being equivalent to half an ounce of lean meat in nutritive value. The case was argued for three days on two of which Willcox gave evidence. He and his colleague Alfred Salaman, were mainly instrumental in obtaining judgment for the plaintiffs on July 15th, damages being assessed by the Judge (there was no jury) at £250 with costs. The appeal was dismissed in April 1915.

Until the Crippen case of 1910 the drug hyoscine had never figured in a court of law as a homicidal poison and it is curious that during his term of office as Home Office Analyst Willcox encountered a second case within four years of the first which resulted in a trial for manslaughter at the Old Bailey of Orlando Miller, the faith healer, and the trial was completed four years and one day after Crippen's conviction. It would be unfair to compare Miller with a convicted murderer for he was doubtless sincere in his beliefs and his methods of treatment of his patients, though he contravened the law by misusing the dangerous drug hyoscine which he should never have had in his possession. Both men were American citizens; they both styled themselves "Dr." with justification for Crippen had an American medical degree and Miller was at any rate a Doctor of Philosophy of Denvers University, posing as a man skilled in medicine though lacking in medical qualifications. But he had studied law and medicine including psychology. Both men came to Britain for a livelihood but there the resemblance ends. Crippen was described as an insignificant-looking little man whereas Miller was a persuasive personality with a great influence on the sick and crippled, which up to a point and in some cases was probably beneficial. The son of a grocer, he worked for a time in the family business until he went to Denvers University. After completion of his studies he started a "rupture cure" business but finally decided to come to Britain to practice as a "Quack", describing himself as a teacher, healer, lecturer on "Biblical Thought" and a student of psychology. He employed medical and mechanical methods of treatment but, more important, the persuasive influence of prayer and psychotherapy.

There has at no time of course been any law to prevent quack medical men from practising in any speciality. There have always been numerous examples of quacks practising in London and other cities often with great success, in many cases well deserved. But Miller's downfall occurred through the death of a crippled woman in his private nursing home, Spring Grove House, at Isleworth, while under his medical care and treatment with the dangerous drug hyoscine which he was not legally entitled to possess. At his nursing home he employed one qualified and several unqualified nurses in charge of thirty to forty patients, paying from three to five guineas weekly.

The death of this particular patient would probably have passed off unnoticed if her own qualified doctor, who was summoned to see her when she was moribund, had signed a death certificate instead of reporting the death to the coroner. Details of treatment were exposed to the full glare of publicity at the inquest in July 1914. On August 29th *John Bull* commented "in the guise of 'Higher Thought Healing' propaganda Miller and his associates have conducted an elaborate scheme of fraud out of which they have continued to make handsome profits".

Miller held services and lectured at the Christian Science meeting place Bechstein Hall where he acquired a large congregation and many patients and students of his cult, some of whom came to Isleworth as patients or to study his methods at a cost of three guineas per week.

Among his congregation was a thirty-seven-years-old reasonably well-to-do lady, Miss Kate Scott, a victim of multiple sclerosis of several years' standing who lived with her sister and was attended constantly by her maid; barely able to walk unsupported, she was able to get about in a wheel chair pushed by her maid and her sister. According to their evidence her health had in fact improved at the time she was admitted to the home on June 2nd. Along with his other methods, Miller employed semi-starvation for thirty-six hours and repeated injections of hyoscine which caused her to become sick and drowsy until, becoming seriously ill, her own doctor was summoned on the night of June 7th, about four hours before she died. According to his evidence she had been in her usual health when he had seen her ten days earlier.

Dr. Christian, who carried out the post-mortem, found numerous pink marks on the skin resulting from injections and an enormously dilated stomach which he attributed, rightly or wrongly, as probably due to the effect of hyoscine. The inquest was adjourned pending analytical investigations. At this stage Willcox came into the case.

On June 12th there appeared at St. Mary's laboratory the Coroner's officer and a detective sergeant bearing the organs of deceased in six jars and a bottle containing a sample of blood. Willcox found no poison except for a trace of the mydriatic alkaloid hyoscine in the stomach, which he agreed was very dilated, the other organs appearing normal. He was unable to say that hyoscine caused death from the result of the analyses alone and considered it likely that death was due to dilatation of the stomach secondary to multiple sclerosis, perhaps hastened by the administration of hyoscine.

The resumed inquest was held on July 11th by Mr. Reginald Kemp, the Coroner, at Hounslow and was concluded the same day.

The deceased's own doctor, Dr. L. Wilson, admitting that his patient was an incurable invalid, considered that a doctor should have been called in at an earlier stage than when he was summoned; that he had attended her for indigestion in the past; and that hyoscine would be a dangerous drug to be used in her case.

At the time of the inquest Willcox had received no information of the details of the illness of deceased. His evidence was accordingly brief and carefully phrased. He did not consider from the evidence available to him that hyoscine was the sole cause of death as there was not a poisonous dose in the organs, but that possibly the patient died from her disease and the treatment in his opinion was most unsuitable.

Recording a verdict of death from natural causes the jury asked the coroner to censure Mr. Miller for not summoning a doctor much sooner than he did and the nurse for taking part in the treatment.

Willcox reported the case to Sir Charles Matthews recommending that it required very full and careful investigation because he suspected that the treatment given had accelerated the death of deceased and considered that further deaths were likely to occur if Miller was allowed to continue his current methods of practice.

Willcox and Matthews consulted on July 17th but there was a delay of a month while steps were taken which led to the arrest of Miller. Evidence was collected from the qualified nurse at Isleworth and the domestic attendant, Samuel Barr, who had served the two Misses Scott.

Meanwhile results of the most momentous consequence to the whole world seemed to throw the case into temporary oblivion. Following the Sarajevo murders the Austro-Hungarian empire delivered its sudden ultimatum to Serbia on July 23rd and on August 1st Germany declared war on Russia. While Willcox took his first holiday for a long time in the first week of August, Britain declared war on Germany and the whole of Europe became involved in the greatest war in history. At the time few realised the horrors that the future four years were to bring. Among the holiday crowds which collected in the Mall and around Buckingham Palace some were seen to be in jubilant optimism that it would all be over by Christmas. Perhaps because of these events, or because it was the holiday season, no further action in the Miller affair took place until August 26th, when Sir Charles Matthews arranged a meeting attended by his deputy, Guy Stephenson, Willcox, Dr. Wilson and Dr. Christian. The joint report of the doctors agreed, after consulting all the evidence, on the essential facts and the conclusions to be drawn from the illness and death of Kate Scott.

When admitted to the nursing home on June 2nd she was in better health than she had been and in no sense was her life in danger. From June 3rd to 5th she was given injections of hyoscine which, admittedly small, were not infinitesimal like homeopathic doses but were repeated first at hourly and then two-hourly intervals. At the same time she was being purged and inadequately nourished. By June 4th she was delirious and semi-conscious, as a result of overdosage with hyoscine which was not surprising in the light of Dr. Wilson's experience that she had tolerated drugs badly compared with normal people. In addition she had vomited at intervals, due to hyoscine causing dilatation of the stomach. They all considered that medical advice should have been sought by June 5th at the latest. Instead Miller had not attempted to seek a qualified doctor's help till two days later when Wilson found her moribund in the evening. They reported that Miller was to blame in administering a dangerous drug in her condition and showed great neglect in failing to summon medical assistance earlier.

Miller was arrested and charged with manslaughter at Brentford Police Court on September 28th. The prosecution was conducted by Mr. Travers Humphreys with whom Willcox consulted several days beforehand. After outlining the history of the illness of the deceased Humphreys claimed here was a case of culpable rashness or want of care amounting to criminal negligence. After the evidence of Willcox and the other doctors and nurse were heard, Miller was committed for trial and appeared at the Old Bailey before Mr. Justice Rowlatt on October 13th. Richard Muir, Travers Humphreys and Percival Clarke appeared for the Director of Public Prosecutions, the defence Counsel being Sir Ernest Wild and Mr. Hancock.

In evidence given on his own behalf Miller claimed that he had successfully treated cases of drug addiction in Chicago since 1898, and in eighteen months had reduced the death rate of delirium tremens in chronic alcoholism to one per cent, using hyoscine and other methods of treatment. He had used hyoscine for disseminated sclerosis and other nervous diseases with success. He admitted that though he commenced hyoscine treatment with very small doses (1/500 grain), the injections were given at first hourly and later two-hourly. The doses were gradually increased up to 1/50th grain, often at the discretion of the nurse in charge. He had never had a death from hyoscine poisoning before. In 1908 he had carried on the same work in Paris, until he was introduced to London by an important member of the British aristocracy. In his evidence which lasted for two hours, Willcox considered that the doses given added up to considerable quantities of hyoscine likely to be risky and dangerous to any person, but especially so to a woman known by her own doctor to be intolerant of drugs and suffering from the debility associated with disseminated sclerosis.

Miller was found guilty of the manslaughter of Miss Kate Scott and was sentenced to three months in the second division. In passing sentence, Mr. Justice Rowlatt said it was clear that Miller was perfectly incapable of attending to the woman after the drug became toxic in its effect. This conviction, he went on, was a very important one because it showed that in spite of all the rhetoric that might be brought to bear on these occasions, all the tall talk about cures and systems of mental treatment and of the unity of the Infinite, a British jury, when people had been subjected to the influence of deadly poisons by incompetent people, would go straight to the business of saying it was manslaughter. In conclusion he delivered justice tempered with mercy:

"I am not going to punish you severely because I hope this conviction has checked it, but I hope others who think of following the same line of business will just take note because, as far as I am concerned, the sentence will be much heavier."

Willcox appeared at the Old Bailey on several occasions in 1914 and 1915 in cases of criminal abortion. The trials of Dawson and Watts in March, and of Riddle and Taylor in November 1914 were of women who carried on their trade, as was so often the case, in pairs. All were convicted. Dawson was sentenced to twelve months' hard labour and Watts to a lesser term. Riddle and Taylor received sentences from Mr. Justice Coleridge of three months and two months respectively, in the second division.

The death of Josephine Baron in November was a far more grave case as she was admitted to the French Hospital in a moribund condition by "Dr. Klein" who, like Crippen, had practised in America, but had no qualifications or medical practice in Britain. His claim to be an American citizen was denied at the American Embassy where he was regarded as an unregistered alien of Hungarian nationality. Spilsbury conducted the post-mortem and sought Willcox's collaboration in the investigations of drugs and instruments after showing him the post-mortem specimens.

The verdict at the Holborn inquest held by Mr. Walter Schroder was "murder by some person unknown". Klein was charged with murder at the Old Bailey, convicted for manslaughter, before Mr. Justice Rowlatt in January 1915 and sentenced to seven years penal servitude and expulsion under the Aliens Act of 1905.

Chapter 8

Wartime Research—1914–1915

Salvarsan

In spite of its evils war has often produced advances in medical knowledge of lasting benefit to mankind. In recent times the first antibiotic penicillin was a striking example: research accelerated by the second world war was attended by such success that it was destined to revolutionize the treatment of infections.

In 1914, Willcox's attention was directed by Sir Robert Morant, First Secretary to the Ministry of Health, to the problem of treatment of syphilis following the declaration of war by Britain against Germany. It was in 1910 that the foundation of chemotherapy was laid when Paul Ehrlich of Frankfurt (1804–1915) discovered the curative value of salvarsan in the treatment of syphilis—treatment which was to be carried on with success for over thirty years. Salvarsan was produced entirely in Germany until the first world war, our supply being automatically cut off on the outbreak of war. How were we to obtain our supplies? The Venereal Diseases Commission, faced with this problem and their responsibility to solve it, turned to Willcox for advice in the light of his knowledge of the toxicology of arsenic. Though the production of drugs was not his line of work, he was the first to be consulted by Morant at a meeting on September 1st at which Mr. (later Sir John) Anderson was present. He offered his services in research work on the efficiency and safety of the new product, suggesting that Sir Herbert Jackson, F.R.S., would be the most suitable scientist to explore the means for its manufacture. This work was directed by a special committee with himself as chairman, and Jackson and Professor A. W. Crossley, F.R.S., as members. They visited the laboratories of Burroughs Wellcome and found that elaborate preparations had already been directed to the production of organic arsenical drugs, the basic means of production of salvarsan being already available. The only other firm in Britain was German—Meister, Lucias and Bruning—their works being at Ellesmere Port in Cheshire. This firm had the patent rights for the manufacture of salvarsan but only the final stages of the process of manufacture had hitherto been carried out in this country. The future production of the preparation of the equivalent of salvarsan was accordingly entrusted to Burroughs Wellcome and Co. Nowadays chemical tests and experimental trials of new drugs are carried out by the firm's own research workers, but in this case Willcox was entrusted with this task by the Medical Research Committee and asked to commence straight away.

Samples of the new preparation were submitted to him at St. Mary's Hospital along with samples of salvarsan. The chemical and physical properties of the two drugs were found to be almost identical, though there was slight difference in solubility. Experiments on rats and mice using relatively large doses by injection showed that the new drug was free from any serious toxic properties. Clinical trials were conducted on patients at St. Mary's Hospital in beds allotted to the Inoculation Department through the kind co-operation of Sir Almroth Wright. In this work he was assisted by Professor (later Sir Alexander) Fleming and Dr. John Webster. It was concluded that the new preparation was every bit as good as salvarsan, no more toxic yet no less effective in the treatment of patients. Slightly altered so as to be more soluble, it was subsequently produced on a large scale by licence of the Board of Trade under the name of Kharsivan. This co-operative and productive research was carried out for urgent reasons within the short period of two months.

Aeroplane Dope

His next research project, equally urgent and important from a national point of view, concerned the aircraft industry and its employees in factories in various parts of the country. Aeroplane "dope" was used for varnishing the wings of aircraft. The toxicity of the substance tetrachlorethane contained in this very volatile liquid had not hitherto been recognised, though Willcox had carried out experiments with it in 1909 in the case of the fatal accident at the hairdressing establishment resulting from the use of carbon tetrachloride (the "top hat" experiments).

It was a curious coincidence that the ball was set rolling when a patient named Gilbert Moody consulted him at the out-patient department at St. Mary's on November 5th—not as Home Office Analyst—but in his capacity as an out-patient physician. Moody had been ill for two weeks suffering from toxic hepatitis with jaundice. Willcox discussed the nature of the work at the Hendon factory with Moody, who himself suspected poisoning because at least ten other workers had developed similar symptoms while others had been unwell who had not handled the dope. Willcox did not see the patient again, but on December 4th he received at the laboratory two specimens of dope from the coroner's officer obtained from Hendon. He was astonished to read the label marked "Dope from aircraft works at Hendon in case of Gilbert Moody", and learned that Moody had later been admitted to the Middlesex Hospital where he died. He made history by being the first victim of aeroplane dope; indeed his death was the means by which other workers were saved. The case set in train detailed investigations of the toxicology of aeroplane dope, its toxic effects on animals and investigations of all employees at Hendon and other aircraft factories, pending the inquest on December 19th, held by Mr. Luxmore Drew with a jury. It was found that the dope consisted of a solution of acetate of cellulose in a mixture of methylated spirit, acetone, benzene and tetrachloride of ethane. The vapour from the liquid was 1·91 times as heavy as air. The same day he examined the factory with Dr. (later Sir Thomas) Legge, H.M.

Inspector of Factories. The smell of the vapour was everywhere—detectable even as far as 30 yards from where the liquid was in use; this was explained by its heavy density, the vapour mixing with air very slowly. The ventilation was by the "plenum" system, very excellent for ordinary ventilation but not for heavy vapours. Many workers there were suffering from symptoms even though they were not employed actually using the dope, some of them at a considerable distance away in a large building. He examined nine of these workers at St. Mary's Hospital, finding the symptoms common to all, in varying degrees of severity. As in the case in 1909 of the hairdressing fatality Willcox described at the inquest his experiments with rats to determine the toxic effect of the constituents of the dope—the most important being tetrachlorethane, which is similar in its physical and chemical properties to carbon tetrachloride. White rats were kept for a week in an atmosphere of the dope, pure tetrachlorethane, benzene and acetone in sequence, after which their livers and other organs were carefully studied by Spilsbury and himself. Changes in the livers and kidneys were similar in rats kept in vapour of the dope as in those in pure tetrachlorethane. These findings confirmed those of 1909. Further, it was shown that extensive changes induced experimentally in the liver resembled those found in the liver of Gilbert Moody; the degree of liver damage corresponded with the severity of the dosage and the length of time the victim was subjected to the vapour.

Both he and Legge were extensively questioned on the case, Legge dealing with the public health aspects, especially the problem of factory ventilation. Again, Spilsbury's evidence corroborated Willcox's opinion on the cause of death of Gilbert Moody. The verdict was "accidental death caused by heart failure consequent on degeneration of the liver caused by tetrachlorethane in the varnish dope at the aircraft works at Hendon". The foreman expressed the thanks of the jury to Drs. Willcox and Spilsbury for their interesting evidence and hoped the investigation would be the means of preventing further deaths and illness occurring in the aircraft industry. Altogether it was calculated that there had been twenty-five cases of serious jaundice with five deaths, excluding many other milder illnesses of a similar kind.

The inquest was extensively reported on in the Press and medical journals, *The Lancet* (December 26th, 1914). A detailed discussion was held at the Medical Society of London at which Willcox, Legge and Spilsbury took part on the subject, "An outbreak of toxic jaundice of a new type among aeroplane workers", (Transactions of the Medical Society of London, Vol. XXXVIII, 1915). As a result of this original research, tetrachlorethane was added to the list of industrial liver poisons and was found to be similar to chloroform, though weight for weight it had been shown in 1909 to be nearly three times as toxic. It is interesting to record that in May 1914 industrial poisoning by tetrachlorethane was reported in Germany. The German dope contained a much higher proportion of tetrachlorethane than the English variety. Although investigations had been carried out, the toxic effect on the liver and kidneys had been entirely overlooked.

As Willcox pointed out, prevention of poisoning by the vapour was of much greater importance than the treatment of patients already suffering from its effects, but it had cost the life of Gilbert Moody to bring about measures whereby the heavy vapour in factories was removed by extractor fans at a low level. The Home Office took prompt action by issuing warning instructions to remove as far as possible all possible risks to factory workers. A harmless substitute, amyl acetate, later replaced tetrachlorethane as aeroplane dope.

Gas Warfare

When the lights of Europe went out in 1914 and Britain was plunged unwillingly into the greatest war in her history, many thought that a few months or a year would see the end of it. During the early months of 1915 both Willcox and Spilsbury offered their services in a military sphere to the War Office but both were considered to be more valuable in a civilian capacity. But Willcox saw an opportunity looming when he was invited to interview Sir Alfred Keogh, Director-General of the Army Medical Services, on May 1st, 1915. This was indeed a red-letter day in Willcox's life because the impression he created then must have been a factor which led to his future eventful career in the Medical Services in the Dardanelles and Mesopotamia.

The subject of Keogh's concern at their interview was the commencement of gas warfare by the German Army at the end of April, contrary to the terms of the Hague Convention of 1899 to which Germany had been a signatory. At the request of Kitchener, Dr. J. S. Haldane, the well known physiologist, had hurriedly set out for the front accompanied by Sir Wilmot Herringham, Consulting Physician to the Army, and Professor H. B. Baker, F.R.S., an expert chemist of the Imperial College of Science. The news of many victims of gas poisoning among troops at the front was in headlines in the Press on May 1st, a leading article in *The Times* being devoted to it. The victims were stricken ill with respiratory distress from intense irritation of the air passages causing either rapid death or bronchopneumonia with a high fatality rate within several days. Keogh was well aware that the Germans had been scientifically developing this secret weapon, and he even knew the composition of their own gas masks. Willcox mentioned that, though he approved of the chemicals used in the gas masks proposed, the addition of ammonium chloride would be an improvement on the German method. The interview ended with Keogh's request that he should assist Professor Baker in his research on the subject of gas mask filters.

Professor Baker consulted him at Welbeck Street on May 3rd when a scientific plan of research was discussed. It is of interest that his notes make no mention of phosgene (carbonyl chloride) though within the next two weeks this substance was found to be the principal gas used for causing asphyxia from lung irritation. Willcox again stressed the importance of including ammonium chloride in the filter and, moreover, suggested this be used (diluted with alcohol) as a first-aid inhalant by affected victims. Baker hurried on with his experiments before their next meeting on May 17th, when he discussed fully the success of their proposed filters; the chemicals finally decided upon in the masks were sodium bicarbonate (instead of sodium carbonate) and ammonium chloride. Agreement was reached that other gases such as arsenuretted hydrogen (As H_3), hydrocyanic acid, isocyanides, carbon disulphide, carbon tetrachloride and ethylene trichloride, would be of far less practical use against an enemy in trench warfare—as subsequently proved to be true. The possibility of contamination of streams and other water supplies with chemical poisons by the Germans was also discussed. The use of tubercle and cholera germs in shells was considered to be beyond the range of practicability. Willcox twice urged Baker to approach Keogh to allow him to visit the front to advise and help in the treatment of gas warfare victims, offers which were politely declined. "I managed to see Keogh last night" wrote Baker on June 1st, "but he asked me to thank you again but he did not think your services were needed at the front as yet. He said he would write if he thought the situation would change". Thus ended Willcox's hopes of being sent to France, but at any rate he and Baker had solved the problem of the most practical chemicals suitable for these early gas masks of the war. But two weeks later Willcox was summoned to the War Office and invited to become Consulting Physician to the Army at the Dardanelles, a post which he immediately accepted, and agreed to embark on July 15th. At this time the fear of gas warfare being used by the Turks must have been to the fore in the minds of authorities at the War Office for he was instructed to report on the matter to the Director of Medical Services at Alexandria on his way to Mudros.

References

"The Toxicology of Salvarsan" by W. H. Willcox and J. Webster, F.I.C., B.M.J. April 1st, 1916.

"A Fatal Case of Poisoning by Tetrachloride of Ethane," by W. H. Willcox, *The Lancet*, December 26th, 1914.

"An Outbreak of Toxic Jaundice of a New Type amongst Aeroplane Workers" by W. H. Willcox, B. H. Spilsbury and T. M. Legge. Transactions of the Medical Society of London, Vol. XXXVIII, 1915.

"The Toxic Effects of Substances of the Carbon Tetrachloride Groups." Address to the Royal Society of Medicine. Proceedings of R.S. Medicine, Feb. 1934, Vol. XXVII, p. 37.

Chapter 9

Problems in Medical Jurisprudence—1915

Professional Secrecy in Criminal Abortion

Before the Great War criminal abortion was one of the commonest and most important of the crimes confronting the Director of Public Prosecutions, Sir Charles Matthews and Willcox, as Home Office Pathologist and Analyst. The latter acted as a bridge between the professions of the Law and Medicine, because Matthews consulted him for advice on any medical matter that arose. Between 1906 and 1915 Willcox investigated at least twenty-three cases in the laboratory and post-mortem room; the work involved analyses of drugs and examination of organs removed. Of eighteen cases which came to trial, Willcox gave evidence at the Old Bailey in at least fifteen cases and in three cases at Assize Courts. When Spilsbury was appointed in 1908, he doubtless became involved in other cases as well. Both men acquired formidable knowledge and experience in this field of sordid work. For every illegal abortion that was discovered, others remained undetected and were the source of an illegal risky trade carried on by "back-street" abortionists. The difficult problem of the doctor's duty, when in medical charge of a patient suffering from the effects of criminal interference with pregnancy, was brought out in open discussion in 1915 following the death on October 16th, 1914, of an unmarried woman, Ellen Armstrong, from septicaemia following an abortion at the fifth month of her pregnancy. She was attended by two doctors before admission to the Women's Hospital, Birmingham, where she was operated on for complications of septicaemia; when he drained the abscess the surgeon found clear evidence that criminal interference had taken place. As a result of the Coroner's inquest Annie Hodgkiss was charged with murder, but at the Magistrate's Court the charge was dismissed.

When the case came up before the Grand Jury at Birmingham Assizes on December 1st, 1914, Mr. Justice Avory not only dismissed the case as one in which there was insufficient evidence to find a "true bill" against the prisoner, but he proceeded to make a judicial ex-cathedra statement concerning the duties of doctors in such cases, and a mild criticism of the doctors concerned in the particular case—a statement that caused embarrassment and perplexity to many doctors in practice. To the learned judge the subject of criminal abortion was not a new one. Horace Avory, before he became a judge, as far back as 1896 gave counsel's opinion before a special committee of the Royal College of Physicians appointed to consider the subject of professional secrecy in cases of criminal abortion. The College's report of 1896 laid the onus of responsibility on the doctor to decide whether or not to divulge to the police information gained while in charge of a patient on whom criminal abortion had been performed. It was a matter to be decided at the discretion of the doctor himself.

In 1913 Charles Matthews had been consulted by the Board of Guardians of Hampstead concerning a case of criminal abortion in an infirmary where the medical officer took the commonly held view that the confidential relationship with a patient should never be infringed even though it was clearly known to the doctor that pregnancy had been illegally interfered with before the admission of the patient to hospital. On that occasion Matthews had consulted Sir Thomas Barlow as President of the Royal College of Physicians, and Willcox, whom he regarded, to use his own words, "as practitioners who, by reason of the high and responsible positions they occupy in the medical world, could answer the questions with the greatest authority". The opinion of Matthews to the Board of Guardians was the mutually agreed views of Sir Thomas and Willcox. The letter need not detain us here, for the views were in broad agreement with, though expressed with greater delicacy than, the judicial statement of the judge in his charge to the Grand Jury at Birmingham on December 1st, 1914, which ran as follows:—

"The Magistrates who have investigated the case have dismissed the charge. The deceased woman, according to the evidence, clearly died as the result of an illegal operation. Three medical men in succession attended her, and to one at least she confided the name of the person who performed the act. No information was given to the Police or the authorities, and the woman died without any deposition being taken or without any statement being made by her on her deathbed which could be used in a Court of Law. With the exception of a letter, which was found among deceased's papers, apparently making an appointment with the accused woman, there is absolutely no evidence against this accused person of having performed any operation upon the deceased woman, and the Magistrates, taking that view, dismissed the charge. I need not remind you that any statement made by the deceased woman to a medical man is not evidence in a Court of Law. I can see no evidence, as the case now stands, which will justify you in finding a true bill against the prisoner for murder. The law provides that in the case of any person who is seriously ill, and who, in the opinion of a medical man, is not likely to recover, the evidence of such a person may be taken by a Justice of the Peace. Under circumstances like those in the present case, I cannot doubt that it is the duty of the medical man to communicate with the Police, or with the authorities, in order that one or other of those steps may be taken for the purpose of assisting in the administration of justice. No one would wish to see disturbed the confidential relation which exists, and which must exist, between the medical man and his patient in order that the medical man may properly discharge his duty towards his patient; but there are cases, of which it appears to me that this was one, where the desire to preserve that confidence must be subordinated to the duty which is cast upon every good citizen to assist in the investigation of a serious crime such as is here imputed to this woman. In consequence of no information having been given, it appears to me that there is no evidence whatever upon which this woman can properly be put upon her trial.

"It may be the moral duty of the medical man, even in cases where the patient is not dying, or not unlikely to recover, to communicate with the authorities when he sees good reason to believe that a criminal offence has been committed. However that may be, I cannot doubt that in such a case as the present, where the woman was, in the opinion of the medical man, likely to die and therefore her evidence was likely to be lost, it was his duty, and that someone of those gentlemen ought to have done it in this case."

The statement of the learned judge, with its implied criticism of the doctor concerned, was published in *The Lancet*, the British Medical Journal, and in several Law journals. But Willcox and Matthews agreed considered that the views of the medical profession should be sounded on a subject of such delicacy and perplexity through the correspondence columns of the medical journals. He accordingly forwarded the depositions of the case of *Rex* v. *Hodgkiss* to the Editor of *The Lancet*, Dr. (later Sir) Squire Sprigge, who published a leading article in the issue of January 2nd, knowing that there was a strong feeling in the profession that the infringement of the rules of professional secrecy, as formulated by Hippocrates himself, should not be countenanced in any circumstances, even when a doctor was aware that criminal interference with his patient had occurred. Sensitive to the divergence of opinion in the profession, Willcox not only exchanged letters with Sprigge but published his views on the subject in his letter to *The Lancet* (January 9th, 1915), views which differed materially from those expressed by the judge and *The Lancet* editor:

"In your last issue you raised a very important and delicate question relating to the action of medical practitioners regarding cases of abortion which may come under their professional care. . . . It is well to bear in mind that abortion from natural causes is an extremely common occurrence and that criminal abortion is fortunately rare. Every practitioner attending a case of abortion is perfectly justified in regarding the case as natural abortion, unless he has definite objective evidence to the contrary which he can see for himself without asking any questions. In attending a case where there is no objective evidence of criminal interference the practitioner will be wise to regard the case as one of natural abortion; any questioning by him as to the possibility of any criminal cause of the abortion is to be most strongly deprecated. It is undoubtedly the duty of the medical man to do the best he can for his patient and any action on his part in the nature of a detective inquiry is to be condemned. The practitioner will wisely refrain from putting questions to his patients or of receiving information from them which will throw upon him the difficult burden of professional secrecy. If a patient desires on her own account to disclose certain facts, it would be wise for the practitioner to caution his patient and to allow her to take such steps on legal advice as she thinks fit, provided that her health is not endangered by doing so. But there is no need for him to be a party to these proceedings. A class of case sometimes occurs where he cannot play a passive part. I refer to cases of abortion where there is conclusive objective evidence of criminal interference. Several such cases have come to my notice—visible perforating wounds or signs of corrosive agents of the uterus or vagina—revealed at operation. In such cases the practitioner who takes no steps at all is unwisely shouldering a grave responsibility which may lead to trouble for others as well as himself. In such cases he should insist on a consultation with a specialist, and if they jointly agree that there is conclusive evidence of criminal interference certain steps must be taken, e.g. when there is no hope of recovery in a desperate case, opportunity should be given to the patient of making a Dying Declaration, or in less desperate cases opportunity should be given for a statutory deposition to be taken by a lawyer, where the health of the patient permits. In every case the health and care of the patient should occupy the foremost place, and the practitioner will be right in forbidding any steps to be taken which are dangerous or detrimental to the condition of his patient. In cases where after consultation with a specialist it is decided that there is conclusive objective evidence of criminal interference, irrespective of any statements made by the patient, then there is no doubt that the duty rests with the practitioner to inform the legal authorities. His duty to the public and to himself must, I think, in such cases override any obligation of secrecy arising from the confidential relationship in which a doctor stands towards his patient."

This letter formed the basis of discussions which subsequently took place before the Censor's Board of the Royal College of Physicians, presided over by the President, Sir Thomas Barlow. Sir Charles Matthews personally and closely identified himself with Willcox's views when he attended the Board to give evidence. The deliberations of the Board were spread over a period of several months, Willcox submitting the substance of his *Lancet* letter as his contribution of evidence on May 11th. But he added one alteration to help the committee to formulate their final report of July 1915. This was the use of a word in a paragraph in which it was stated that "every doctor convinced that criminal abortion has been practised on his patient should *urge* her, especially if she is likely to die, to make a statement to be taken as evidence against the person who has performed the illegal operation."

Willcox's letter to *The Lancet* met with no opposition by other correspondents, a sign which he considered to indicate the approval of the medical profession. Moreover, the final report of the Censors exactly expressed his views on this difficult subject, and met with the approval of the legal profession at the same time. The perplexity of certain doctors aroused by the somewhat crude and pontifical statement of the learned judge was overcome, and Willcox had come to be regarded as an important bridge between the two professions. At any rate Matthews thought so, for he wrote to Willcox expressing his thanks for the service he had rendered both to his own department and to the cause of justice.

Fraudulent Treatment Exposed

Early in 1915, when news from the battle-front in Europe loomed large in the daily news and the Neuve Chapelle campaign was being launched, the City of London police were prosecuting a quack who was

conducting a successful fraudulent medical practice in the City by exploiting the neurotic and gullible members of society—an easy prey to unusual
forms of treatment. The practice of Arthur Dennison Light could not be
compared with that of Orlando Miller. The latter, who was at least honest
in his beliefs, was far more dangerous, for as an unqualified practitioner
he undertook the care of patients however seriously ill. Light's rudimentary
medical knowledge was obtained from herbalists of his acquaintance.
He was the superintendent of the "British Health Institute" whose headquarters were opposite Cannon Street station. He employed four girl
typists and a clerk, and conducted his practice in a consulting room in the
premises. He had no qualification as a doctor or pharmacist, but the
police learned from his records that he was consulted by 275 patients there
during the year 1914. He advertised his practice by the publication of his
periodical "Power, Purity and Progress", and numerous pamphlets
issued by the institute, most of which dealt with sexual problems in men.

The exposure of his methods was revealed to the police by a clerk at the
institute in an amusing way. Light claimed to possess the power of diagnosis by studying the symptoms of a patient's complaint coupled with the
examination of a specimen of urine sent by post, for a fee of 1s. 6d. Various
pamphlets were sent by post to his patient, and treatment commenced
by a course of so-called psycho-physio culture assisted by the administration of medicated douches and pink powders, a course costing a guinea
and a half.

Suspecting the fraudulent nature of his activities, two young men laid
a trap for Light which was to prove his undoing. Using assumed names,
they applied for treatment in writing, sending two carefully prepared
specimens of "urine". In the first case a coloured solution of bismark
brown and potassium dichromate, and in the second saffron and bismark
brown, resembled human urine. A little soap solution was added to each
to produce a froth on shaking. In the first case Light's diagnosis of his
patient's complaint of nervousness and lack of energy was catarrh of the
bladder for which he strongly recommended a course of his culture
treatment, and medicated douches. In the second case the urine was
pronounced to be normal, and the opinion (correct, as it chanced to be)
was given that the patient "enjoyed very fair health."

When the case was reported to the police, Inspector Wagstaff decided to
become a "patient" himself, submitting an application and his own specimen of "urine", consisting of weak tea tinged with bismark brown and
soap solution added. But he did not go so far as to submit to treatment.
Light was arrested on December 22nd, 1914.

Willcox was consulted by the City Solicitor Sir Holmwood Crawford and
Richard Muir on January 13th. His investigations of the three specimens
of "urine" showed the absence of urea and salts of real urine, and the
presence of vegetable matter never present in ordinary urine. The sample of
medicated powders obtained from the headquarters of the institute proved
to be powdered common salt coloured with an aniline dye. Light was tried
at the Old Bailey on January 14th before the Recorder of London on a
charge of attempting to obtain money by false pretences. Muir and

Roland Oliver appeared as prosecuting counsel. The trial lasted for five days. Light was found guilty and sentenced to three months' imprisonment.

Suicide or Accident ?

The sudden death of Joseph Muller from oxalic acid poisoning on February 6th at Shoreditch appeared at first sight to be a clear case of suicide, but on investigation suspicion of accidental poisoning arose through the curious circumstances surrounding the tragedy. Of Austrian nationality and forty-seven years of age, Muller was employed as a lavatory attendant—which was one explanation of his access to the use of oxalic acid at work. He retired to bed at 9 p.m. and three hours later was found dead in bed by his daughter. Though afflicted by an obscure type of paralysis of his legs, his health had otherwise been reasonable though he was mentally depressed; he had been unfit for work for six months and disturbed by his inability to communicate with his mother in Austria owing to wartime restrictions. On the mantelpiece of his room an opened packet of Epsom salts bearing a Boots label and a packet containing menthol snuff were found. A cup containing white crystals of oxalic acid was found on a table.

Oxalic acid used to be a not uncommon cause of death by suicide. Though widely used in industry, its domestic use for cleaning and bleaching has nowadays been, to a great extent, superseded. The crystals (salts of lemon) closely resemble Epsom salts in appearance, but not in taste; it is a strong corrosive poison.

The police surgeon found striking signs of corrosion of the upper end of the stomach and there was evidence of oxalic acid in the almost empty cup. At the inquest at Shoreditch held by Mr. Wynn Westcott, Muller's wife said that deceased had been in the habit of taking Epsom salts at regular intervals, and that he had been depressed by his physical disability, and certain financial hardship resulting from it. When the packet of Epsom salts was examined by the police surgeon and doctor, they agreed that the taste was of oxalic acid and not of Epsom salts. The inquest was adjourned and the police commenced enquiries. When the findings of the inquest reached the head office of Boots, the directors immediately consulted Scotland Yard and the Shoreditch public analyst, H. G. Harrison, to whom were submitted the Boots' packet from the house of deceased and numerous samples of Epsom salts obtained from Boots' London depot at Bishopsgate, and their main depot at Nottingham. No evidence of any source of contamination of samples could be found, some of them being obtained from branch shops of the firm in the neighbourhood of deceased's home.

Willcox was consulted by the solicitors acting for Boots and their counsel Richard Muir on February 20th. Their purpose was to establish evidence to exonerate the firm of Boots from any possible charge that their supply of Epsom salts had been contaminated by oxalic acid. It was even suggested that this might have been one of those rare cases of suicide in which the victim leaves behind evidence to suggest that death was accidental. In this case the packet had been carefully opened in such a way as to leave the Boots' label intact. In an earlier case a man had bought potassium cyanide from another chemist and a Seidlitz powder from Boots. He put part of the cyanide into one of the powder packets and swallowed the rest, with fatal results, inferring that Boots and Co. had supplied cyanide instead of the powder. The motive for the deception lay in the Life Assurance Policy of the deceased by which his family stood to gain £1,000 by his death if accidental. In the case of Muller there was no insurance policy; nevertheless he may have wished to escape from the stigma and blame likely to be attached to his death by suicide.

Willcox carried out research in three directions. First, he had a long consultation with Harrison who shared all the information he had so far gained. Together they discovered under the microscope that the crystals of oxalic acid from the packet of deceased were quite different from the samples obtained from Boots. Harrison had found 7·4 grains of oxalic acid in the fatal cup and 271·5 grains in the packet labelled Epsom Salts. Secondly, Willcox made a detailed examination of the stomach which bore signs of typical oxalic acid corrosion of its upper part. Thirdly, he tested six separate samples of oxalic acid obtained from Boots' branches in the Shoreditch district, and six samples from chemists' shops, other than Boots. All these specimens yielded after combustion a far greater percentage of ash than from the substance taken from deceased's packet. He thus was able to show that the oxalic acid in this packet was obtained from a source other than Boots, or any local chemist's shop, and in fact all samples of Boots' Epsom salts were pronounced pure and free from any source of contamination. At the resumed inquest on February 27th an open verdict of oxalic acid poisoning was recorded. The coroner noted that no blame for the tragedy was to be attached to Messrs. Boots and Company. The case was unquestionably one of suicide. One significant point was noted by Willcox in his evidence. Mrs. Muller had testified that deceased always took Epsom salts in the morning as patients customarily do, but on this occasion deceased took his fatal cup at night.

The Infected Ampoules

The technique of sterilisation of ampoules containing liquid preparations of drugs and biological substances given by injection became so perfected in the early part of the century that the risk of infection from this source was soon overcome. Nowadays it is scarcely thought of even as a remote possibility, although thousands of injections are given daily—preventive inoculations, insulin and drugs. Even when infection does occur it is now easily controlled by antibiotics.

The tragic death of a woman from septicaemia following treatment by injection of pituitary gland extract (pituitrin) was a unique event in Willcox's experience. The inquest in April 1915 was described by Mr. Vere Benson, the East Sussex Coroner, as one of the two most important and difficult cases in his whole career, the other being the case of Hugh Trevanion (1912, page 61).

Mrs. Woodman, the wife of Captain Woodman of the Sussex Yeomanry, died at her home at Willingdon near Eastbourne on April 2nd after receiving four injections of pituitary extract on alternate days from her doctor acting on the advice of a Harley Street specialist. The fact that the treatment was given for a comparatively trivial complaint, and not as a life-saving remedy, made the shock of the tragedy far more grievous than would have been the case otherwise; she suffered merely from the unpleasant symptoms commonly experienced by women at the change of life.

Captain Woodman was so convinced, and rightly so, that his wife had died as a result of treatment or poisoning, to use his own words, that he reported the case to the coroner, informing the doctor that he would not agree to his certifying her death as due to erysipelas (an illness caused by streptococcal infection). With the coroner's permission and probably at his suggestion, Woodman privately consulted Willcox immediately after his wife's death, requesting him to spare no expense in launching a complete investigation into the case in order to see where the blame lay, and how to prevent any further tragedies of like nature.

Willcox commenced investigations by consulting the specialist who had already been in contact with the deceased's own doctor. He was handed two ampoules of the extract of a batch manufactured by a well-known pharmaceutical firm. The fluid in the ampoules, instead of being clear, was decidedly turbid. There had been no other complaints of the ampoules produced by the firm. Willcox obtained full information about the treatment of the patient. Mrs. Woodman had developed pain due to an abscess in the buttock following the fourth injection, each injection being given on alternate days. Five days later—on April 2nd—she died of septicaemia.

At this stage Willcox brought Bernard Spilsbury into the case. On April 4th they travelled to Eastbourne and conducted the post-mortem at Willingdon in the presence of the local doctors. Together they took samples for bacteriological tests and Willcox took home certain organs for detailed analysis. Profuse growths of bacteria—staphylococci and streptococci—were obtained from cultures from the abscess and from the blood from the heart. Meanwhile Dr. Walter Emery, bacteriologist to King's College Hospital, cultured corresponding bacteria from the contents of the ampoules. There was no doubt that the illness and death of deceased was caused by septicaemia from infection from the ampoules, or the pituitary extract itself. Spilsbury and Willcox had found no other possible cause of death.

The inquest at Willingdon was opened before the East Sussex Coroner, Mr. Vere Benson, on April 6th when factual evidence was taken from the deceased's doctor and from Captain Woodman.

The resumed inquest of April 20th was of unusual importance, not only for its scientific nature but also for the attendance of four leading counsel representing respectively Captain Woodman, the pharmaceutical firm, the specialist who had been consulted by the deceased and the Medical Defence Union acting for Dr. Emerson, the doctor who had carried out the treatment. Richard Muir, as counsel for the firm, was in the unusual position of being in a sense in opposition to Willcox, his old associate in so many cases, whose evidence had been sought by the deceased's widower, Captain Woodman.

Emery described the tests he had carried out on the two infected ampoules and the unusual turbidity of their contents, from which he grew living bacteria corresponding to those obtained at the post-mortem tests. Willcox agreed with his views and defended the treatment initiated by the specialist and carried out by Dr. Emerson. Cross-examined by Muir, he said that the prescribing of treatment by the doctors was beyond criticism. The fault lay in the accidental infection of the pituitary extract but so far as he knew this was the first recorded instance of any ill-effect experienced from any preparation of the extract or from any substance prepared for injection by the firm concerned.

The pharmaceutical chemists responsible for the manufacture of the extracts were unable to throw any light on the mystery as to how this particular batch of ampoules had become infected. They submitted that they had never had any previous experience of this kind.

The verdict of death from misadventure was an eminently fair one. The jury considered that there was no criticism of the doctor or of his injection technique but that more care should have been taken in the preparation of the extract.

The next day Willcox, who had taken the precaution of interviewing the firm's solicitor a few days before the inquest, received letters of thanks from the director of the firm and from the coroner for the absolute fairness of his evidence which had been confined to facts and conclusions that were strictly necessary. But the inquiry had failed to solve the mystery. How had the ampoules of this particular batch become infected? Willcox hazarded a guess that an employee engaged in the preparation of the extract must have accidentally contaminated the material from contact by an infected hand, but this idea was no more than conjecture. The story did not, however, end there. There was an interesting sequel to the inquest. To prevent the possibility of any recurrent tragedy, the director of the firm consulted Willcox for advice on the future technique of sterilisation of ampoules for all liquid substances given by injection. Willcox brought another colleague into the case. John Freeman, who with Alexander Fleming and others worked in Sir Almroth Wright's team of bacteriologists at St. Mary's Hospital, attended a consultation with Willcox and the firm's director to plan modifications of the technique of sterilisation of ampoules to ensure their future safety and the firm's reputation.

Chapter 10

The Brides in the Baths
(*Rex* v. *G. J. Smith*, 1915)

The expansion of the armed forces in the first winter of the Great War caused a serious manpower shortage which affected the police forces as seriously as any other class of occupation. It was aptly claimed that crime could more easily escape detection. The first battle of Ypres had taken place in December and the second battle soon followed with its appalling casualties. Then came the Dardanelles campaign of the Spring of 1915. Nearly all the news in the daily papers was about the battle-front and the war effort at home. Crime received little or no attention by the Press. Nevertheless, there was one exception. This was the police investigation during the first half of the year of a series of murders by drowning—a series of crimes without precedent which attracted great publicity. Police statements were taken from 150 persons of whom 112 appeared as witnesses at the trial of George Joseph Smith in June.

The "Brides in the Baths" case, as it came to be called, was the last of the great trials in which Willcox figured as a Home Office pathologist. To him it was the end of an era. When he appeared at the Old Bailey in June, he was already under orders from the War Office to embark for Mudros as Consulting Physician to the Army at the Dardanelles on July 15th. Thereafter, he was engaged in military activities for the next four years.

Soon after Christmas he was consulted by Sir Charles Matthews about the case of Mrs. Lloyd, who had been found drowned in her bath in circumstances which appeared suspicious to the police in view of information received from a Buckinghamshire fruit farmer. Acting on Willcox's advice, Matthews decided to investigate—which meant an exhumation was required. For if murder by drowning was suspected, how could it be assumed that death was due to drowning as the inquest jury at Islington had supposed? Why not drugs or poison?

Willcox knew all about the case of Mrs. Lloyd when he was requested by the Under-Secretary of State to take part in the investigations in connection with the exhumation of the body at Finchley Cemetery. His first duty was to carry out the analysis of the remains for poisons and drugs. He and Spilsbury were furnished with Inspector Neil's report and the inquest depositions. When Spilsbury performed the post-mortem at the exhumation of Mrs. Lloyd on February 4th he was already briefed for two other exhumations of brides who had died in a very similar fashion.

On the evening of December 17th Mr. and Mrs. Lloyd, had engaged furnished rooms in the house of Miss Blatch in Highgate. They made no mention that they had been married at Bath on the previous day. In fact Mrs. Lloyd said she felt unwell and had already consulted Dr. Bates at his surgery in Archway Road—within a short distance of Seddon's home. They went to bed early and the next day Mrs. Lloyd felt much better. On the following evening Miss Blatch prepared a bath for Mrs. Lloyd. While she was in the bath her husband played the harmonium. After that there was silence. She thought he had gone upstairs, but in response to a knock at the front door fifteen minutes later she let Lloyd in from the street, saying he had purchased tomatoes, which he carried. Lloyd called to his wife, but received no reply from the bathroom. Going upstairs together, they discovered Mrs. Lloyd dead in the bath, three parts full of water. The candle had been extinguished. They lifted her out of the bath, then summoned Dr. Bates and the police. The doctor came quickly and pronounced life extinct.

Mrs. Lloyd had lived with her mother and sister at Bristol until December 15th when she left home without any warning, unexpectedly, and to their dismay. On the day of the tragedy, to make matters worse, they received a letter from 14, Bismark Road, Highgate, dated the 17th, saying that she had married John Lloyd at the Bath Registry Office, that she had preferred to keep her marriage secret by running away from home for fear of disapproval and that she had corresponded with Lloyd secretly for the same reason. She ended by saying how happy she was with her husband. This was the first knowledge her family had ever had of her association with any man.

A post-mortem was conducted by Dr. Bates, and the inquest opened by Mr. (later Sir Walter) Schroder, on December 22nd. It was adjourned owing to an injury to Miss Blatch's knee, but she gave her evidence on New Year's day.

The proceedings ended with a verdict of accidental death by drowning being returned by the jury, though the Coroner would have preferred an open verdict. But there was no reason to suspect that she had been murdered. In his evidence, Dr. Bates said that death was caused by asphyxia from drowning, adding that influenza coupled with a hot bath might have caused an attack of syncope or fainting.

Meanwhile the deceased's sister, Miss Lofty, had written to her cousin, a London solicitor named Kilvington, requesting him to make thorough inquiries into the cause of the tragedy. Wasting no time, he arrived at Bismark Road to interview Lloyd the day after the tragedy. It must have been an embarrassing meeting for Lloyd, for he had to explain his reason or excuse for not having let his wife's family know about the accident. Lloyd explained that he had been led by his wife to believe that she had no surviving relatives—that she was alone in the world. He denied any knowledge of his wife's letter to her mother and sister.

Lloyd and Kilvington were the only mourners at the funeral on December 23rd, and Lloyd supplied no wreath or flowers. Immediately after the inquest was completed, Lloyd disappeared from his lodgings and his whereabouts were obscure. Earlier, he had seen Dr. Bates to get his signature to a claim form for his wife's Life Assurance money from the

The History and Fate of the Seven Brides of G. J. Smith

Name	Bride	Place of Marriage	Date	Fate of Bride	Possessions gained by Smith	Inquest	Exhumation
Oliver Love	Caroline Thornhill	Leicester	January 17th, 1898	Emigrated to Canada 1900	—	—	—
George J. Smith	Edith Pegler	Bristol	July 30th, 1908	Survived	—	—	—
George Rose	S. A. Faulkner	Southampton	October 1909	Deserted at National Gallery	£300	—	—
Henry Williams	Bessie Mundy	Weymouth	August 26th, 1910	Separated 1910–1912 Drowned in bath at Herne Bay, July 13th 1912	£2,500	July 15th, 1912 Drowning in epileptic fit	February 18th, 1915 Herne Bay
George J. Smith	Alice Burnham	Portsmouth	November 4th, 1913	Drowned in bath at Blackpool, December 12th, 1913	£140 plus Life Assurance for £500	December 13th 1913. Accidental drowning	February 9th 1915 Blackpool
Oliver James	Alice Reavil	Woolwich	September 17th 1914	Deserted September 23rd, 1914, at Brockwell Park	£78, piano and furniture and clothes	—	—
John Lloyd	Margaret Lofty	Bath	December 17th, 1914	Drowned in bath at Highgate, December 18th 1914	£19 plus Life Assurance for £700	December 22nd, 1914 and January 1st, 1915 at Islington Accidental drowning	February 4th, 1915 Finchley

Yorkshire Assurance Company amounting to £700. Lloyd had also benefited by his wife's Will, already made, but only by the small sum of £19 in the Savings Bank.

The death of Mrs. Lloyd would have faded into oblivion and her murder passed undetected had it not been that by a curious chance a Buckingham fruit farmer who lived at Aston Clinton happened to read an account of the inquest in the *News of the World*. Charles Burnham, who was to figure prominently in subsequent events, was still mourning the death of his daughter Alice who had died in a very similar way almost exactly a year ago—on December 12th, 1913. She had married a man named Smith on November 4th at Portsmouth Registry Office against his consent. He had taken a dislike to George Joseph Smith on first acquaintance. Immediately after her marriage Alice had asked her father for the sum of £100 which he had hitherto held in trust for her. Guessing that Smith was attempting to acquire the money—or at any rate to share in it—he at first refused, but after some acrimonious correspondence and threats from his son-in-law and acting on the advice of his solicitor, he forwarded the money to Alice. A few days later he received a telegram from Smith dated December 13th: "Alice died last night in her bath—letter following." The letter, addressed to his mother-in-law, described how he had found his wife drowned in the bath. When they had arrived in Blackpool Alice had complained of pains in her head for which they consulted a doctor only a few hours before the tragedy.

So it was that Charles Burnham initiated the whole chain of investigations which led to the astonishing conclusion that three undetected murders had been committed. No doubt his instinctive dislike and distrust of Smith prompted him to suggest to his solicitor that Lloyd and Smith were one and the same man. Certainly to the police it was strange indeed and so unlikely that two wives of the same man should die accidentally in such similar circumstances. But was it the same man? Both deaths were followed by inquests, and in both cases the verdicts were accidental death, though in the case of Mrs. Smith she was said to have suffered from fits and died after having a fit or faint in her bath. Directly the Aylesbury police were notified, not only were inquiries made by Scotland Yard detectives at Blackpool and Highgate, but it was learned that yet a third woman—Mrs. Williams—had succumbed to a similar fate in her bath at Herne Bay in July 1912. In this case, "Mr. Williams" had purchased a house using his wife's money, and had benefited by her Will to the extent of £2,400 in gilt-edged securities.

Step by step Inspector Neil, who was in charge of the investigations, built up the complicated life story of G. J. Smith—a story which would make an enthralling biography. It became clear that John Lloyd, G. J. Smith and Henry Williams were in fact the same person. Smith had been married seven times since 1898 when, as Oliver Love, he had married Caroline Thornhill who emigrated to Canada two years later. His second wife (née Edith Pegler) became the first Mrs. Smith in 1908. They acquired a junk shop in Bristol which Edith cared for while Smith travelled about the country ostensibly in quest of antiques. If Smith ever loved anyone it was Edith. To her he always returned sooner or later, between his marriages and crimes of which she was entirely ignorant.

Every effort was made to find Smith's whereabouts lest he escape abroad as Crippen nearly succeeded in doing. On February 4th he was arrested at a solicitor's office in Shepherds Bush on a charge of the false entry of his bigamous marriage at Bath—for it was known that three months earlier he had married Alice Reavil at Woolwich. Though he had deserted her within a week, the marriage contract was not terminated. At identity parades Smith was recognised by many witnesses who had in some way or another been associated with him and his three wives at the time of their deaths. The most important of these witnesses was, of course, Charles Burnham.

Smith's complicated business dealings in connection with his three deceased wives were laid bare by police inquiries at banks and insurance companies. They formed a major part of the tedious—but important—evidence at the trial. Apart from the financial gain to Smith by the deaths of Mrs. Williams (née Mundy), and Mrs. Lloyd (née Lofty), he gained £140 from the Will of Alice Smith (née Burnham) and £500 from her Life Assurance policy.

Bernard Spilsbury carried out the three exhumations in the reverse order to that in which the victims died. On February 4th he was at Finchley concerning Mrs. Lloyd. He was at Blackpool on February 9th and at Herne Bay on February 18th; in these two cases he found moderately advanced decomposition of the remains. But he found no sign of any disease to explain the cause of death in the three cases. Likewise John Webster and Willcox found no trace of drugs or poisons in the organs submitted for analysis.

Between January 26th and May 11th Willcox and Spilsbury conferred together on four occasions. The last meeting was attended by Mr. Archibald Bodkin, who was to lead for the prosecution at the trial. In his notes, Willcox summarised the discussions briefly under three main themes.

Q. Was drowning accidental? e.g. fit or syncope followed by asphyxia?
A. From evidence we think "No".
Q. Was death suicide?
A. No evidence of suicidal tendencies in these cases, nor of mental instability.
Q. Was death homicidal?
A. We think "Right hand on head of woman. Left forearm of assailant beneath both knees. Left forearm of assailant suddenly raised while right hand is pressed down on head of woman. Then the trunk of body slides down towards the foot end of the bath, the head being submerged in water."

They considered that this was the only possible method of murder by drowning in a bath, in such a way as to obviate sufficient noise to attract the attention of other occupants of the house.

Smith appeared at Bow Street charged with the murder of his three wives. The hearing was conducted intermittently over a period of about six weeks. The scientific evidence was heard on the last day—May 13th. The greater part of the time was taken up with Spilsbury's evidence. His factual evidence was his own—based on his post mortem work. But the opinion which he gave to account for the three deaths was in reality that of Willcox and himself formed by mutual consent and agreement at their earlier meeting. Dealing with Mrs. Lloyd deceased, Spilsbury said that she was five feet seven inches tall. The bottom of the bath measured only 3 feet 2 inches. It was therefore impossible for her to have drowned accidently unless she had lain face downwards. Again, in the case of Mrs. Williams, the doctor had found her legs raised with the knees bent, the feet against the bottom of the bath—a finding inconsistent with death during a fit. He next put forward the theory of homicidal drowning (referred to earlier). The sudden immersion of the head would give rise to shock and probably early unconsciousness, perhaps in a matter of seconds. Once the head was completely immersed, no sound could be possible, though struggling would occur until unconsciousness supervened. In the case of sudden or unexpected immersion, loss of consciousness would be much more rapid. The bruising found on the arm of Mrs. Lloyd might have been caused by striking, or by pressure on the side of the bath during the struggle.

Willcox said that he entirely agreed with Spilsbury's views. His own clinical opinions were added. "With regard to Mrs. Williams (the Herne Bay case), he thought that there was no evidence that she had ever had a fit at all. The sudden appearance of a first epileptic fit in a previously healthy woman of 35 was extremely unlikely in the absence of a family history of epilepsy. The thickening of the mitral valve of the heart of Mrs. Smith (the Blackpool case) was not a serious matter. It was a comparatively common post mortem finding and would not predispose to sudden fainting attacks."

Six weeks were to elapse between the police court proceedings and the trial of G. J. Smith at the Old Bailey. Willcox had for some time been hopeful of being accepted by the War Office for military service, but his offer had been declined on the grounds that at the Home Office he was almost irreplaceable. But as a practising physician his chances of employment in a military sphere were, at any rate, greater than those of Spilsbury, whose experience was confined entirely to pathology—for Spilsbury had never practised in a clinical capacity as a doctor since completing his residential hospital appointments soon after qualifying. When Willcox was summoned to the War Office on June 15th to be offered the post of Consulting Physician to the army at the Dardanelles, he immediately accepted, though unaware that the decision would be one of the great turning points of his career. He had joined the Territorial Army in 1912 as Captain on the roll of the 3rd London General Hospital. At the end of 1914 his offer of service had been declined, but now he was given the opportunity to contribute his services to the war effort in the roll of a practising physician in an active theatre of operations. He was given orders to be in readiness to embark for Mudros on July 15th. By that time the trial of Smith was over.

The trial at the Old Bailey commenced on June 23rd. Smith was charged with the murder of Mrs. Williams (née Mundy)—the Herne Bay case. The case lasted for eight days and would have been much longer had a triple murder charge been made. The reason for the selection of this particular murder charge need not be fully discussed here, but certainly Smith benefited to a greater extent by the death of Mrs. Williams than those of his other two brides. Then there was the theory of death during an epileptic fit which, it was considered by Bodkin, would be easy to demolish. Bodkin, the leading counsel for the prosecution, was assisted by Travers Humphreys and Cecil Whiteley. Edward Marshall Hall had the unenviable task of defending Smith. Having failed in an attempt to persuade the judge, Mr. Justice Scrutton, to exclude the evidence relating to the other two cases of drowning, he became involved in a hopeless cause almost from the start. The public interest was centred more on the character of the prisoner than the skill of the lawyers taking part, and no doubt it was his sex appeal which accounted for the presence of so many women that they occupied two-thirds of the seats in court. The proceedings were interrupted by outbursts of indignation and protests from the prisoner. The Herne Bay and Blackpool baths were there as exhibits for the jury to see. Willcox and Spilsbury had seen the Highgate bath as well. They had taken accurate measurements of the baths, and of the shape and stature of the three deceased brides. During the trial a detective experimented with a nurse lying in a bath in a bathing costume. Playing the part of an assailant, he raised her legs with one arm while submerging her head with the other hand, in order to satisfy himself of the reasonableness of the theory propounded by the scientific experts. The small size of the bath was a point against the argument for accidental drowning in a fit or faint. Spilsbury and Willcox gave evidence on the sixth and seventh days. Willcox was in the box less than half as long as Spilsbury, but as usual their evidence was mutually agreed beforehand; it was substantially the same as at Bow Street.

The jury returned a verdict of Guilty after deliberation for only half an hour. Smith's appeal failed and he was executed at Maidstone on August 13th, 1915.

To the public, the great interest of the trial lay more in the history and character of the prisoner than the details of the legal and scientific evidence. The character of G. J. Smith was so evil, yet so complex, that it is difficult to sum him up in a few words. That he was one of the most interesting personalities ever convicted of murder at the Old Bailey there can be no doubt. He was cleverer than Seddon, whose single crime fades into a shadow compared with Smith's multiple murder of helpless brides. They have certainly provided fascinating material for biographers and crime writers. The biographers of Sir Travers Humphreys and Sir Edward Marshall Hall describe him respectively as "the most atrocious English criminal since Palmer" and "an unspeakable hypocrite and human monster". Exploiting women entirely for gain, he made a more profitable living than was apparently possible from his second-hand junk shop, or his antique dealers' business. He had no dealings with men and no male friends. Instead, aware of his power of attraction to women, he exploited it fully. Some of them he married, with others he formed friendships which he would abandon, obtaining as much of their property as he could. He met Alice Burnham at a Congregational chapel, yet proceeded to murder her within a few weeks.

One of the most heartrending stories in the depositions is that of Alice Reavil who married Smith—styled Oliver James—as his sixth wife after casually meeting him on the front at Bournemouth. She allowed him to gain possession of all her worldly belongings, consisting of £70 in the bank, furniture, a piano, and even her clothing, except what she was wearing. He took her for a walk in Brockwell Park and deserted her with the excuse that he was visiting a public convenience. She never saw him again until she identified him after his arrest. The story of Flora Jarvis was similar, except that he did not go so far as to marry her.

The staging of two undetected murders of two brides is evidence of Smith's extraordinary cleverness and ingenuity. It was merely by chance that the third attempt was unlucky. In the three cases the bride was married hurriedly and secretly, well away from the bride's relatives; in each case the bridegroom had a different name; each marriage was conducted far away from the others; in each case all the ready cash the bride possessed was realised, a Will was made in Smith's favour. There were the preliminary visits to the doctors, the murders at the week-end, the hastily arranged inquests followed by the disappearance of Smith.

To the first and second of his wives he showed signs of real affection. The first left him and emigrated to Canada to escape. The second, Edith Pegler, was ignorant of his escapades and remained faithful to the end. She received his last letter before his execution.

Born in 1872, Smith was the son of an insurance company agent of Bethnal Green—hence his skilful plan to take out insurance policies for the lives of two of his brides (Alice Burnham and Margaret Lofty) who owned no property or substantial amounts of money. He was sent to a reformatory at the age of nine, and at eighteen he received a six months' prison sentence for stealing. Then he served in the Northamptonshire Regiment for two years. Masquerading as George Baker, he received twelve months' hard labour for larceny in 1896, and a two year sentence in 1900. By exploiting his first wife as a maid in domestic service and an accomplice in thefts from private houses, he committed many larcenies at south coast resorts and in London. She was sentenced to three months' hard labour in 1899, while he himself escaped. Though he so successfully exploited women for profit, his art dealer's shop shared with Edith Pegler can scarcely be called successful. He was certainly a man of initiative and enterprise. He had run a baker's shop and been a gymnastic instructor at different times.

Sir Bernard Spilsbury's biographers wrote of him as "a vulgar and all but illiterate ruffian", but the description is not at all accurate. It is true that his education had been poor and his letters showed a striking inability to spell quite simple words. Yet strangely enough, he had an astonishing appreciation and love of poetry, especially of Shakespeare. He could play the piano and draw quite well—skills which were lacking among many of the distinguished persons in court. The prison chaplain described him as intelligent and well read. Towards the end he changed from being an atheist to a sincere and penitent Christian.

At intervals he submitted correspondence to *The Bath and Wilts Chronicle* on the subjects of "Manners", "Prison Punishment", "Sanitation", "Criminal Reform", and "Objectionable Literature". No doubt his spelling and grammatical errors were corrected by the editor. His pose as a social reformer reveals him as a hypocrite, but these letters, which have never been republished since his death, are those of a thinker ahead of his time and make pertinent reading to-day.

Modern Education

Sir,

If the new system of education, as calculated by the authorities, be far more serviceable and substantial than it was twenty years ago, how is it we do not see the the fruits in the general behaviour of children, especially those between the ages of 12 and 16? Take, for instance, the quality of obedience. Can any grown-up person, either country or town bred, deny the fact that when they themselves were children their obedience to parents and superiors was more observed than it is to-day? Take, as another instance, and no less important, the coarse manner, the lack of true brotherly and sisterly feeling, and the late hours indulged in by children. The maximum time for children to return home was 8 p.m. but now any time will do. Let me quote another instance to compare with twenty years ago— the vast amount of inferior literature, such as the "penny dreadfuls" read by children—the circulation of which is enormous. In conclusion, the training of children is undoubtedly a great problem, and cannot be solved by the State alone. Thus it becomes the duty of parents to do their share, inasmuch as there are two educations—the one which is taught at school, and the other which comes from parents, the latter being as important as the former.

GEORGE SMITH.

91, Ashley Down Road,
Bristol.   August 9th, 1911.

Sanitation

To the Editor "Bath and Wilts Chronicle".

Sir,

I wonder if any of your readers can inform me as to the number of towns or districts, if any, besides Twerton, where refuse is removed from dwelling houses and shops only once a fortnight?

I have lived in many towns in England, large and small, and I have found no such regulation as this in existence elsewhere.

The removing of refuse in good time, especially from the poorer districts, is essential to public health, and in that case it should be one of the first and foremost duties of those in commission to employ ways and means for its urgent removal.

In a great many houses iron boxes are used to contain refuse, which undoubtedly are very serviceable, providing the boxes are kept properly covered. But many of the poorer class have no money for iron boxes; consequently any kind of vessel is used, some of which are very poor substitutes. Many of the small wooden boxes used for this purpose by large families are only capable of containing five or six days' refuse, and for the remaining eight days it is often piled up in heaps near the wood fence in the corners of the yard.

Until this fortnightly regulation is altered and a better system established, sore throats and many other ailments are inevitable. Therefore I hope, for the sake of public health and decency, that the authorities will take the matter up seriously, and follow the example of other towns, where all refuse is removed at least once a week.

GEORGE SMITH.

28, Brougham Hayes,
BATH.   December 12th.

Objectionable Literature

To the Editor "Bath and Wilts Chronicle".

Sir,
I note in your issue of the 26th instant that the Home Secretary is at last about to take steps for the suppression once and for all of the publication of inferior literature, and other offensive matter. I trust that when this provision is made law it will be promptly and consistently carried out, and not gradually allowed to sink into oblivion as did the "Black List".

I maintain that inferior literature is doing more harm and accountable for more law-breaking than excessive drinking and that unless our shops are cleansed from such a living curse—and the young prevented from further opportunities of obtaining such poison—our new generation, instead of rising to credit us, will live to disgrace us. As I pointed out in a previous letter regarding education, inasmuch as if parents do their share in these matters, they themselves would not only reap the benefit, but it would also tend to assist the schoolmasters and authorities.

GEORGE SMITH.

28, Brougham Hayes,
BATH.   December 27th, 1911.

Criminal Reform

Sir,

In my opinion, the problem of criminal reform is quite as important as the problem of unemployment, and, consequently necessitates the same amount of public attention; for undoubtedly unemployment tends to create criminality; and likewise criminality tends to create idleness. It is impossible to purify any sphere of society, while the hardened unreformed criminal is in our midst. Yet the public, as a whole, seldom, if ever, turns its attention towards this downfallen class, never troubling in the least as to what system the authorities are using in order to reform, as well as punish, these unfortunate beings. It is only when the public is reminded from time to time by the astounding revelations made known through the Press by some of the more observant and intellectual of discharged prisoners, that any regard is paid in that direction, and the whole matter, unfortunately, soon falls into oblivion.

G. Smith.

Cyanide Poisoning

It was appropriate that Willcox's last duty as Home Office Analyst should have been to solve the cause of the tragic death by poison of an eighteen year old student, Edmund Cronin, for the West Ham Coroner at the resumed inquest on June 23rd—the day on which the trial of G. J. Smith commenced. The inquest had been adjourned pending the analysis of the organs. Signs of irritant poisoning had been found by the pathologist, but no poison was obtained from the bedroom of deceased, only a tumbler containing a sediment which turned out to be Epsom salts. He had been studying for a civil service examination which included a course in chemistry. To Willcox, it was a straightforward problem for a chemical pathologist. The gullet and stomach showed the typical features of potassium cyanide poisoning, the stomach containing half a fatal dose. An open verdict was recorded. Potassium cyanide was a fairly common cause of suicidal and accidental death in circumstances where it could be easily obtained—in this case from the laboratory where deceased had worked.

Willcox had similarly investigated the sudden death of a fifteen year old girl, whose inquest brought him to Huntingdon on November 6th, 1914. In this tragedy, the girl had obtained the poison while employed in domestic service in a house where photographic equipment was lying about. But whether it was taken by accident or intention was never established at the inquest, an open verdict being returned.

References

The Trial of G. J. Smith by Eric Watson, Notable British Trials, 1915.
Bernard Spilsbury, His Life and Cases, by Douglas G. Browne and E. V. Tullett, Harrap, 1951.
Sir Travers Humphreys—A Biography by Douglas G. Browne, 1960.
Sir Edward Marshall Hall by Edward Marjoribanks, 1929.

PART 3

CONSULTING PHYSICIAN TO THE ARMY

Chapter 11

The Dardanelles Campaign—1915

Appointed by the War Office as Consulting Physician with the rank of temporary Lt.-Colonel, Willcox left London on July 15th, 1915, for Marseilles via Paris, arriving on 17th. He embarked the next day and reached Malta on 20th and Alexandria on 23rd. A happy reunion occurred with his sister Minnie who was a nursing sister at the 15th General Hospital and later became Matron of the Officers' Hospital in Cairo. During a week in Alexandria he visited several hospitals and interviewed General Sir William Babtie, D.M.S., of the Mediterranean forces and a V.C. of the South African War. He left a fourteen-page report on "Toxicological Problems relating to the War". This report dealt with chlorine, bromine, sulphur dioxide and nitrous oxide fumes and methods of protection devised by Baker and himself at home. The modification of the "Pimlico" helmet containing soda lime was recommended, against phosgene and hydro-cyanic acid. The prevention of irritation of the eyes by lachrymating gases received attention because xylene and bromine had already been used by the Germans in France. He recommended methods of spraying affected trenches with suitable chemical solutions and steps to be taken in dealing with water contaminated by the enemy with cyanide, arsenic, phosgene, copper and lead.

He arrived at Mudros on August 3rd and immediately settled down to his numerous duties as consulting physician. It is well at this stage to consider the duties involved in such a post. During the second World War, consulting physicians and surgeons were far more numerous in all theatres and carried the rank of Brigadier though their powers were limited to reporting to local Directors of Medical Services (D.M.S.). They visited hospitals and other units over wider areas, but visits were limited in time and consisted in details of organisation rather than pro-blems of individual patients. In the First World War consultants carried the rank of Lieutenant Colonel or Colonel, but as in the case of Willcox and others, they were in certain cases empowered to report direct to the War Office if the necessity arose.

Most of Willcox's work during the next six months was concerned with hospitals and patients, but this did not prevent him interesting himself in public health problems and even those concerning gas warfare, because he found there a team of analysts working on water supplies and other public health problems—a team headed by Major J. T. Hewitt, R.E., D.Sc., F.R.S., and Major le Sueur. During his travels in the forward areas, Willcox collected for analysis exploded bombs and shells which had contained lachrymating gases, samples of water from various hospitals for tests of purity and even tins of condensed milk. But his time was otherwise entirely taken up in hospital work of intense interest—"the most interesting work of my professional life" as he later described it. In Mudros itself there were eight hospitals which he visited at least once weekly, and more often when the occasion merited emergency visits. The terrible conditions in which war raged on the peninsula caused not only enormous numbers of battle casualties, but physical illness abounded as well—as was to be expected in a country where good hygiene could not be maintained by troops under constant bombardment through conditions of excessive heat and cold. Dysentery of several types was by far the greatest scourge though malaria, cerebrospinal fever, infective jaundice, typhoid and paratyphoid and relapsing fever were common, and even frost-bite cases were seen. In reports he stressed the importance of early clinical diagnosis of typhoid fevers where laboratory facilities were not available in forward areas and in the notification of infectious cases so that steps could quickly be taken for their prevention. In an article in the *Lancet* of March 11th, 1916, he reported 26 cases of beri-beri seen at Mudros —a disease which had already been described by Gowland Hopkins and others as a deficiency disease, later to be shown to be due to vitamin B deficiency. In the Dardanelles cases, the disease manifested itself following other infections such as dysentery, typhoid fever or jaundice, and death occurred in two cases. Willcox noted several cases of scurvy which had long been known to occur in people deprived of fresh fruit, and later recognised to be due to vitamin C deficiency. In his report he urged the provision of the necessary steps to improve the diet of the troops and the necessity of universal inoculation of mixed typhoid and paratyphoid vaccines among all troops arriving at the peninsula.

Within a month of his arrival at Mudros, he had succeeded in the establishment of a new building as a chemical laboratory for analytical work in connection with water supply and food problems, a field laboratory at Mudros and branches of this service in forward areas—all under the command of Captain R. G. Archibald, R.A.M.C. He made many friends among the doctors in the hospitals in Mudros and Salonica. Among them was his old friend Major (later Sir Arthur) Hurst of the 2nd Australian Stationary Hospital at Lemnos—who was later appointed Consulting Physician at Salonica.

On November 26th there was a great storm over the peninsula (the Suvla Blizzard) during which torrential rain swamped the trenches and the wind blew down many of the hospital tents so that patients had to be saved from smothering. This weather was followed by intense cold and frost which accounted for an outbreak of "trench foot"—a painful form of frost-bite aggravated by exposure to moisture. Towards the end of August 1915 following the second failure at Suvla the decision was reached to evacuate the Gallipoli peninsular—a confession of failure of a campaign which some military historians had regarded as doomed from the start. Nevertheless, as in the case at Dunkirk, the evacuation was carried out with unexpectedly brilliant success and very few casualties. Thus ended a campaign which had cost an enormous number of allied casualties both of sick and wounded. Early in 1916 Willcox was recalled to proceed home on leave. He embarked on the Mauretania from Mudros on January 17th. Doubtless he expected to be given another military posting after a short period of leave—as turned out to be the case.

Chapter 12

The Advance and the Conquest of Baghdad—1916–17

On January 25th Willcox returned to London from Mudros and reported to the War Office the next day. The next six weeks was a period of relaxation, but it could scarcely be termed a holiday, for he was from time to time summoned to the War Office to report to Keogh and Horrocks about the medical organisation and sickness among troops at the Dardanelles.

At this time the frequency of self-inflicted wounds and firearms injuries was a source of concern to the War Office and the Army Medical Department. Diagnosis of a self-inflicted injury by Medical Officers was often extremely difficult; and even when the evidence of self-infliction was there, few doctors were prepared to support it at trials by courts martial. Willcox was requested to carry out experimental work on this difficult subject, the results of his work being published in the R.A.M.C. Journal of June 1916.

Using British and American service rifles and targets of cardboard lined with chamois leather, he fired the weapons at distances from three to twenty-four inches and photographed in each case the targets to record the varying degree of blackening, scorching and peppering such as would be seen in self-inflicted wounds of the human body. This work, conducted with the help of E. L. Churchill, the gunsmith, was an extension of the research on revolver bullet wounds carried out in 1907, as previously described, and proved a help in the difficult problem of diagnosis both in military and civilian practice.

The impression Willcox made on Keogh and Horrocks through his services at the Dardanelles was such as to merit his selection for the appointment of Consulting Physician to the Army in Mesopotamia, an achievement evidently envied by some of his professional colleagues in London. His selection—and that of Sir Victor Horsley at the same time, as Consulting Surgeon—was made in response to severe criticism of the medical services at the front in Mesopotamia in the early months of 1916.

At the age of forty-six Willcox was in the prime of life, active and vigorous, having enjoyed excellent health in spite of hard work in the hot and cold climates of the Dardanelles. Those who knew him only in later life would not have guessed that he was tough enough to enjoy the rigours of military life, like a duck taking to water. Others were doubtless surprised that a Home Office analyst, skilled at laboratory analyses and well known as a medical witness in courts of law, should have been selected for an important and responsible military post in one of the major campaigns of the war—a post which was to involve him in work of quite a different kind altogether. Though he was not a man who suffered fools gladly, he had already demonstrated his capacity to co-operate with all ranks and to give advice to superior officers without causing offence or jealousy. All these factors combined to turn the scales in favour of his selection.

At the age of fifty-nine Sir Victor Horsley was at the same time appointed Consulting Surgeon to the same Army, having earlier volunteered to go when he heard about the difficulties in the organisation of the medical services there. He was already in command of a surgical unit at Alexandria. They did not, therefore, travel out together. Horsley left Port Said for Bombay on March 15th, 1916; Willcox left Southampton on the Essequibo on the same day, having said farewell to Mildred there. The previous day he had had a long interview with Keogh, Horrocks and other officers, receiving detailed briefing about his duties and the problems to be confronted. Both Horsley and himself were empowered to communicate direct to the War Office and to G.H.Q. India, a salutory power which ensured, as nothing else could have done, that their representations would receive attention ("Loyalties", Sir Arnold Wilson). As Willcox explained after the war (*St. Mary's Hospital Gazette*, May 1919) little attention had been paid at home to the campaign until early 1916, when rumours filtered through which caused anxiety about transport arrangements and deficiencies in the care of sick and wounded—the responsibility of the Government of India. During the period following the surrender at Kut on April 29th, the Government of India endeavoured to forestall criticism of its administration by appointing a commission consisting of Sir William Vincent, a distinguished Civil Servant, and Major-General Bingley "to inquire into the medical arrangements in Mesopotamia during and subsequent to January 1916 and to report to the Chief of the General Staff" ("Loyalties" 1914–1917, p. 170).

Operations which had begun in November 1914 had been eminently successful until the period preceding the Kut disaster. They had been directed to drive the Turks out of the Persian Gulf to free the Arabs from Turkish domination and the oilfields from their control. Troops landed at the mouth of the Shatt-al-Arab under the command of General Delamain while reinforcements under General Sir Arthur Barrett proceeded and landed about 30 miles upstream. Within a month Basra and Kurna had been captured. Under General Nixon's command from April 1915 most brilliant victories were achieved at Ahwaz—the key to the oilfields, Amara and Naziriyah. A large Turkish force was defeated at Kut-el-Amara and at Ctesiphon, about 20 miles south of Baghdad. The siege of Kut was the attempt to stabilise the front at this region, rendered necessary by heavy casualties and strong enemy reinforcements assisted by trained German troops. The appalling treatment of the survivors of the seige is well known, but at that time details were never allowed to reach the public at home through the Press, except in very diluted form.

There was heated discussion, however, of the causes of the reverses and the breakdown in organisation and transport services on the Tigris and Euphrates, rivers not by any means suitable for big ships. It was the old story of great successes and military advances resulting in far too lengthy lines of communication, poor reinforcements and supplies, followed by inevitable reverses in the face of increasingly powerful opposition. Criticism was directed to the Government of India from the Viceroy, Lord Hardinge of Penshurst, downwards, to Sir John Nixon, who became one of the chief military scapegoats in spite of his earlier brilliant victories so highly praised by Mr. Asquith in the House of Commons on November 2nd.

Until January 1917 the Tigris front lay below Kut, a distance of 300 miles from the base at Basra. Without considerable improvement in river transport which had to be increased from all available resources (India, Burma and Egypt) the campaign could never have been carried on in 1916 as the roads were undeveloped, and motor transport in comparatively short supply.

Willcox arrived at Alexandria on March 27th and left for Suez the next day. Seven days spent there waiting for a boat provided few idle moments, for he visited all the hospitals there, conducted consultations, and gave a medical address. He saw some patients evacuated from Mesopotamia and learnt something of the work which awaited him at his final destination. He encountered an outbreak of Relapsing Fever there, and was able to witness the successful treatment by methods previously developed at Mudros.

He arrived at Bombay on April 10th and visited several hospitals, interviewing medical officers about deficiencies in supplies and services for troops evacuated from the Persian Gulf. He stayed four days at Simla from April 21st, with Sir Pardey Lukis, Director of Medical Services for India. At a conference with the Commander in Chief, General Sir Beauchamp Duff, he was already prepared with sufficient evidence to urge recommendation on a wide variety of requirements for the medical services: improvement in river transport, ten extra hospital steamers for the Tigris and Euphrates, two more hospital ships for evacuation of casualties from Basra to Bombay, increased hospital accommodation and laboratory facilities at Bombay. This forecast for hospital requirements in Bombay proved accurate. Additional hospital accommodation was soon provided and, as events turned out, was able to meet all requirements in 1916 and 1917. Turning to various diseases, he urged the necessary preventive measures for dealing with the deficiency diseases scurvy and beri-beri by attention to improvement in diet, fresh lime juice, vegetables, yeast, marmite, and refrigerators—requirements based on reports received from officers returned from the front.

He arrived at Basra on May 11th, and quickly commenced hospital inspections in an attempt to assess the relative priority of requirements for improving the care of medical and surgical casualties. He found Horsley, having already made complaints and requests for various improvements, was suffering from a considerable sense of frustration at the lack of response from authorities in India. Among other recommendations they urged that the laboratory services in British and Indian hospitals must be improved, and that cookhouses and latrines should be rendered fly-proof as soon as possible. Proceeding by steamer up-river to Amara, Willcox realised that no arrangements existed for water chlorination for personnel travelling in this way. The provision of N.C.O.'s trained in water chlorination to supervise the water supply on all river transport was soon arranged in order to minimise the risk of personnel acquiring dysentery and enteric infections. In hospitals at Amara he discovered 300 cases of enteric fever, mostly in British troops. Most of these cases were examples of paratyphoid infection, which had not been prevented by routine inoculation against typhoid fever. The adoption of triple vaccine against these infections was accordingly urged, with success.

Early in May he was awarded the C.M.G. in recognition of his services at the Dardanelles, receiving congratulatory letters from several old friends including his old headmasters, the Revd. T. Glasspool and the Revd. James West.

He was instrumental in moving the Infectious Diseases Hospital and the Indian General Hospital at Basra, the sites of both being unsatisfactory, and urged the provision of electric light and fans where they were most urgently required. The daily sick rate among about 4,000 personnel stationed there had reached the alarming rate of 600 for whom hospital accommodation could not be provided, but somehow further sick bays were improvised for short term illnesses. The locally purchased milk supply at the British General Hospital was condensed milk from Holland and Italy; it was condemned as quite unsuitable, but fortunately from July 30th satisfactory condensed milk from England was supplied at regular intervals.

Willcox did not confine his attention to base hospitals, but visited field ambulances and combatant units at the front. He reported by telegram both to the D.M.S. at Basra and to G.H.Q. India, listing the many deficiencies urgently required for the ordinary care of the sick—suitable tents, beds, mattresses, mosquito nets, water supplies, apparatus for chlorination, fresh vegetables and fruit, fresh eggs, meat, ice and refrigerators, motor launches and ambulances. Though Horsley had already agitated, as he thought, in vain, the defects were steadily, though slowly, remedied during 1916 under the able direction of the D.M.S., Major General Treherne, assisted by Col. Matthew Fell, his deputy, with the co-operation of Col. E. A. Dickson of Supply H.Q. Basra. The fact that Willcox had come direct with War Office authority behind him added urgency to his recommendations. The Army Commander, General Sir Percy Lake, took the greatest interest and did all in his power to supply everything in the way of hospital units, personnel and equipment. The foundations were thus laid for further military advances within a few months, by which time the medical services could be compared favourably with those in any other theatre of war. New ration scales were introduced in July 1916 which included vitamin B in the form of Marmite and yeast and fresh meat, and other sources of vitamin C whereby the incidence of beri-beri and scurvy was almost completely controlled by the end of 1916. The overwhelming proportion of casualties at the front were medical illnesses; and Mesopotamia has been called the physician's paradise. Many of the Indian troops newly arrived were found to be debilitated by a long and trying journey. In the hot weather of 1916, for example, heat stroke affected 130 cases on a hospital ship on its way from Basra to Bombay, of which 25 were fatal.

Willcox observed that scurvy was a disease that should and could have been prevented at an earlier stage of the campaign. As his colleague and consulting physician Col. H. G. Melville, I.M.S., noted, many of the Indian troops whom he observed on arrival were on the borderline of malnutrition, and therefore predisposed to fall quick victims to scurvy. Melville had been Professor of Medicine at Lahore and had volunteered for service in spite of being considerably senior in age to Willcox. In spite of indifferent health, he had great qualities of perseverance in an exacting climate. He kept in close contact with his colleague, his great experience of Indian personnel being of special value to the service. Melville died in harness in Baghdad in December 1918.

The enormous wastage of troops due to scurvy was seen in the statistics: 11,445 cases occurred in the last six months of 1916, though the incidence had fallen by about three quarters at the end of the year. Most of these cases in Indian troops had to be evacuated as being unfit for further service. Scurvy fortunately did not affect British troops, owing to the higher meat ration in British rations.

Willcox and Melville made a detailed study of the Indian ration system hitherto in operation. Financial allowance was made to each soldier equal to the cost of items in the Field Service Ration. He bought his ration from the "bunniah" or food contractor of his unit. In order to save money for his family the Indian sepoy often took no trouble to draw his ration for his own consumption, no doubt starving himself for a few annas. As a result, many troops arrived in an unsatisfactory state of health; anaemic, debilitated and suffering from pyorrhoea. They were easy victims of scurvy if put under hardships of dietetic restrictions in the field, with little balance in the bank of antiscorbutic vitamin C. The British troops, on the other hand, were well nourished when they went out, and seldom developed vitamin deficiency. Basra and Amara being centres of production of fruit and vegetables, the troops there had a low incidence of scurvy, but further afield troops had to rely solely on food supplied by river transport. Attempts to grow locally vegetables for the army were unsuccessful, owing to water shortage in outlying districts. No special provision for transport of fresh fruit and vegetables was made until near the end of 1916, the provisions actually supplied being in many cases in a damaged condition or insufficient.

In the official history Willcox was given much of the credit for the alteration in the Indian rations sanctioned by the Army Commander, Sir Percy Lake in July 1916 and again by his successor General Sir Stanley Maude in October 1916. In the revised diet fresh lime juice was supplied, the meat ration was raised to 6 ozs. and tamarind and coccum containing vitamin C were included. But Willcox gave much of the credit for the eradication of dietetic deficiencies amongst the troops to those responsible for transport and supplies, notably Sir George McMunn, Inspector-General of Communications, and officers under him, to whom credit was due for their success in supplying by the end of the year fresh limes and vegetables in greater quantity. Many of the Indian troops, as a result of social or religious customs, had failed to consume their daily meat ration of 4 ozs.

Hitherto the ordinary lime juice included in Indian rations was probably about six months old before reaching the troops, having lost most of its antiscorbutic value. At Willcox's suggestion fresh lime juice was prepared in 5 per cent alcohol, and salicylic acid (2 grains per pint) added as preservative. It was effective in both prevention and treatment of scurvy. It was transported in special casks with the date of preparation marked on the label. This was allocated specially to Indian troops.

Though beri-beri played a less important part in the campaign, over 300 cases occurred in British troops in 1915. Deficiency in vitamin B occurred as a result of deficient transport of food supplies to, rather than deficient ration scales for, British troops. By adding oatmeal and dhall to British rations, and atta (25 per cent) to the composition of flour in bread, a substantial need of vitamin B was met as early as February 1916. Willcox had suggested to the War Office (*Lancet*, March 11th, 1916) that an extract of yeast should be included in British rations. Experiments instituted by Colonel William Horrocks and carried out by Professor Starling, Dr. S. M. Copeman, Miss Chick and Miss Hume (of the Lister Institute) resulted in the issue of Marmite to British troops in Mesopotamia in October 1916—the first issue of this extract of yeast to the British Army. The nutritional value of yeast had been recognised at the end of the 19th century, and it had been used in the Dardanelles campaign to prevent and treat beri-beri. The concentrated extract of autolysed yeast known as Marmite was first produced in 1902, but it was shown at the Lister Institute to be equally effective in preventing beri-beri in pigeons as any other yeast preparation. It lost none of its qualities after transport and storage. In this way beri-beri was easily controlled. Both scurvy and beri-beri were made notifiable diseases, and in 1917 special hospitals for nutritional diseases were established at Basra and Amara. Due to the initiative of the D.M.S., Major-General Francis Treherne and Willcox, a memorandum on the prevention of these deficiency diseases was circulated to all officers in command of units. In this way and others they were enabled to ensure the best possible nutritional state of combatant and non-combatant units.

Much was achieved to improve motor transport in outlying areas far from the Tigris and Euphrates in preparation for the military successes achieved in the advance to Baghdad at the end of 1916.

Willcox arrived at Amara with the D.M.S. about a month after Horsley's arrival, finding him impatient at the poverty of supplies to forward troops of water, food, transport and surgical equipment. Sir Victor was devoted to his surgical work, and spent much of his spare time writing reports and complaints which were apt to embarrass some of the senior officers. There was no doubt that the Indian Government had failed to make adequate provision for a campaign on the large scale it had turned out to be. With the arrival of Willcox he was relieved to be able to hand over the task of organisation to his colleague. At this stage the campaign was static.

Troops were entrenched at most places, the bulk of the medical work being non-surgical. Along the right bank of the Tigris the Turks were being gradually repulsed with the result that our troops became infected with cholera, dysentery and typhoid fevers acquired from captured camp sites. This experience was repeated in the Burma campaign in the Second World War when the Japanese forces retreated in Burma, leaving infected typhus sites behind from which our troops were infected on a large scale.

Horsley spent nearly all his time in the very forward areas, and walked long distances at all hours of the day. When Willcox and Horsley met (on several occasions) in May, Horsley felt extraordinarily fit and claimed that the heat suited him. Nevertheless on July 16th he succumbed to an attack of paratyphoid fever complicated by heat stroke. His sad loss, though a great blow to the army, was more so to the profession of which he was one of its most distinguished leaders and surgeons. After the war Willcox wrote of him "Horsley possessed in a remarkable degree qualities of fearlessness, disregard of self and personal discomfort, tireless industry and personal charm, to which can be added a sporting instinct and love of adventure—as exemplified by his service in the war. While in India, and thereafter, he did much to stimulate the authorities about the medical needs for the forces in Mesopotamia and his advice was fully appreciated and acted upon. After reaching Basra he immediately set out for the front to appreciate the actual surgical needs there. His letters from Amara in May and June describe the climatic discomforts and hardships of the campaign. It was a tragic misfortune that this calamity occurred then, for it was known that he had intended leaving for India early in June to use his influence at G.H.Q. to improve conditions and supplies for the front. He had delayed his departure in order to meet the Army Commander who was coming up river. During the mornings he visited the hospitals at Amara, walking several miles (in the absence of motor transport) in the intense heat, in order to do his work. There is not the least doubt that the exposure caused the fatal attack of heat stroke."

The period from Horsley's death until the end of 1916 was one of military and medical preparation for the offensive towards Baghdad. Supplies were built up and of course river and motor transport improved on a large scale. General Sir Stanley Maude was appointed to succeed Lake as Army Commander at the end of August. Lake was in indifferent health as a result of his activities as a successful Army Commander who took a great interest in the medical services. In one of his last dispatches speaking of the difficulties of the medical services he wrote: "Much thought and hard work have been devoted to overcoming these difficulties, and meeting the medical needs of the force . . . The advent of the hot weather in May with a sudden rise in temperature increased the number of sick. The heat was aggravated at the front by the absence of shade and the failure of the 'shamal' or north wind, which did not commence until July 19th. The admissions to hospital then at once lessened and are still decreasing . . . An outbreak of cholera occurred on the Tigris front at the end of April, but was got under control in a short time since when only a few cases are reported from time to time in various parts of the country. I am much indebted to Surgeon General F. H. Treherne for the valuable assistance he has consistently rendered since his arrival, and to Col. W. H. Willcox, Consulting Physician, whose high professional knowledge has always been at the service of the force. Much credit is due to the Nursing Sisters who have carried out their duties with great devotion . . . in alleviating the suffering of those who have passed through their hands. By the untimely death of Colonel Sir V. Horsley both the force and the medical profession have sustained a severe loss." Willcox was often summoned by the new Army Commander for discussions on medical arrangements both before and after the conquest of Baghdad. Maude, an old Etonian and son of a famous general holding the V.C., was equally interested in the medical services as Lake had been. They had previously met at the Dardanelles and now formed a mutual liking for each other. Maude already was familiar with most of the problems involved, having been in command of the 13th Division. Speaking of Colonel Willcox to Colonel Dickson, the Controller of Local Produce, Maude had said: "I consider his work in improving the health of my force is equal to two divisions. Whatever it costs in work and money you must see that the country provides everything that Willcox thinks necessary." (Callwell, p. 305.)

Following the visit of General Sir Charles Monro, C.-in-C. India, to the front on October 27th, Maude was laid low with an attack of sandfly fever, and came under the care of Willcox who later reported "His only care then, after hearing the diagnosis and the treatment necessary, was that his work should be interfered with as little as possible. Removal to hospital was unnecessary and part of the time required for rest was occupied in his journey up the Karun river to visit the oilfields. He made a complete recovery from this illness, which to most patients means a week or more in hospital, but to him was two days rest in bed, after which he was able to resume his duties with certain restrictions as to exertion." He was pronounced medically completely fit again on November 3rd and for the next month was extremely busy with details of the forthcoming offensive which commenced on December 13th.

Another noteable patient in September was Miss Gertrude Bell, the well-known Arabic explorer and linguist who, through her vast knowledge of Arabic customs and politics and her acquaintance with local rulers, had been attached to the political department under the control of that supreme adviser Sir Percy Cox. She contracted catarrhal jaundice (hepatitis) in September at Basra. She recovered well but slowly and perhaps became active more quickly than he expected.

Basra—October 23rd, 1916.

Dear Colonel Willcox,

How kind of you to come and see me. I am very sorry I missed you. I am well, thank you, but not very gloriously well. Perhaps some more of the most potent tonic you gave me would not be a bad thing. As long as I have it I felt much better. The I.G.C. does you great credit.

Yours sincerely,
Gertrude Bell.

During the autumn outbreaks of dysentery and cholera continued to cause anxiety at the front. Special attention was paid to the treatment of these cases at the Advanced Base at Amara. He visited advanced units at the front beyond Sheikh Saad. Most hospital cases were examples of illnesses as opposed to battle casualties. The fight against cholera was intensified by preventive measures and vaccine inoculation in newly arrived troops. The intravenous saline treatment designed first by Sir Leonard Rogers, I.M.S., an old friend at St. Mary's Hospital, was arranged on a large scale for all sufferers but in the hottest season of the year the mortality still approached 40 per cent.

The Conquest of Baghdad

With the advent of the cooler weather the planned offensive took place towards Baghdad from December 10th ending with brilliant success on March 18th, 1917, when General Maude entered the city by river almost unnoticed except by a small crowd of Arabs who had collected at his landing site. Though this was not the end of the campaign it marked the army commander as one of the most successful generals of the war at the time. Baghdad subsequently made a base for supplies and for new base hospitals to be set up. Local supplies of food were subsequently obtainable under the control of General Dickson, director of local resources. From 1917 onwards the lower sickness rate in spite of the great heat of that summer was due to improved hygiene and rations of fresh foods and meat obtained locally. Improved hospital facilities in Baghdad reduced the number of sick who had to be evacuated to Basra, a distance of 500 miles downstream. An excellent laboratory service under the command of Major Mackie, I.M.S., X-ray departments, and specialists in these subjects soon provided services as good as in any other theatre of war. Principal diseases were sandfly fever, malaria, dysentery, enteric fevers, typhus, relapsing fever, smallpox, catarrhal jaundice, cholera, heat exhaustion and heat stroke. No doubt contact with the civilian population and the use of Turkish camp sites predisposed troops to the ravages of some of these diseases when the hot season of 1917 came on—the hottest season in the memory of the local population. From July 10th to 24th the temperature on three days reached 122 °F. in the shade. In tents, though they were of the double fly type, the temperature would reach a maximum of 135 °F. There were 6,242 cases of heat stroke (mortality 8·4 per cent) in 1917 compared with 574 (mortality 5·4 per cent) in 1918 which was a cooler summer in which the temperature attained 115 °F. on only two days (Willcox, B.M.J., March 20th, 1920). It was during July that the unsuccessful attack on Ramadi took place. Maude was seen pacing up and down his room saying "God help those poor fellows" at the time the attack commenced.

Maude gave the Turks no respite but rapidly pushed his forces northwards up the Tigris and Euphrates. Willcox made several long journeys by motor (Ford) transport across the desert to outlying units to see casualties in the most forward areas. From time to time he would be summoned, when in Baghdad, to the Army Commander's house for consultation. Occasionally he would receive an invitation to dinner—worded in Maude's typical courteous and informal style, written in pencil, but never as a command.

Army Commander's House (Baghdad)

May 10th, 1917.

Dear Colonel Willcox,
The Army Commander hopes you will come to dinner tonight at 7.30 p.m.

Yours sincerely,

George Ogilvie Forbes
(Staff Officer)

In June Willcox was awarded the C.B. as a result of Maude's recommendation of March. As Sir Arnold Wilson later wrote (Loyalties, Vol. 1, p. 276) Willcox "enjoyed General Maude's confidence and esteem in a quite exceptional degree." He made no note, however, in his diary, but preserved an amusing letter from Miss Bell.

June 1917.

My dear C.B.,
A thousand congratulations. But if it had been K.G. it would not have surpassed your deserts. Would Tuesday morning suit you for visiting Daud Bey's horses? If so will you pick me up here at 6.15?

Yours very sincerely,

Gertrude Bell.

He attended her again for heat exhaustion late in July. Less than a month later she picked up an attack of sandfly fever as she graphically describes in a letter to her father:

Baghdad, September 5, 1917.

To H.B.,
I didn't go to Samarra after all. Doom struck out, as the poet says, like a blind camel and he caught me straight and full. For with my box and bedding packed, my dinner almost carried to General Lubbock's hospital board—I was going to dine with the Father of Railways on my way to the train—I began to feel curiouser and curiouser and anyhow very certain that I had fever. And then Col. Willcox drifted in (Providence always directs the angelic man to my door just when I want him) took my temperature and shattered my plans. I held out for two miserable days in my own house, too achy and above all too headachy to stir, and then came into hospital with a temperature of 102. Sandfly fever. Everyone has it. I don't know how I've escaped it so long. They don't know what it is really; they haven't caught its microbe yet. But you get your money's worth out of it, if only from the intolerable headache. Quinine is no good. They give you febrifuges and phenacetin and feed you only on slops, all of which things being unfit, so to speak, for human consumption, you find yourself pretty ragged when at last the devil thing goes.

I'm really over the thing—it's gone. But there's no doubt I shall feel cheap for a bit and as soon as I can I shall go away for a fortnight. Col. Willcox is very keen that I should do this and I think it will be salvation. It's so beautifully cool now that one can go anywhere. They are extremely kind to me in this hospital. They treat me as if I were a Major General.

Damnable as sandfly fever is it isn't a matter for the smallest anxiety so please feel none, you and mother. I feel ashamed of behaving like this.

She recovered quickly from this and wrote:

Dear Colonel Willcox,
How very kind of you. Could you please thank Captain MacDermott also? I'm better today—I feel more like a human being.

Yours sincerely,

Gertrude Bell.

At the end of May the Bishop of Nagpur visited Baghdad to carry out duties in connection with the chaplain's department including confirmations. He stayed at Maude's house at G.H.Q. throughout his visit. In response to his request to visit Babylon, about fifty miles distance, Maude arranged motor transport and an armed escort for the party consisting of the Bishop, Colonel J. H. Stanley, Captain Norman Brookes (his assistant) the famous tennis player and singles champion of Wimbledon in 1907 and 1914, and Willcox. Though Maude insisted on the armed escort for fear of the Bishop's safety from attack by desert arabs, the escort did not turn up at the appointed time of departure, but eventually caught up with the party en route about half way on the journey. It was a memorable visit during which they saw the ruined palaces of Nebuchadnezzar and the ruins of Birs Nimrod popularly supposed to be the tower of Babel. On returning the Bishop remarked that he had collected material for at least a dozen sermons. Though the journey was a rough and bumpy one it provided Willcox with the nearest approach to a holiday that he had enjoyed since his arrival in the country. When the military situation permitted, he was allotted the use of a horse for riding to hospitals in Baghdad and often enjoyed rides in the desert, sometimes in the company of Miss Bell who was equally fond of horses and riding. He also was able to enjoy his other favourite sport of shooting and took the opportunities provided for sand grouse shooting at Samarrah in November.

During May he had the opportunity of entertaining to dinner Captain V. Z. (now Sir Zachary) Cope. He was one of the two junior surgeons on the staff of St. Mary's Hospital who did distinguished surgical work at the front. The other was Major C. A. Pannett (later Professor of Surgery at St. Mary's) who was stationed at Sheikh Saad in 1916 and 1917.

The Consulting Surgeons Col. E. V. Hugo, I.M.S., and Col. T. P. Legge and Willcox all lived together in the Red Cross Mess at Baghdad. On September 8th they had the honour of entertaining General Maude and his staff officers to dinner there—probably the last occasion they met him informally.

The Death of General Maude

The death of the Army Commander, the conqueror of Baghdad, who had achieved imperishable renown since he took over the command, was unique in the annals of British military history and the greatest tragedy in the campaign next to the disaster of Kut. It was an instance of the danger of cholera in military operations in a hot climate. In describing Willcox's life it is necessary to describe this illness in some detail, not only because of the esteem and affection he felt for him—as indeed was the case of all ranks of the army there—but Willcox was present throughout his illness when it took on a serious aspect and was the senior doctor in charge of him as patient, though the consulting surgeons and other medical officers lent advice and technical help. Yet neither Willcox nor any of the other doctors was able to pull him through a virulent attack of cholera in spite of the most detailed care and constant effort. It was certainly the most tragic yet historic illness he ever attended; and probably the saddest moment of his life was when Maude died. Let the illness and appreciation be described in his own words in his report to the War Office:

In January 1917 I was at G.H.Q. Sinn when the active operations around Kut were in progress and I had the privilege of an interview with General Maude. He was at that time living in an 80-pound tent and undergoing the same hardships as his troops. He was taking the greatest interest in all the medical arrangements and was most solicitous as to the care of the sick and wounded during these operations.

After the occupation of Baghdad on March 11th, 1917, it was frequently my privilege to meet General Maude, and to discuss with him matters relating to the prevention of illness among the troops and any practical suggestions always received his utmost support. He took the greatest interest in the prevention of scurvy which had been a great scourge amongst the Indian troops and he gave instructions to his Director of Local Resources General E. Dickson that at all costs fresh vegetables and supplies were to be issued to the fullest medical requirements. These instructions were faithfully carried out and as a consequence scurvy speedily disappeared from the Force.

After the occupation of Baghdad General Maude took the keenest interest in every detail of the medical arrangements and it was largely due to his active support that the very high degree of efficiency was attained.

The hospitals in Baghdad and the medical arrangements generally were as efficient in every way as regards medical care, nursing and equipment as any hospitals in London or in any theatre of war.

General Maude personally visited the hospital at least twice a week and by his kindly interest and sympathy did a very great deal to alleviate the sufferings of the patients and to encourage them in their progress towards recovery. He took special interest in the Indian patients, and as an example of his thoughtfulness and sympathy he learnt Hindustani in order to be able to converse with them on his visits to the Indian hospitals.

It is impossible to exaggerate the great help and sympathy which the Medical Service in Mesopotamia received from General Maude during the whole time of his service as G.O.C. His personal interest and great sympathy were the prime causes of the perfection of the medical arrangements in the hospitals and in the field.

In October and November 1917 an epidemic of cholera occurred in Baghdad, and General Maude issued orders on the advice of the D.M.S. as regards the precautionary measures to be adopted, including inoculation of troops against cholera.

During this period he was working very hard and planning out the various operations necessary for the complete expulsion of the enemy from Mesopotamia. No detail of any part of the Army Administration escaped his attention.

On November 16th, General Maude was not feeling well. He had had slight diarrhoea for two or three days and he saw at his office at 7.45 a.m. Lieut. Molony I.M.S. the medical officer of G.H.Q. At this time no symptoms of illness were present and he continued at work until 1 p.m.

He then returned to his residence but continued at work in his bedroom during the afternoon. At 6.15 p.m. on November 16th, 1917, I saw General Maude in consultation with Lieut. Molony and at this time no symptoms of any kind were complained of or were present. On my arrival General Maude was busy dictating telegrams and giving instructions as regards the various details connected with the Force under his command.

After some persuasion he consented to retire to bed and give up work. He very much wished to fulfil an engagement for dinner on that evening but on my urgent request decided to forgo this.

About 7.45 p.m. severe symptoms of cholera commenced with great suddenness, and in a few minutes a state of extreme collapse occurred. Without delay immediate treatment was adopted and everything possible was done to combat the acute symptoms. Lieut. Molony and myself as consulting physician remained with General Maude throughout his illness. Colonel Legg A.M.S. and Colonel Hugo I.M.S., consulting surgeons to the Force were called into consultation and remained in attendance during the illness. Miss Walker the Matron of No. 31 British Stationary Hospital and four specially selected nurses carried out with the greatest care and devotion their nursing duties.

Some slight improvement followed, and some of the severe symptoms were alleviated but the condition of extreme cardiac weakness remained throughout, and there was little if any hope of recovery from the very onset of the symptoms of cholera. No permanent improvement followed on the intravenous saline treatment which was carried out without delay from the onset of severe symptoms.

General Maude retained his mental activity in spite of his great weakness until two hours before the end. He instinctively knew after the onset of the severe symptoms that he was suffering from cholera and his first request was that none of his staff should run any risk of infection.

During his illness his constant thought was the Army under his command, and he anxiously enquired as to certain recommendations for awards to his men which he had made, and it was necessary for him to be assured that these had been forwarded.

A few hours before his death he received a telegram from Lady Maude and dictated an encouraging reply.

At 4.30 p.m. on Sunday, November 18th, 1917, unconsciousness supervened and General Maude passed peacefully away at 6.25 p.m. The cause of death was cardiac failure consequent on the toxaemia of a very severe cholera infection.

Some rumours occurred in Baghdad and I believe in England as to the possibility of General Maude's illness being due to poison. I would like most emphatically to contradict the possibility of this having been the case. Throughout the illness most careful bacteriological examinations were made at the Central Laboratory Baghdad by Major Gloster I.M.S. and his staff and most definite evidence was obtained of the presence of a very virulent infection of cholera, thus confirming entirely the clinical diagnosis.

As regards the date of infection, it seems very probable that this was contracted on Wednesday evening November 14th, 1917. On that evening a dramatic performance was given in aid of a local charity by the civil population in a part of Baghdad where cholera was present. General Maude had earlier consented to be Patron of the entertainment, and he was unwilling to disappoint the local population by being absent, though he was advised to abstain from attending. At the performance General Maude partook of some light refreshment and had coffee with which he took some milk. In that area of the city at that time it would be very likely that the milk would be infected with cholera organisms and it seems very probable that the actual infection occurred in this way. There is no reason to suspect that the infection of the milk was otherwise than an accidental infection from the water of the area which was known to be under great suspicion at that time.

The death of General Sir Stanley Maude was an irreparable loss to the Mesopotamian Force and to the Empire. He had endeared himself to every member of his Army and he was personally mourned by everyone for he was loved by all.

His devotion to duty, military genius and nobility of character were well known to every man serving in Mesopotamia and each instinctively gave of his very best in consequence.

One cannot read the account of the closing scene described by the Chaplain, the Revd. A. C. E. Jarvis, without sharing the grief of those present and of all his troops.

At the end it was all very beautiful. His immediate personal staff, the doctors, nurses and orderly stood round the ordinary camp bed. Outside, the measured tread of the Gurka guard. A peaceful calm filled the room. I began the service of Commendation at five past six, and at twenty-five minutes past he passed peacefully into Paradise. Thus our beloved Commander left us, victor over the last great enemy.

During the course of the illness Major-General A. P. Blenkinsop D.M.S. sent his account to Sir Alfred Keogh; the last paragraph read:

The Chief went to a Jewish dramatic performance on Wednesday and while there, drank some coffee and milk. He had been warned not to eat or drink anything in the city and he knew that all issues of fresh milk to troops had been stopped since the appearance of cholera and I had told him that milk was under suspicion.

Though the illness was bacteriologically proved as cholera, the theory of poisoning which was subsequently held in the city prevailed for several years. It was even said that one of Maude's closest relatives still believed this, over twenty years later. It was obviously quite untenable. Maude had taken no steps to be inoculated against the disease in spite of the fact that his troops on his own orders had received vaccine. He was an entirely selfless man, an extreme extrovert, so concerned with details of his army and the health of his troops that he took no trouble to safeguard his own, having supreme confidence in his own inherent strength and resistance—evidence of a slight obstinancy of character which had been revealed at various times in his earlier career (Callwell).

Looking back to this illness after a period of over fifty years, one is tempted to ask whether Maude's life could have been saved under present-day standards of treatment. If he had been an ordinary soldier the probability is that he would have agreed to treatment at an earlier stage of the illness, whereas he had to be persuaded reluctantly to decline an invitation to dinner an hour or so before the illness took a serious course. In all probability Maude's illness would be the same again in view of his habit of concealing his own illnesses in order to avoid abandoning his duties for reasons of ill health.

In the autumn of 1917 Willcox was preoccupied in work in hospitals in Baghdad and its environs and was confronted with outbreaks of smallpox, cholera, typhus and relapsing fever. Smallpox had of course always been a problem. In 1917 and 1918 there were 332 cases in British troops (mortality 18 per cent) and 131 in Indian troops (mortality 9·5 per cent) in Baghdad alone, apart from those in units in outlying districts, which required visiting. Until late in 1917 typhus and relapsing fever had been uncommon as there had been little contact of troops with the local arabs. But the number of Turkish prisoners was increasing rapidly, bringing typhus with them; and there was far closer contact with Kurds and Persians enrolled in native labour corps as the area of occupation by our forces increased. The risk of infection was greater in medical personnel, transport drivers, police and those in charge of labour units. Typhus was prevalent only in the winter, being conveyed by louse infestation. The further our forces advanced into Northern Mesopotamia and Persia the greater problem they became owing to larger numbers of prisoners and the prevalence of disease in the local population. The Turkish Army left a dangerous legacy. A medical officer described typhus as the "faithful follower" of their army. Their entire 6th Army was plagued; more than 15,000 cases were said to have occurred at Kut among their forces (mortality 8 per cent). This factor must have contributed to their defeat. Von der Goltz Pasha, their Commander, died of typhus.

Throughout his lengthy period in Baghdad and its environs from 1917 onwards, Willcox was used as a consultant by civilian doctors attached to the Political Department headed by Sir Percy Cox. Thus, in visits to various centres he would visit both civilian and military hospitals in consultation. He forged a link between the Civilian and Military Hospitals which was of obvious importance from the point of view of preventive medicine and control of infectious diseases. Having at his right hand the resources of the British Red Cross Society he was able to help the deficiency in medical supplies in civilian hospitals—a privilege of which he made the utmost use. Not only so, he was able also to benefit by the close co-operation and friendship with civilian doctors. Among these he met Major (later Sir Thomas) Carey Evans, I.M.S., a surgeon and superintendent

of the Civilian Hospital in Baghdad. He was the son-in-law of Lloyd
George, and later became the first Medical Superintendent of the Postgraduate Hospital at Hammersmith. Willcox was called by him to the
cases of the Nagib of Baghdad and his daughter, both suffering from
typhus, early in 1918. They both recovered.

In the cooler weather he managed to spare more time for riding, being
the lucky possessor of two arab horses, one of which he could spare for
another officer, or he could accompany Miss Bell for a visit to arab chiefs
of her acquaintance. Shooting was a sport he less often enjoyed, but in
December at Samarrah and again at Birs Nimrod the following March
he was able to shoot sand grouse to supplement the rather monotonous
diet at the Red Cross Mess. Melville often mentioned his own shooting
expeditions in his letters.

In February 1918 he learned with grief that his brother Octavius
("Ockie") had been killed in France. Sir Percy Cox, who had previously
lost his only son killed in action, learnt of this, and kindly wrote:

Feb. 19th, 1918.

My dear Willcox,

I was so sorry to hear, while I was away, that you had lost your brother
killed in France. In case many days elapse before we meet I send this
line, rather belated I'm afraid, to offer you my sympathy. It is very hard
these continual sacrifices, but it only makes one feel the more passionately
that we cannot stop until we make sure that they have not been in vain.
Trusting you are very fit.

Yours sincerely,

P. Z. Cox.

References

Loyalties, by Sir Arnold Wilson, K.C.I.E., C.S.I., C.M.G., D.S.O., Oxford University
Press, 1931.
"Beri-beri, with Special Reference to Prophylaxis and Treatment", by W. H. Willcox,
The Lancet, March 11th, 1916.
The Life of Sir Stanley Maude, by Major-General Sir C. F. Callwell, K.C.B.,
Constable & Co., 1920.
The Letters of Gertrude Bell, by Lady Bell, D.B.E., Ernest Benn Ltd., 1927.

Chapter 13

Northern Persia and India—1918–1919

There are many memorials in Baghdad to Sir Stanley Maude but the one which would have pleased him most was the continued success of his army under the able generalship of his successor, Sir William Marshall. The sphere of operations became widely extended so that new medical problems constantly arose. Our troops advanced northwards to Enzeli, the post on the southern shore of the Caspian Sea. Though attended by little military resistance, the operations involved the army in an enormous amount of philanthropic work for famine relief. In the spring a serious outbreak of typhus occurred in Northern Persia, spreading to the civilian population, and refugees fled south towards Baghdad by any transport that could be found—camels, mules and donkeys. Willcox was instrumental in planning, with the aid of any help he could find, segregation camps and special measures of disinfestation and segregation of cases along the line to Baghdad. Fortunately as a result of these measures an epidemic was avoided, few cases occurring in the native population of Mesopotamia.

The country was devastated by famine and the native population were dying by thousands from simple starvation. The country had been devastated by both Turks and Russians, and the food supplies had become exhausted. Many of their primitive dwellings had been destroyed, so that the overcrowded living conditions promoted the spread of typhus. The clothing of the natives was filthy and scanty. The natives of the region received little help from the Persian Government if such existed, and their medical officers were quite unable to cope. Units of the army rendered most valuable assistance which was to a certain extent successful in alleviating the horrors of death by starvation, and was at the same time of political value for propaganda purposes. On his first visit to Persia, which lasted from July 1st to 17th, he was accompanied by General Dickson, Director of Local Resources, and Captain Norman Brookes of the Red Cross Society. A full report on the requirements for medical units, hospitals and personnel on the lines of communications was submitted to the D.M.S. From August, 70,000 Armenian and Assyrian refugees trekked southwards from the region round Lake Urmia near the Caspian Sea and they were finally cared for in an enormous camp at Baquba, about 30 miles north of Baghdad. They were fleeing from Turkish atrocities, having only animal transport and little food, some travelling on foot. At intervals over a distance of about 500 miles our troops played a notable part in sustaining as best they could these destitute people; but considerable numbers perished on the way. Typhus fever broke out among those reaching Baquba. Blenkinsop, helped by

Willcox, organised the segregation and disinfestation of these people with great success, the incidence and mortality rapidly declining. To quote from the Official History (Vol. iv, p. 401): "A large quarantine camp was formed where all refugees were examined as a preventive measure. Few of the medical officers had seen cases of this fever and, had the diagnosis not been made by the Consulting Physician at the time, the disease would probably have spread to the men of the labour corps". The British Red Cross Society played a prominent part in famine relief, and was ably directed by Col. S. M. Moens and J. H. Stanley. In his report to the D.M.S., Willcox paid great tributes to British doctors for their work for refugees at a time when the civilian medical services were quite unable to cope.

His experience in military hygiene resulted in the termination of an outbreak of cholera in the holy city of Kerbela by the Euphrates in September, occasioned by the arrival of pilgrims to a religious festival. The source of infection was traced to a canal which supplied the town with water; at the bed of this suspicious source of water it was customary to wash bodies before burial. Directly this branch of the canal was drained the epidemic subsided. He then proceeded to give an address on cholera to local doctors, which was duly interpreted. A local cholera unit was set up by Captain Vint, R.A.M.C., and proved to be popular and successful.

Late in September he was ordered by the G.O.C. of the area to organise hospital services at Enzeli, a port on the borders of the Caspian Sea, where 15,000 Armenian refugees had arrived after fleeing from Turkish persecution. In October and November he returned to Enzeli and Hamadan (a town en route south to Baghdad) where he found great improvements in the medical services had occurred since July. Nevertheless, the condition of the migrating refugees from North Persia must have been one of the most pitiful sights of the war. Their state is best described in his report to the G.O.C.

October 28th 1918.

"To: G.O.C. Norperforce, from Colonel W. H. Willcox,
    Consulting Physician, Mesop: Ex: Force.

Report re Persian Refugees:

From October 11th until October 27th I have been staying at Enzeli, and have visited Resht on two occasions while there. Large numbers of destitute and emaciated Persian refugees are to be seen along the roads in the Resht and Enzeli districts, and all along the road to Menjil. There is no doubt that these people are starving and most of them are only scantily clothed in filthy rags. Numerous dead bodies are found at Enzeli, Kazian and Resht and along the roads daily. Along the roadside one sees refugees who are lying ill and dying. It is said that there are about 2,000 Persian refugees at Enzeli. It was a common occurrence to see them eating garbage collected out of the refuse heaps in the town, and they receive no help whatever from the Persian population of Resht and Enzeli. At a conference with the Persian Governor of Enzeli, the Mayor, Persian Doctors and the

Town Commandant on medical matters which I attended, it was obvious that the Persian Municipal authorities of Enzeli resented most strongly the presence of their own refugee countrypeople, and they showed scant sympathy towards them. I believe the attitude of the local Persians at Resht is similar. These refugees are Kurds and Persians and the districts from which they come are known. They are too weak and destitute to help one another. It is a most urgent need that something be done quickly for these unfortunate people who are dying daily in scores. Some system of organisation and government seems to be absolutely necessary and Persia is quite unable to furnish this.

Signed W. H. Willcox. Col. A.M.S.

Consulting Physician, Mes. Ex. Force."

Northern Persia did not escape from the spread of influenza from Europe which affected British and Indian troops. On his last visit there he investigated a severe outbreak complicated by the presence of malignant malaria in a proportion of cases (Lettsomian Lectures, 1919) and a careful plan of treatment went a long way to mitigate the severity of this epidemic.

India and Home

On November 17th he returned to Baghdad to find his duties had apparently declined following the termination of hostilities on all fronts. His opportunities towards Christmas for riding and shooting became more frequent. Yet another bereavement occurred with the death of Colonel Melville, after a brief illness, from heart failure on November 30th. His friendship and loyal co-operation through thick and thin had been dearly appreciated, all his interesting letters being carefully filed. Sir John Hewett, a distinguished retired Indian civil servant, took up residence in Baghdad from December to March under orders from the War Office to report and make recommendations on the present and future civil administration of the country. They had several professional meetings concerning the future medical administration of the country, for which Willcox outlined a plan in considerable detail. He received orders to leave for Bombay on January 18th. His last important duty was to submit a report to the D.M.S. on the history of scurvy in Mesopotamia since 1916, the main purport of the report being to stress the importance of the maintenance of an adequate diet for the future welfare of the troops.

A similar but less technical report on this subject was submitted to the Army Commander, Lt.-General Sir William Marshall, at whose house he was entertained at dinner on Christmas Day. His last ride with Miss Bell took place on January 3rd. A farewell dinner for him was held on January 16th presided over by Sir John Hewitt. Blenkinsop, Dickson, Stanley, Moens were all there together with a number of his other friends. At the time of embarking Dickson and Stanley arrived to see him off, but a hurricane was blowing, the ship became unmanageable, and it was decided to tie up for a night. He was thus able to enjoy another night at the Red Cross Mess, leaving uneventfully the following day. After a night spent at Basra with General MacMunn he left for Bombay, arriving there on February 8th. During the next four days he surveyed all the hospitals which had dealt with patients evacuated from Basra during the last three years of the war; the Colaba, Freeman Thomas, and Cumballa hospitals for British troops; and the Lady Hardinge, and Marine Lines War Hospitals for Indian troops. He was able to give high praise to their excellent construction and administration by their respective commanding officers and the work carried out by the nursing staff. In his report he stressed the importance of encouraging Indian women to take up nursing as far as this was possible. He also congratulated the laboratory service under the command of Lt.-Col. Glen Liston, and the rehabilitation unit for Indian disabled troops under the command of Lt.-Colonel Hirch, I.M.S., for which Lady Willingdon had devoted so much personal interest and energy in raising funds for its maintenance.

He spent four days in Delhi on a mission to help with the future planning of the Indian Medical Service. At an interview with Surgeon-General W. R. Edwards, the Director-General, discussions took place which went a long way to assist the committee set up by the Secretary of State to ascertain the views of the I.M.S. doctors on the causes of discontent with the conditions of the service before the war. The committee had first met in February 1918 and was presided over by Surgeon-General Edwards. Their reports traced the history of the decline in popularity of the service as a career for doctors as far back as 1912 when the B.M.A. reported on the subject. Sir Pardey Lukis had fought hard with Whitehall to remove the inadequacies, the insufficiency of pay and home leave, the inferior position of doctors in the I.M.S. compared with the R.A.M.C., and other complaints, but his was a voice crying in the wilderness of Whitehall. Willcox read all the reports while he was in Delhi and made his own report on the subject, being unable to remain in Delhi long enough to give evidence to the committee, owing to his orders to return home. General Edwards' letter of thanks shows that his views were in full agreement with those of the committee:—

"24.2.1919   Office of Director General,
                                               Indian Medical Service,
                                                             Delhi.

My dear Willcox,
    Very many thanks for your kindness and courtesy in sending me a copy of your notes on the I.M.S. I have just read them and consider them of the greatest value, and I am practically in entire agreement with you. I gather, however, that the general feeling of the committee now is that the immediate formation of a unified service is not practical, and that their recommendations will be that the present I.M.S. shall be turned into a Corps, given the station hospital system, retain its civil appointments, and as far as possible have its present disabilities remedied. Unification might again be considered in five or ten years. Personally, I believe that by doing this the best men would again be attracted, and that the I.M.S. as the I.M.C. would once more become the best medical service in the world. In the past the Regimental system has given such hopelessly inefficient training that any thinking member of the service predicted a breakdown. The service

would have broken down if no man had become civil, and in that case we should have been still worse off, because we should have had no good surgeons and physicians. Your evidence at the India Office, and the War Office, will undoubtedly carry great weight.

Yours sincerely,

W. R. Edwards."

His work in Mesopotamia and India now completed, he could not leave that fascinating country without seeing some of the historic buildings of Delhi, both new and old. He spent about 24 hours at Agra, visiting the Fort and Taj Mahal, and the beautiful deserted palaces of Fatehpur Sikri built by the Mogul Emperor Akbar, taking several photographs. He left Bombay on February 22nd on the Merkara on which he sailed home via Aden, the Suez Canal, Marseilles and Gibraltar. This period of three weeks at sea must have provided him with much needed recuperation and rest. He had had no leave for almost exactly three years. He had at times looked haggard, underweight and tired. But he had enjoyed good health throughout. His diary recorded only one day in bed unwell— shortly after the death of General Maude. He had been lucky, too, in the privilege of serving three of the most able Army Commanders, Lake, Maude, and Marshall, all of whom interested themselves in the medical welfare and health of their troops. Of these it can be said that Maude, had he survived his fatal illness, would have been proclaimed as one of the most successful generals of the war; he had served two D.M.S.'s who shared with him friendship and co-operation in a special degree under most trying climatic conditions in work of enormous responsibility. And there must have been feelings of sorrow at the loss of those who never returned—Maude, Horsley, Melville and many others of lesser degree. He had come to admire the work of all the medical officers working there, and in later years he found the bonds of friendship forged in that campaign were profound and long lasting. There must have been feelings of personal satisfaction for having himself contributed in no small degree to the improvement in the organisation of the medical services from 1916 onwards, in an army engaged in one of the most difficult tasks in the war; in a theatre of war in which the medical services had contributed a great part in achieving victory out of defeat—perhaps a greater part than had ever been played in the history of the British and Indian Armies. He had fought for the welfare of the Indian troops, especially towards improvement in their rations, which he expected and hoped would on a permanent basis continue in times of peace at home. He had made firm recommendations resulting in a medical service for Mesopotamia after the war to be continued after the formation of the British Mandate and the accession of King Feisal in 1921. And he had made a helpful contribution to the reform of the Indian Medical Service to the status it was later to enjoy between the two world wars.

From a professional and medical point of view the campaign had furnished outstanding opportunities for bringing into play the principles of medical organisation, military hygiene, and medical and surgical treatment, in a way that had not previously been recognised to be so vitally necessary in one of the most exacting climates in the world. All these experiences would, he hoped, be of substantial benefit to students of military and medical history, and to the War Office for future planning. Indeed, it can be said that this turned out to be true, for many of the lessons learned there were of value in the military campaigns of the second World War of 1939–1945.

He disembarked at Plymouth on March 20th, arriving home the same evening. Amongst correspondence awaiting him was a letter of welcome from the Chief of the A.M.S.:

East Grinstead, Sussex.

"April 23rd 1919

My dear Willcox,

Welcome Home! I shall be delighted to see you again, and I hope you are none the worse for your prolonged tour abroad. You certainly have stuck it most manfully and have shown no restlessness or desire for change like so many others. You are a born Army Medical Officer, and to my mind that is the best thing that can be said of any of us. You ought to have gone into the army as so many young and able medical men should do. I am at present taking a holiday, and return at the end of the month. A phone message will always find me, and so when you have a spare hour we can arrange a meeting.

Yours very sincerely,

Alfred Keogh."

Correspondence

From Lady Horsley.

25. Cavendish Square, W.
September 24th 1916.

"Dear Colonel Willcox,

I saw Mrs. Willcox the other day as she most kindly offered to come and see me, and she was good enough to promise she would tell you that I was only waiting to write to you personally, till the personal effects etc. should have arrived. But they have not yet done so and I feel therefore that I cannot defer any longer writing to thank you for your great kindness in taking all the trouble that you have on my behalf and for all the information (of the utmost value to me) which you have sent me. The cooler weather has come now and with it, I hope, greater safety for you. I know you will have to run heavy risks, but take as much care as you can. You cannot realise the utter desolation of those who are left, nor what this awful war means to the women of the country.

Very gratefully yours,

Eldred Horsley."

From Sir Percy Cox, K.C.S.I., K.C.I.E.

27/10/17

"My dear Willcox,

Very many thanks from us both for your kind note of sympathy.

Our poor boy was our only child so his loss means a great deal and I really had no ambition, had we both been spared to see the war out, than to hang up my hat at home and help him in his career.

However the curtain has rung down on that vista. Fortunately one has not time for intrusive thinking and can but peg away at the common task. Please God our boy and thousands of other peoples boys who have given their lives for the supreme object in view, have not done it in vain.

Yours sincerely,

P. Cox."

From Colonel J. H. Stanley,
Red Cross Commissioner.

Bagdad.
18th January 1918.

"My dear Colonel Willcox,

In parting with you I feel that I am parting with a very dear friend, and so far from you thanking me for the little I have done, I am profoundly impressed with the debt of gratitude we all owe to you for your ever ready sympathy, advice and assistance in any work that made for the wellbeing of our sick and wounded, quite apart from all you were doing for the Army.

With every kind wish,

Believe me always

Yours very sincerely,

J. H. Stanley."

From Sir Alfred Keogh, G.C.B., M.D., F.R.C.P., D.G., A.M.S., Rector, Imperial College of Science and Technology, 1910–1922.

"May 4th 1918

My dear Willcox,

Your very interesting letter reached me after I had left to return to my work here, but it was none the less interesting on that account. In a sense I was sorry to leave the work for it was an intense gratification to me to be able to help and direct things from the centre, but the needs of the work here were great and I was faced, in common fairness to my colleagues here, with the alternatives of resigning my position at S. Kensington or returning there. I chose the latter, fully convinced that the W.O. work could go on without me. It had become routine, and frankly, routine bores me! But as I have said, the work abroad interests me intensely and I was glad to get your letter.

The death of your Chief was a great blow, the more so that it was avoidable had he only been imbued with the necessity of taking those precautions for himself that he was required to see taken on behalf of others. It is a melancholy story, for his was a fine character.

Although you have reached so high a standard of excellence in Mesopotamia, the situation there must always be for you one of great anxiety, for the potentialities for evil are immense and the blow may come from any quarter if sanitary vigilance is relaxed. By this time you will have the hot weather well upon you. I hope you keep well. You appear to have stood it admirably in the periods of comfort and discomfort. I hope you will take every opportunity of taking a trip to India, for the country is worth seeing apart from the relaxation and rest a journey to the hills would give you.

You will perhaps be as well posted in European affairs as we are, and will have gathered what people are doing and saying concerning the war or the period after the war. Preparations are being made for the new world that is to come, but if we are not better at preparing for peace than we have been in preparing for war I fear the times in front of us will not be without anxiety. Still, there is this to be said. The national conscience has been aroused and I think the Government Departments will be thereby kept alive to the necessity of dealing with national problems much more seriously than in the past, for these problems will be very pressing and the danger of neglecting them much more obvious than heretofore.

To you and to me the great interest is of course the question of the national health, its relation to national efficiency, to housing, to poverty and the relation of industrialism thereto. I have some—but not very strong —hopes that the medical profession will come to realise that its part in these great questions is bigger than they have been in the habit of imagining. But we have to get away from the ideas that are so prevalent, if not voiced, that we are merely technical advisers and cannot like other professions produce leaders of men. If I have any hope in this direction it is that the war may have produced a class of man in Medicine as a result of military experience different from that which has usually been produced by the schools. If all this experience has not produced sound thinking on the future of the profession then indeed I am without hope for the great subjects which, for their efficient management, depend upon the profession. I see little sign that 'Public Health' is really recognised to be that which it is. All the talk is of sick benefit clubs, halfcrowns for the practitioner and so on. The great things are forgotten.

My own work here is of another and a very different kind, but I cannot help looking back at the profession which I have now for good and all left, without wondering how the members will comfort themselves in the 'new world', and how they are going to deal with the educational problems which the new aspect of affairs suggests. But I must not preach to you on my hobby. Keep well and take great care of yourself and propagate the gospel of the future of Medicine.

Yours very sincerely,

Alfred Keogh."

Basrah.
23rd January, 1918.

"Colonel W. H. Willcox, C.B. C.M.G. A.M.S.
   Consulting Physician,
     Mes. Exp. Force.

Memorandum.

I have just received the following letter from the General Secretary of the Joint War Committee, Indian Branch, British Red Cross & Order of St. John.
'I am directed to say that Sir Claude Hill has read with interest your reference to the services of Colonel Willcox, C.B. C.M.G. A.M.S. Consulting Physician to the Force, and desires that his thanks, as well as those of the Joint War Committee, Indian Branch, may be conveyed to Colonel Willcox for the valuable aid rendered by him to the cause of the sick and wounded in Mesopotamia'.
The following is an extract from my Report.
'I append to this report some letters of thanks and would especially draw attention to that of Colonel Willcox, C.B. C.M.G. A.M.S. Consulting Physician to the Force. Colonel Willcox, whose personal friendship and whose help and advice in all matters connected with the Red Cross in Mesopotamia I shall always value more than I care to express in a report which deals exclusively with "dull catalogues of common things" has had long experience in Mesopotamia. Few men know better than he the difficulties which confronted the Medical Authorities in the earlier days of the campaign and few, if any, have contributed more to ameliorating the condition of the sick and wounded of this Force. Permit me to take this opportunity of placing these facts before the Joint War Committee in connection with the valuable services which Colonel Willcox has rendered both directly and indirectly to Red Cross work in Mesopotamia'.

S. M. Moens. Lieut.-Colonel.
Red Cross Commissioner.
Mes. Ex. Force."

"To   Delhi.
    The Director Medical Services, India.   February 17th 1919.

From
    Colonel W. H. Willcox, A.M.S.
      Consulting Physician
      Mesopotamian Expeditionary Force.

Sir,

Report re Rations for Indian Soldiers serving in India.

I have the honour to report that I arrived in India from Mesopotamia on February 8th, in accordance with orders from Government of India, dated 3rd May 1916.

I have served in Mesopotamia as Consulting Physician to the Expeditionary Force since the beginning of May 1916. During this period I have been brought very closely into touch with the relationship of 'Rations to the Health of Troops', and I have on numerous occasions given advice and written reports to Director Medical Services, Mesopotamian Expeditionary Force, on this very important subject. It is very doubtful if any campaign has ever furnished such very important and interesting data on the very close bearing which Rations have on the health of the Soldier, and the great danger of Vitamin Deficiency in a Ration has been demonstrated on a very large scale.

I enclose the following Papers which give a summary of the Relations of Rations to Disease in Mesopotamia. viz:—

    (1) Report on Scurvy to Director Medical Services, Mesp. Expd. Force, January 12th, 1919,
    (2) Notes re Rations for Mesopotamian Expd. Force, January 1st, 1919,
    (3) Abstract of Lecture delivered before Amara Medical Society, December 29th, 1916,

also Memoranda on Beri-beri and on Scurvy respectively which I wrote for Director Mesopotamia Expeditionary Force for official circulation in Mesopotamia.

The above documents give an account of the Diseases which occurred in Mesopotamia as the result of defective rations, and of the measures which were taken to combat these diseases.

The prophylactic measures taken were followed by the greatest success so that in a short time Diseases due to Deficiency in Rations were stamped out.

Valuable lessons are to be learnt from the history of Deficiency Diseases in Mesopotamia, and the sufferers from these diseases will not have suffered in vain if the knowledge gained thereby is utilised in ensuring such a satisfactory rationing to troops in future as shall render impossible the occurrence of Deficiency diseases, and also keep the soldier in the best condition of health possible and shall maintain his Military efficiency thereby at the highest level.

On my arrival in India on February 8th, I found that the system of Rationing *Indian* troops in India still left a great deal to be desired and I desire to call attention to what in my opinion are great defects in the present system.

The 'Peace Scale Ration' for Indian Troops introduced February 17th 1917 (No. 2438 Govt. of India) is very greatly deficient in Antiscorbutic Vitamins and I have no doubt that such a ration if not supplemented will certainly be productive of Scurvy if soldiers live on this for a few months.

The Scurvy incidence would be much increased if the soldier were exposed to hard conditions whether climatic or of physical endurance.

The 'Field Scale Rations' for Indian soldiers differ only as regards their vitamin efficiency in the addition of Onions 2 oz. per diem. This Ration is greatly deficient in Antiscorbutic Vitamins and the criticism of the 'Peace Scale Ration' applies to this also.

I am aware that a money allowance of 10 annas per month is allowed to Indian soldiers for the purpose of supplementing their rations. In my judgement this system of supplementing by a money allowance a defective ration is a bad one and should be discontinued. I most strongly urge that in the interests of the Indian Troops in India a Ration should be issued which is entirely satisfactory as regards the maintenance of health and efficiency in a high degree. As a satisfactory Ration I would quote the Ration to Indian Troops in Mesopotamia vide Annexure to G.R.O. Mesopotamia Exped. Force October 10th, 1917.

A comparison will show that the Peace Scale Rations and the Field Scale Rations at present issued to Indian Troops in India have no fresh meat at all whereas 6 to 8 ounces per diem are very necessary for the prevention of Scurvy, also there is a great deficiency in the issue of the important Antiscorbutic article viz fresh vegetables and fresh fruit.

It has been overwhelmingly proved by the experience of the Mesopotamian Expeditionary Force that it is a great economy to provide the soldier with a Ration which is physiologically good. The low sickness rate much more than compensates for extra financial expense, and on a good ration the soldier proves himself physically and morally thoroughly efficient and ready for any demands made upon him. On a Ration physiologically bad (under this term I include the 'Peace Scale Ration' and the 'Field Scale Ration' at present in force in India for Indian soldiers) there is bound to be a high sickness rate and the soldier cannot be expected to be physically and morally efficient for any severe demands that may be called upon him.

Health, courage, cheerfulness and efficiency are qualities of which the expression in a large body of men is very largely dependent on physiologically good nutrition.

I am aware that very important and valuable enquiries are being made into the question of Rationing of troops by the Committee assembled by order of His Excellency the Commander-in-Chief of India. I sincerely hope that this Report and the accompanying documents may be of help to this Committee in their important investigations and recommendations.

I have the honour to be,

Sir,

Your obedient servant,

(Signed)　　W. H. Willcox.
　　　　　　　Colonel, A. M. S."

Reference

The Official History of the Great War, Medical Services, Vol. IV, by Major-General Sir W. G. Macpherson and Major T. J. Mitchell, 1924.

PART 4

CRIMES CLAIMS AND CAMPAIGNS—1919–1935

Chapter 14

Readjustment—1919–1921

Willcox arrived home looking a good deal slimmer than when he departed in 1916 but had already had a welcome rest on the voyage. His next task was to rebuild his career. His practice had disappeared and his contacts with London doctors were far fewer owing to deaths and retirement. But his military contacts persisted and replaced them, for his diaries and case-books register appointments with many officers and personnel returned from India and Iraq, or their friends and relatives. Before his demobilisation on May 1st he was asked by the Colonial Office to advise on details of the planning of the Civil Medical Service for Iraq and to make arrangements for treatment of service personnel returned from overseas at St. Mary's Hospital; work in which he took as great pleasure as in the more remunerative work of private practice against strong competition, which only gradually returned. But he always believed that by hard work and efficiency success could be achieved.

The Dean of St. Mary's Hospital was Sir John Broadbent whose father, Sir William, had earlier been a physician on the staff and a physician to Queen Victoria. He had great difficulty keeping the Medical School going, owing to depletion of its staff on war-time service; the financial position was precarious, and the Medical School buildings very much out-dated for the post-war world—problems of administration which were the source of earnest consideration and anxiety for the medical staff for several years to come. On the retirement of Sydney Phillips, the senior physician, in 1919, Willcox was promoted to be a physician to in-patients in charge of beds, while at the same time Dr. Charles Wilson (later Sir Charles, and now Lord Moran) joined the staff as a physician to out-patients. It is worth recording that in those days, and indeed, until the formation of the National Health Service in 1948, the junior members of the Consultant staff performed only out-patient duties at voluntary (including teaching) hospitals. Each in turn was promoted to have charge of beds by the retirement or death of the senior members of the staff. Willcox thus came to find himself in a position where teaching students would occupy more time and responsibility. At this stage he had to make one of the most important decisions of his career. Could he find time to perform efficiently this important work, on which the reputation of the hospital so largely depended, while continuing to carry on the great pressure of Home Office work he had on his shoulders in 1915? Always having an eye for the future, he realised that it would be impossible to carry on both tasks at the same time with the efficiency and attention to detail which were features of his character. He reluctantly decided to resign his appointment as Home Office analyst, and to pursue his clinical career as physician to the hospital. This decision was motivated by the fact that for the last three years his work abroad had been almost entirely clinical; his recent writings and publications had been in this field—on deficiency diseases, heat stroke, liver disorders, malaria, typhoid, and other fevers. He felt he would have something substantial to add in the way of clinical experience to that of his medical colleagues, Broadbent, Harris, Miller, and Langmead. Moreover, he had acquired a greater liking for illnesses and patients than for investigations of unnatural deaths, exhumations, post mortems, and the like. During the war years the Home Office work had been handled entirely by Webster and by Spilsbury who, according to his biographers, was overburdened with work. There had been few, if any, cases of great toxicological importance. While in Mesopotamia he had been kept posted about unusual cases by Sir Charles Matthews, Director of Public Prosecutions, and in 1916 by Sir Edward Troup, Permanent Under-Secretary of State.

> "December 10th 1916.   Home Office,
>   Whitehall, S.W.
>
> Dear Colonel Willcox,
>   Very many thanks for your most interesting note. I am glad to hear of your doings in Mcsopotamia, and delighted to hear that the medical arrangements are now so satisfactory.
>   I don't think we have had any criminal problems of the medico-legal class since you left. The men who would naturally be poisoning their wives are better employed in killing Huns. We have, however, had to deal with a difficult matter in stopping the sale of cocaine to soldiers— which was doing much mischief. A stringent Defence of the Realm Regulation has, I think, been very effective—but a difficulty arose about its use by unregistered dentists, and a month or two ago I rang up to find out if by any chance you had come home—if you had, we should have asked you to serve on a small committee which had to be set up to consider their claims. The Home Secretary would have been glad to have had your help, but in the end we got together a fairly good Committee which ought to report before Christmas.
>   We have had a rather miserable ten days of Ministerial crisis—bickerings about leadership and peace, while the Germans are sweeping Roumania and sinking our merchant ships. I hope the new Government will be more energetic than the old—if so, it will be very energetic indeed.
>
>   With best wishes for Xmas and the New Year,
>
>   Yours very sincerely,
>
>   Edward Troup."

Drug addiction had even then appeared as a threat to the community, a problem destined to engage the attention of the Home Office in the future.

During the war years Webster, who had served the department of Chemical Pathology for several years, had been solely responsible for all the Home Office toxicology. It seemed only fair to Willcox that Webster should continue as Senior Analyst on a permanent basis, knowing that Roche Lynch, who had assisted them before the war, was keen to return after his release from service in the Royal Navy in 1919. So Webster became senior and Roche Lynch junior analysts to the Home Office, with Willcox as Medical Adviser.

Though Webster was not medically qualified he had a distinguished and interesting medico-legal career though his testimony in courts of law tended to be evidence of fact rather than of opinion; but at the time he was the most experienced analyst of the three, regarded by Willcox as a man of meticulous accuracy and brilliant technique. At the trials of Seddon, Greenwood, and Armstrong their joint testimony was unassailable evidence for the Crown. Their mutual co-operation was continued in other cases until Webster's death from pneumonia in 1927. Roche Lynch, who succeeded him, had a long distinguished career at St. Mary's as Chemical Pathologist, succeeding Willcox as lecturer in this subject in 1926 and in Forensic Medicine in 1935. He died in 1957.

Appointed Medical Adviser to the Home Office in 1919 at his own suggestion, Willcox offered to render every possible service in an honorary capacity in any problem that might crop up from time to time in connection with Forensic Medicine and Toxicology. This appointment was held until his death in 1941. The title subsequently lapsed, and there has been no other holder of it.

His services for the Red Cross and Order of St. John in connection with the military and civilian sick in Mesopotamia and for famine relief in North Persia received recognition by his appointment as a Knight of Grace of the Order of St. John of Jerusalem bestowed on him at an Investiture at Buckingham Palace on May 29th. At the same time he received the C.M.G. and C.B (military) decorations awarded in 1916 and 1917 respectively.

During 1919 and 1920 he was frequently invited to give lectures and addresses to various learned societies on subjects connected with war experiences. To the Medical Society of London he gave three Lettsomian Lectures on Jaundice in which liver poisons and jaundice of military importance were exhaustively dealt with. To the same society he contributed to a discussion on malaria treatment on November 24th, which promoted lengthy correspondence in the B.M.J. by himself and Sir Ronald Ross on the merits of quinine given by injection compared with tablets given by mouth for cases of malignant malaria. Those interested in malaria would find this discussion of historical interest, as Ross was the original discoverer of malarial transmission by the mosquito, though as a pathologist he had not himself had an exceptional experience of treatment of sufferers. The following March Willcox read a paper on heat stroke to this same Society. To the Royal Society of Medicine he read papers on "Deficiencies of Diet" dealing with scurvy and beri-beri and "Typhus and Relapsing Fever". To the St. Mary's Hospital

Medical Society he gave an address on "Mesopotamia 1916–1919" dealing with the influence of the medical diseases and organisation in the course of the campaign, and a similar address to the Kensington Division of the British Red Cross Society followed in July 1920.

His link with Iraq was maintained when in 1921 he was appointed Honorary Medical Adviser to the Colonial Office, to be responsible to give advice on the suitability and health of personnel, including nurses, posted to Iraq, in view of the irksome climatic conditions prevailing there.

His work increased so much during 1919 that he was unable to enjoy more than three days' holiday at Hope Cove in South Devon with Mildred and the children—Gerald, Nancy, John and Philip, who were all on holiday from school—Gerald from Oundle, Nancy from her day school in London, and John and Philip from their preparatory school at St. Leonards. Several sessions of sea fishing were much enjoyed.

His routine work consisted of rounds at St. Mary's Hospital twice weekly in the afternoon, and at St. Luke's Hostel, a private charitable nursing home for the clergy and families, which he served for the rest of his working career in an honorary capacity. He was a firm believer in taking a genuine interest in the careers of his House Physicians and Registrars at St. Mary's. Though the students attached to his "firm" changed every three months, he liked to get to know them personally. For this purpose, and according to a tradition passed on from his seniors, he developed the custom of inviting twice yearly all his clerks, his House Physician and Registrar, to dinner at Welbeck Street—parties for which the menu and wines were carefully planned by himself and Mildred. Any of the grown-up members of the family at home were also present at these parties.

He was by now examiner in Forensic Medicine at Manchester University which meant staying in Manchester for several days in June and December, at the Pharmaceutical Society, and at the Conjoint Diploma (M.R.C.S., L.R.C.P.) examinations held at Queen Square. On his return from India in 1919 he had been invited by Sir Thomas Horder (as he then was) to join the "Clinical Club" consisting of a small group of physicians with common interests who met in each other's houses in the evenings of the third Wednesdays of each month for informal discussions on subjects of public importance in the medical world. Dr. Lewis Smith was a co-founder, the other original members being John Fawcett, Herbert French, Robert Young, Langdon Brown, Cecil Wall, Farquhar Buzzard and Reginald Miller, Willcox's younger colleague at St. Mary's. It was at these meetings that he extended his interests to the work of his colleagues and at the same time made his own personal contributions to the discussions.

So far in his life Willcox had never before experienced any breach of happy relationships with medical colleagues of junior or senior status at the hospitals he served. The period 1920 to 1921 at St. Mary's was regrettable by reason of several disagreements that arose among the staff. First and foremost was the resignation of Bernard Spilsbury from his post as pathologist in November 1920. Very averse from making quarrels himself, Willcox was too tactful to intervene in a disagreement which was no business of his own. Yet he was upset and embarrassed by a private disagreement between Spilsbury and a senior member of the staff, though there is no evidence that Willcox's help as a mediator was ever sought; Spilsbury was quite mature enough to stand on his own feet and to maintain his own point of view and authority to the point of resignation. Even if the cause of the dispute was fully understood, no useful purpose would be served by further discussion of it. Details were never made public, and sank into oblivion. In no way was the happy friendship between the two persons involved. Indeed, until the second world war, Spilsbury continued to remain a friend of the family and to attend social contacts at Welbeck Street. Both habitually retired to bed late at night. From time to time Spilsbury would call at a late hour and be welcomed for a quiet talk for purposes of mutual help or professional advice on problems usually of medico-legal importance. Spilsbury was subsequently appointed to a corresponding post at St. Bartholomew's Hospital and continued his career unhindered.

For financial reasons and on account of its derelict buildings, the position of the medical school at St. Mary's was seriously threatened with extinction. The new Dean, Dr. Charles Wilson, and the medical committee, fought hard to preserve its status as an undergraduate teaching hospital by obtaining grants from the government with the support of the University Grants Committee and by raising money from other sources, (The History of St. Mary's Hospital, by Sir Zachary Cope). These struggles were successful and by 1921 clinical units in Medicine and Surgery were set up with Chairs in these subjects, the first professors appointed being Professor F. S. Langmead and Professor C. A. Pannett.

Willcox was not afraid to stand by the welfare of hospital patients and relatives even at the expense of being over-ruled by a majority decision of a medical committee. The question of post-mortem consent was an example which came under discussion at the hospital in 1921.

At the present time, at any rate in provincial hospitals in England and Wales, when a patient in hospital dies from natural causes (not a coroner's case) it is customary for the nearest relative to be asked permission for a post-mortem to be made before the examination is carried out. Such was the custom at St. Mary's Hospital until 1921. A proposal was made at the medical committee that on the printed form which a patient or relative signs on admission to hospital the words be added "in the event of the death of the patient a post-mortem examination will be made". No decision was made at the first meeting but Willcox's view was strongly opposed to the suggested change. The committee members, being ignorant of the law on this point, were anxious to know whether such an addition to the admission form would give the hospital doctors the right to hold a post-mortem without further permission of the relatives, or whether there was legal objection to the change of procedure. Willcox's feelings on the subject were so strong that he consulted his friend and distinguished counsel Sir Richard Muir, and Sir Mackenzie Chalmers, who was Chairman of the Departmental Committee to enquire into "the Law relating to Coroners" and Chairman of the London Fever Hospital. Both Muir and Chalmers were in agreement. Chalmers expressed the opinion "that he was opposed to the proposed change because on legal grounds the permission given by the signing of a printed form by a relative would be valueless. Though there was no property in a corpse the taking possession of a body against the wish of the nearest relative was a misdemeanour in Common Law. It would be detrimental to the interests of a hospital to introduce such an innovation at the present time and contrary to the principles underlying voluntary hospital administration and might adversely affect voluntary contributions, and the public reputation of a hospital."

In spite of receiving these important opinions on July 5th, 1921, the resolution was passed by four votes to three at the medical committee, Willcox being opposed, that "post-mortem examinations shall be made without permission of any kind being asked verbally or written, and before the death certificate is supplied". Willcox had also consulted with the Professor of Forensic Medicine at Manchester University, a Pathologist, who stated that such a procedure would not be tolerated at Manchester and that he would not dream of suggesting it. Willcox did not let the matter rest there but wrote to the Chairman of the Board of Management registering his disagreement "in a personal letter and not as an official communication", in which he continued: "As Lecturer in Forensic Medicine I am on medico-legal grounds very strongly against the suggested change of procedure which on legal grounds is wrong and likely to damage the reputation of the hospital and against the principles underlying the voluntary system of hospital maintenance in this country. On sentimental grounds the change of procedure is indefensible. The previous custom of obtaining the permission of the nearest relative verbally has never given rise to difficulty. It is the one adopted in most hospitals and in my experience has sufficed. No medical practitioner would dream of introducing such a change of procedure into his private practice, which would quickly disappear if he did. It appears desirable to me that patients in voluntary hospitals should be treated with the same consideration as patients in private practice. This is a principle I have always adopted in my hospital work. I find that relatives most reasonably respond to courteous consideration and grant any sensible requests for post-mortem examinations."

The Board of Management were embarrassed at being compelled to make a final decision on the proposal of the medical committee, a proposal passed by four votes against three at a poorly attended meeting. They came to a reasonable compromise which must have gone some way to satisfy both parties. Their resolution of October 1921 represents the present arrangements still in force:

"the Board of Management reserves to itself, in the interests of the Public for the advantage of future patients and as one of the conditions of admission to the hospital, the right of causing a Post-Mortem examination to be made on the body of every patient dying in the hospital by the Pathologist or his Assistant, for the purpose of accurately determining the cause of death.

In the event of the friends or nearest relatives of the deceased patient being opposed to such examination they are to communicate their wishes to the Secretary of the Hospital, who is authorised to dispense with the Post-Mortem Examination."

In spite of this resolution affecting general hospital policy at St. Mary's Willcox continued to carry out the policy he had previously followed in the case of the patients under his own care.

In the King's Birthday Honours on June 4th, 1921, Willcox was made K.C.I.E. in recognition of his "Military services as Consulting Physician and services to the Civil Administration in Iraq". The event was modestly recorded in his diary "K.C.I.E. awarded". The honour had been delayed by the establishment in Whitehall for nearly two years despite repeated recommendations by the government of India which had been responsible for the direction of the epic campaign in Iraq. To himself this personal honour was not entirely unexpected because Sir Stanley Maude had recommended an equivalent decoration as early as 1917 but it had been altered to C.B. by the War Office. If Maude had survived his fatal attack of cholera his wish would have been fulfilled in 1918. Paradoxically, at no time in his career did Willcox receive public recognition for his Home Office or other work, all his decorations having been for war-time services; nor did he expect or covet any further advancement thereafter. The honour was bestowed by King George V at the Investiture of July 19th. This touching tribute for his work for the British and Indian troops was specially appreciated in that only four other medical men held the same decoration.

While the family spent their holiday at a farm in Northamptonshire during the long spell of hot weather and the memorable drought of August he accompanied Colonel J. H. Stanley, The Red Cross Commissioner, on a five-day visit to the battlefields of France and in September he spent two weeks at a Rheumatology Congress at Aix-les-Bains.

Chapter 15

The Poison Mystery of Kidwelly—1920
(Rex v. Greenwood)

At the time when A. H. Bradbury, the coal merchant, was being prosecuted for tax evasion and defended by Sir Richard Muir with help from Willcox, the stage was being set for one of the great trials of this century. Harold Greenwood, the solicitor of Kidwelly, was charged with the murder of his wife by the administration of arsenic. The trial, extraordinary for its complexity and the conflicting opinions of witnesses, took place in November 1920—almost eighteen months after the death of Mrs. Greenwood. For this reason the evidence of witnesses was based on their memory of events long past, and the true course of events that occurred on that fatal day of her death—June 16th, 1919—will always remain a matter of opinion and conjecture. The fascination of a crime often lies in the setting in which it takes place. In this case we have a solicitor and his family living in a large house in comfortable circumstances with an ample domestic staff of two maids and a cook in the old town of Kidwelly; a large garden extending to the river edge tended by a full time and part-time gardener. We read of the comings and goings of a family and a visitor on a fine Sunday in June, the walks in the garden and the game of clock golf played by Greenwood and the local doctor between the visits to his wife on the last day of her life. No wonder the case attracted the interest of the press and public as it did not only in Wales but throughout the country. For fifty years the interest has not waned among students of legal and medical history. Willcox played a major part in all events following the exhumation and throughout the trial. This account, based on his files and notes—hitherto unpublished—is written from his own aspect of the case in his capacity as Medical Adviser to the Home Office.

On April 17th, 1920, Police Sergeant Hodge Lewis of Kidwelly delivered at St. Mary's Hospital laboratory three sealed jars containing organs obtained from the body of Mrs. Greenwood, from the grave in Kidwelly Churchyard, the previous day. The analysis for poison was quickly commenced by Mr. John Webster, the Home Office analyst, while Willcox carried out as detailed an examination of the remains as was possible in spite of a degree of putrefaction to be expected after a period of nine months since burial. As far as could be discovered the kidneys, lungs, liver, spleen, brain, oesophagus, stomach and intestines showed no sign of physical disease, while the heart—though considerably putrefied—showed no gross enlargement nor defect. There was a fibrous tumour of the uterus no larger than a thrush's egg without any cancerous change. Willcox considered, in the light of Webster's preliminary analysis, that the appearances were consistent with arsenical poisoning but that such a degree of putrefaction had occurred that it was impossible to draw any accurate conclusions as to the cause of death from the examinations of the organs, though they were relatively well preserved considering the time that had elapsed since burial. His suspicion that arsenical poisoning was the cause of death was based on the clinical history of the fatal illness and his knowledge of Webster's preliminary tests for arsenic. The Inquest of April 16th was adjourned to allow for further police enquiries, Webster's detailed quantitative analyses of each organ and Willcox's reports on all the available evidence. The course of the adjourned Inquest, police court proceedings and trial were the logical sequence of the evidence which accumulated in the hands of the police and Willcox's reports to the Director of Public Prosecutions.

Mrs. Greenwood's fatal illness lasted less than twelve hours and she died in the early hours of Monday morning from acute gastro-enteritis after a period of fairly good health. Not unexpectedly local gossip and comments from the nurse in attendance reached the ears of the local police. "Trifles light as air are to the jealous confirmation strong as proofs of Holy Writ" was the comment of Sir Edward Marshall Hall, Greenwood's counsel, in opening the case for the defence. His early re-marriage on October 1st was another event of Greenwood's life that strengthened early suspicions of foul play. The report of the Chief Constable of Carmarthenshire, Mr. Picton Phillipps, of March 9th, 1920, to the Coroner and to the Home Secretary, Edward Shortt, represented the police evidence collected from various sources. It summarises the course of events and hitherto has never been published:—

"I beg to bring to your notice the following particulars which concern the death of Mabel Greenwood, with a view to the exhumation and examination of her body, should you consider there to be sufficient justification for making the order.

"Mabel Greenwood was the wife of Harold Greenwood of Rumsey House, Kidwelly in this County. She died on the 16th June last and was buried in an ordinary grave in Kidwelly Churchyard. They lived at Kidwelly for the last 20 years and there are three children,* the eldest being 22. Mrs. Greenwood had private means.

"Harold Greenwood is a Solicitor, and has an office at Llanelly. His small practice has mostly to do with Jews, Moneylenders, and dealings in house property.

"He has a poor reputation both as a lawyer and generally. No one seems to have a good word for him.

"He was too friendly with other women during his deceased wife's life which caused a certain amount of domestic infelicity, so that their married life could not be described as a particularly happy one. As an illustration, during his late wife's absence from home in 1918, he invited to his house for the weekend his present wife whom he married 15 weeks after the death of the first wife. She was a Miss Jones of Llanelly.

"Mrs. Greenwood suffered from a weak heart and was treated for it by

* This was inaccurate. There were four: Irene, Eileen, Ivor and Kenneth.

Dr. W. B. Cheadle's Last Lecture at St. Mary's Hospital Medical School, 1904. Willcox is seated in the front row on the near side of the gangway, Spilsbury at the near end of the front row and Fleming on the far side of the gangway.

(Published in the St Mary's Hospital Gazette in March 1935 on the occasion of Willcox's retirement from the Staff.)

Sir Thomas Stevenson, Toxicologist, and Home Office Analyst from 1872 to 1908.

[facing page 146

Crippen Again at Bow-street

DOCTORS WHO GAVE REMARKABLE EVIDENCE.

From left to right: Dr. Spilsbury,
Mr. Travers Humphreys and Dr. Willcox
leaving the resumed inquest at Bow-street.

*(By permission of the Daily Mirror, September 17th
1910.)*

Cellar in Crippen's House at Hilldrop Crescent.

(By permission of the Commissioner of Metropolitan Police.)

THE WESTERN UNION TELEGRAPH COMPANY.

THE LARGEST TELEGRAPHIC SYSTEM IN EXISTENCE.

DIRECT ROUTE FOR ALL PARTS OF THE UNITED STATES,
CANADA, CENTRAL AMERICA, WEST INDIES,
SOUTH AMERICA, &c. TRANSPACIFIC CABLE to AUSTRALIA,
NEW ZEALAND, FANING, FIJI AND NORFOLK ISLANDS.

ATLANTIC CABLES direct to CANADA and to NEW YORK CITY.

DIRECT WIRES TO ALL THE PRINCIPAL CITIES.

To Handcuffs Dew Esq

Crippen and Le neve
arrested write later
Dew

The telegram from Inspector Dew announcing
the arrest at sea of Crippen and Miss Le Neve,
July 31st, 1910.

(By permission of the Commissioner of Metropolitan Police.)

The Seddons in the dock at the Old Bailey.

(*Notable British Trials, The Trial of the Seddons, by Filson Young. William Hodge & Co. Ltd.*)

Arsenical Mirror

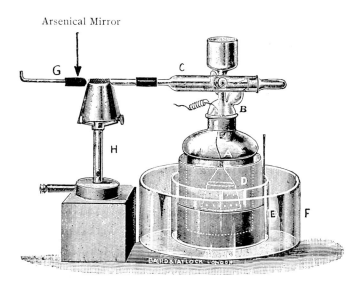

Diagram of the Electrolytic Marsh-Test Apparatus designed by Professor Thorpe.

Sir Richard Muir, Treasury Counsel.

(From "Sir Richard Muir; A memoir of a Public Prosecutor" by Sidney Felstead. The Bodley Head Ltd, 1927.)

Sir Edward Marshall Hall.

(From Notable British Trials, The Trial of Harold Greenwood, 1930, by Winifred Duke. William Hodge & Co. Ltd.)

the local doctor (since retired) Thomas Robert Griffiths, who did not think there was any danger of sudden death, and did not expect her to die when she did.

"Dr. Griffiths is a bachelor living with his sister and has a private income. His practice depended principally upon a levy from the Industrial workers. The principal private patients in the district are attended by Doctors from neighbouring towns. He is not regarded by many who are quite friendly with him as particularly competent, rather the contrary, especially at diagnosis. He has been the sole practitioner at Kidwelly for many years.

"On 14th June last Mrs. Greenwood went to a Tennis Meeting at Ferryside—4 miles away, and after her return in the evening was visited by a friend Miss Florence Phillips, who states that she was unusually well and very cheerful. What particularly struck Miss Phillips was that her complexion was very much improved. She describes it as a 'lovely sort of pink'. It is thought that this might have been due to arsenic.

"On the 15th (Sunday) Mrs. Greenwood spent the morning writing letters on the lawn, and when seen by Miss Phillips, a truthful and reliable person, she 'seemed pinched' and spoke very quietly. She was on the lawn again in the afternoon and the parlour-maid states she appeared quite well when she cleared the table after tea. The meals served during the day up to that time were: *Breakfast*. Eggs poached or otherwise, bread and butter and coffee. *Luncheon*. Roast Beef, potatoes and another vegetable, gooseberry tart and custard. *Tea*. Bread and butter and cake and tea.

"After tea Mrs. Greenwood was taken ill and about 6 p.m. Greenwood went (whether at the request of Mrs. Greenwood or not, we don't know) for the Doctor, who lives across the road directly opposite Rumsey House.

"The Doctor returned with him and found Mrs. Greenwood sitting on a couch in her bedroom. She was sick and he treated her for biliousness, which he attributed to the gooseberry tart eaten for lunch. He ordered her to bed and prescribed milk and soda, barley water, sips of brandy, and ice if procurable.

"Greenwood and the Doctor then walked round the garden and played clock golf, the latter staying altogether about an hour. He saw Mrs. Greenwood before he left, and said he would send over a bottle of medicine, which he did. It contained bismuth.

"About 7 p.m. Miss Phillips came to the house, having been invited to supper; the usual supper time being 7.30. She saw the Doctor and Greenwood who were in the garden, and the latter told her to go upstairs, as Mrs. Greenwood was ill.

"Miss Greenwood (eldest daughter) coming out of her mother's room met her and said 'Mother is very ill. I am undressing her'. On her own initiative Miss Phillips went for the District Nurse who lives about 300 yards away. The latter came in about a quarter of an hour and was at Rumsey House about 7.45.

"The nurse took charge of the case. Miss Phillips and Miss Greenwood under her direction prepared hot water bottles while the nurse and Greenwood remained with Mrs. Greenwood.

"About 8 p.m. Greenwood at the request of the Nurse went for the Doctor, Miss Phillips and Miss Greenwood, at the bedroom windows facing the Doctor's house, anxiously waiting for his return. Miss Phillips states that they waited for about an hour and then she told Miss Greenwood that she ought to go and fetch her father, which she did.

"During his absence Greenwood was in the drawing room of the Doctor's house with the Doctor's sister. The servant was out as she regularly is on Sunday evenings. There has been a long standing flirtation between Greenwood and the Doctor's sister.

"Miss Griffiths (who has told her friends privately a good deal more) says Greenwood was 'in very good spirits and jocular in his manner' and told her, referring to Mrs. Greenwood, 'She is worse than usual and I don't think she will get over it this time'. Miss Griffiths states she does not think that Greenwood could have been more than 10 minutes in the house before Miss Greenwood came to fetch him. She probably does not want to give herself away more than she need as to the time spent in the drawing room, otherwise I have no doubt she is truthful but could say more.

"Assuming that Greenwood has in some way brought about the wife's death, this will seem an extraordinary thing for him to have said, but he acts in rather an extraordinary way all through and cannot be judged by ordinary standards.

"About 9 p.m. as soon as he was told, the Doctor went across. He saw Mrs. Greenwood and gave the nurse 2 pills (pil opii gr $\frac{1}{2}$) one to be given at once and the second in an hour or so.

"At 10.30 Greenwood met the Doctor near the entrance to his house and told him that Mrs. Greenwood 'was easier' so the Doctor did not go to see her then.

"The Doctor states that he was not called afterwards till about 3 a.m. when Mrs. Greenwood was sinking fast.

"The condition of Mrs. Greenwood during the last 4 or 5 hours of her life, when Greenwood and the Nurse were with her, is described in the accompanying statements made by them.

"They contradict each other and are inaccurate in many respects, and neither is supported by the Doctor as to his visits and the time of them.

"It would appear from what they state that Mrs. Greenwood was in a more or less critical condition for some hours, and during that vital period (when, according to the Nurse, the heart was not responding to treatment which worried her, whenever Greenwood asked his wife how she felt he received the reply 'very bad', the circulation was failing and the fingers of both hands had become quite blue) it seems an astounding fact that the Doctor, practically on the spot, was not called in.

"It does not agree with Greenwood's alleged anxiety to keep the Doctor on the premises earlier in the evening but quite accords with his behaviour in the Doctor's drawing room as described by Miss Griffiths.

"The Doctor is quite positive that there was no call after his 9 o'clock visit until about 3.0 a.m. and his sister, who always rouses him if he does not hear a knock, confirms it. If this is so, there is no reason to doubt it, the visits which the Nurse refers to at 11 p.m. and 1 a.m. (and Greenwood refers to at 4 a.m.), never took place.

"The Doctor would no doubt have again seen Mrs. Greenwood between those hours had he thought she might not recover, a result he did not anticipate, and naturally he relied upon the Nurse to call him if his services were required.

"He certified that death was due to valvular disease of the heart but would not say that the condition which he ascribed to the gooseberry tart might not have been produced by other causes. I understand that poisoning by tartrate of antimony or arsenic would produce similar symptoms.

"I am informed on good authority that Dr. Griffiths told Dr. Owen Williams, of Burry Port, that Mrs. Greenwood died from 'ptomaine' poisoning.

"A month previous to the death, Greenwood's present wife's sister told a Miss David, Llanelly, that Mrs. Greenwood was seriously ill, unconscious, and not likely to recover and that her brother had come to see her. Miss David wrote a letter of sympathy to Miss Greenwood. On enquiry she found there was no truth in the statement. Greenwood wrote her an insulting letter accusing her of telling lies, by stating Mrs. Greenwood had not been ill and that her brother had not been to see her. As a matter of fact her brother was not in Kidwelly until after Mrs. Greenwood's death, and Dr. Griffiths was not called in. There must have been some object in spreading this report. It might not unreasonably be attributed to an attempt to create an impression that Mrs. Greenwood was in such a case of health that she might die suddenly, so that when she did it would not be unexpected.

"Probably, however, after the burial there would have been no further development but for some very significant statements made by the Nurse. These roused suspicion and caused rumours which started police enquiry.

"To Mrs. Smart (President of the local Nursing Association) she said 'The case worried me a lot. I did not quite understand it. I have never seen a case like it before. I wish I had my time over again I would insist on a p.m. although I don't like them'.

"To Miss Phillips: 'The sickness and diarrhoea were not like anything I had seen before'.

"To the Vicar: 'I think there ought to have been a consultation'.

"To the Police: In addition to admitting the above statements. 'The diarrhoea was not ordinary. I have never seen anything like it before. It was quite flakey. It was a funny case'.

"These remarks justify the view that there was something mysterious, certainly not understood by the Nurse, about the death, and she had the best opportunity of forming an opinion, generally and professionally. The Nurse evidently thought a p.m. would reveal something. The Vicar, who was seen at the Vicarage by the Nurse four hours after death in the early morning, also thinks so.

"It would appear as if it were on her mind that there was something wrong and that she couldn't keep it to herself.

"She had not been known to talk about her cases which would also probably be consistent with her professional training. She had been nursing for 18 years* (6 at Kidwelly).

"At the same time when faced with the question, she wouldn't go to the extent of saying she thought there was foul play, but whilst not prepared to take that responsibility which can hardly be expected, she said sufficient to create that impression and to cause the people of Kidwelly to believe that Greenwood has poisoned his wife.

"Believing herself at fault because she did not send for the Doctor

---

* This was inaccurate. According to her own evidence it was 23 years, two of which had been at Kidwelly.

during the critical hours, thinking perhaps she had said too much, and probably unwilling to get Greenwood into serious trouble, she was placed in an awkward position, which might account for her subsequent shiftiness and disinclination to give information, as if there was something she wished to conceal.

"The responsibility of having said enough to bring the police into the matter, and the possibility that what she had insinuated might not be substantiated, must have weighed heavily upon her.

"The reason why the Nurse did not send for the Doctor can only be surmised, but something would seem to have restrained her, for on her own showing Mrs. Greenwood was in a very critical state.

"She was on friendly terms with the Greenwoods. On more than one occasion, I am informed, in their house she told Greenwood's fortune and to do so took him into another room alone. This may seem trivial but it is mentioned only to indicate the degree of intimacy between them.

"To the police during investigation her conduct has been most unsatisfactory. She resented giving information, was neither candid nor straightforward, and on one occasion refused to say anything further unless compelled to.

"We imagine she has been advised to this by Greenwood whose house she still goes to.

"When first seen by Sergeant Lewis she said there was nothing unusual about the death, that she had seen many cases like it and added 'You can look through me, Sergeant, I am telling you the truth', but she afterwards dropped that attitude.

"She did not in the main deny what she had told others, she could not do so very well as they are people who would be believed, but to additional details as to the Doctor's visits etc. at 11 p.m. and 1 a.m. we cannot attach any credence. They are denied by the Doctor and even Greenwood does not refer to them.

"Greenwood when cautioned, before being questioned by Supt. Jones, did not act in the manner one would regard as that of an innocent man. It must have been obvious to him that foul play was suspected in connection with his wife's death. He showed no indignation and did not resent the implication (contained in the caution) that he was suspected of being involved, and acted as if he knew there was something to explain.

"He dwelt very much on the pills given by the Doctor as being too strong and causing her death, as if he wanted to shift the responsibility on to someone else.

"It's singular that both the Nurse and Greenwood should have changed the time the pills were given from 9 p.m. to 1 a.m. in the case of the Nurse, and to 3 a.m. by Greenwood.

"When rumours were mentioned to him, he did not enquire what the rumours were, nor has he made any attempt to ascertain who were responsible for them, although he was ready enough in the case of Miss David. His whole account is full of mis-statements.

"He makes much of his alleged fears and what he did to keep the Doctor in the garden when he was first called in (although his house was only 10 yards away), his sending Miss Phillips for the Nurse (which he never did), Mrs. Greenwood's severe heart attacks in the garden (which were not even mentioned to the Doctor). But these statements coincide with his indifference in allowing his wife to be without medical assistance, which was immediately available, whilst slowly dying for hours in his presence, and with his conduct and feelings as indicated to Miss Griffiths in the drawing room.

"That he may not have realised how seriously ill Mrs. Greenwood was, is contradicted by his expressed opinion that she would not get over it this time.

"He states that Mrs. Greenwood may have had whisky and soda with her lunch. The Parlour maid says Mrs. Greenwood had port wine. 'She always took port wine and was never known to take whisky'.

"He refers to diarrhoea in the afternoon and the day before when she went to Ferryside and when, according to Miss Phillips, she looked unusually well and was very cheerful, but doesn't say anything about the continual sickness and diarrhoea during the night when, according to the Nurse, it was such a prominent feature, both being symptoms of poisoning by arsenic or antimony.

"He does not refer to the second occasion the Doctor was sent for, which should have been more impressed on his mind than any other, for he himself was sent for and did not return for such a long time that he had to be fetched by his daughter. He could scarcely have forgotten that visit and his conversation with Miss Griffiths.

"Nor does he refer to his conversation with the Doctor outside about 10.30 p.m. when, in consequence of what he said, the Doctor did not think it necessary to see Mrs. Greenwood.

"About 3.0 a.m. when he again went for the Doctor at the Nurse's request after Mrs. Greenwood's pulse seemed to have stopped, he says he 'failed to rouse him'. The Nurse had no difficulty and it was not necessary for the Doctor's sister to wake him which she was in the habit of doing if he didn't hear a knock.

"The 3.0 a.m. visit of the Doctor is completely mis-represented. Far from saying Mrs. Greenwood 'was better in herself', she was in extremis at the time and obviously was not given any pills then, as Greenwood states. He also fixes that as the time when Mrs. Greenwood sent her daughter to bed and not at 11 p.m., as stated by Miss Phillips who is no doubt correct.

"Whether this was intended to shew that Mrs. Greenwood was not so ill as she really was at that time, and to provide an excuse for not having sent for the Doctor before, is a question.

"He states that Mrs. Greenwood's income passed to the children. Mrs. Greenwood's sister says that this is not so, that he also benefits.*

"Referring to the death afterwards in conversation with his sister-in-law, he was heard by Miss Phillips to say 'Doctor was so good, he was over every half hour'.

"It is impossible to estimate what importance should be attached to anything he says. He is ordinarily a man of the irresponsible and unreliable type. At the commencement of his statement he says that Mrs. Greenwood died about 3 a.m. By the time he reaches the end of it it is extended to 4.15 a.m.

"During the morning of the 15th Greenwood went to the china pantry twice. According to the parlourmaid he had never been known to do so before. From the pantry he went to the dining room.

---

* Greenwood's statement was substantially correct. The children were in fact the chief beneficiaries.

"Two certificates of death were issued to Greenwood by the Registrar, but the purpose of the second one is not known. Greenwood said his wife was not insured.

"At the interview with Supt. Jones, Greenwood was told that 'having regard to the rumours which were about and the matter being so very much talked of by the people, I am afraid we shall have to apply for an order to exhume the body'. He replied 'Just the very thing. I am quite agreeable'.

"He might have thought that any objection would increase suspicion.

"There is a very prevalent belief, freely voiced, in Kidwelly and Llanelly that Mrs. Greenwood met her death through foul play. Miss Phillips, who does not hesitate to say it, thought so when she was at the bedside during the evening of the 15th and still thinks so, but of course she has only psychological grounds for it. As an indication of the local feeling I may instance the opinion of Mr. Smart (Mrs. Smart's husband) who informed me that he was perfectly satisfied in his own mind that Greenwood had poisoned his wife. He knows Greenwood very well and they have always been on good terms. Even the Vicar has been heard to say that he had very grave suspicion (this was before the Police had moved) and told Sergeant Lewis later 'When that body is got up people will stiffen their backs and you will get to know a good deal more'.

"The Nurse (although tired out as she stated) went to the Vicarage and saw the Vicar about 4 hours after the death. The Vicar called at Rumsey House about 10 o'clock, but Greenwood and the children had already gone to Llanelly.

"These are the suspicious circumstances connected with a death surrounded by mystery, falsehood, and as it seems to me, culpable negligence and callousness, which I have respectfully to submit as reasons why the body should be exhumed, either in the interests of justice, or if that should happily not be so, then to relieve the husband of a terrible suspicion which will otherwise probably cling to him for life."

The Home Secretary did not reply until March 22nd and was scarcely qualified to criticise the police for delay in the conduct of investigations.

"With reference to your letter of the 9th instant giving particulars of the circumstances attending the death of Mabel Greenwood, I am directed by the Secretary of State to say that he has consulted the Director of Public Prosecutions and considers that the facts should be reported at once to the Coroner, who has power to order exhumation and hold an inquest. The Secretary of State is of opinion that it would have been better if this step had been taken sooner, but, in the absence of dates on the documents, he is unable to gather the reason for the delay.

"If the Coroner decides to order exhumation, the articles for analysis should be sent by him to the Home Office analyst: (Wm. Hy. Willcox, Esq. C.B. C.M.G. M.D.) St. Mary's Hospital, Paddington, London, W.

"After the facts have been reported to the Coroner watch should be kept on Mr. Greenwood in case he seeks to leave the neighbourhood".

At this stage the case came within the jurisdiction of the Director of Public Prosecutions. Chief Inspector Ernest Haigh, of Scotland Yard, consulted Willcox, Webster, and representatives of the D.P.P. on June 7th and 12th. Willcox's answers to various questions were given in the form of reports which were the substance of his evidence at the Inquest:—

1. The symptoms described by Dr. Griffiths and Nurse Jones were those of acute gastro-enteritis which could have been due to food poisoning or poisoning with arsenic, antimony or other irritant poison.

2. The clinical history, symptoms and the results of the analysis indicated that death was certainly due to acute arsenical poisoning and were typical.

3. The post mortem appearances were consistent with arsenical poisoning but it was impossible to draw accurate conclusions as to the cause of death from the appearance of the organs.

4. No specimens of muscle, hair, nails or skin were submitted, and they would have provided confirmatory evidence of arsenical poisoning.

5. This amount of arsenic could not have occurred as a result of medical administration of arsenic. There was no evidence of accidental ingestion.

6. Arsenic does not accumulate in the body but it takes a little time to be excreted, depending on the circumstances of administration, the form in which it is taken and the health of the patient.

7. The smallest fatal dose of arsenic was considered to be 2 grains. The medicinal dose is 1/60 to 1/15 grain. Dr. Griffiths denied having given any medicine containing arsenic.

8. Arsenic was present in all the organs analysed: the stomach, intestines, oesophagus, rectum, liver, spleen, kidneys, uterus, heart, lungs and brain. The total found was 18·07 mgs (0·28 grains). It is calculated that there must have been between $\frac{1}{2}$ and 1 grain in the whole body, probably about $\frac{3}{4}$ grain. This indicates that the poison was taken by mouth. The wide distribution of arsenic in the body shows that it had been taken several hours before death; the small amount in the stomach (0·6 mg) shows that it was probably not taken within three hours of death.

9. Severe vomiting and diarrhoea which occurred for several hours before death would have caused the elimination of a considerable amount of arsenic from the stomach and bowels. A dose of at least 2 grains of arsenic must have been taken within 24 hours of death. It was probably taken between 1.30 p.m. when lunch was taken, and 6.30 or up till midnight, probably during the evening before death.

10. Arsenic (arsenious oxide) can be powdered and dissolved slowly in cold water or other drinks and is almost tasteless. Likewise arsenical weed killers, which commonly contain 20 per cent or more of arsenic. These substances can be added to food or drink without causing noticeable detection by taste.

The Inquest was resumed on June 15th and lasted for two days. The verdict of the jury after retiring for fifty minutes and a brief consultation with the Coroner, J. W. Nicholas, was read out by him:—"We are unanimously of the opinion that the death of Mabel Greenwood was caused by acute arsenical poisoning as certified by Dr. Willcox and that the poison was administered by Harold Greenwood". It must be a rare event for the name of a medical expert to appear in an official coroner's verdict. In this case it was made clear that the verdict was based on the medical evidence resulting from the procedure of exhumation which in turn was carried out as a result of suspicious evidence collected by police inquiries. Webster's evidence that arsenic was present in considerable amount in all the organs examined was factual and decisive in its effects. As an expert chemist and analyst, and not a qualified doctor, he was not questioned about the medical evidence of the illness of deceased. It was, therefore, left to Willcox to express his opinion as to the cause of death, and the probable time the poison was administered. Dr. Griffiths' evidence did not conflict with Willcox's opinion in spite of the fact that he had issued a death certificate. Other evidence was given by nurse Jones who attended the deceased through her fatal illness, and by Miss Phillips, Miss David and Miss Martha Morris, friends of the Greenwood family, and by Miss Griffiths (also a friend and sister of the doctor). Others to give evidence were the domestic staff of Rumsey House, Miss Bowater, (sister of the deceased), the local chemist who sold the weedkiller, an expert of the firm of Cooper's weedicide and the Vicar of Kidwelly. Neither Greenwood nor his daughter Irene attended the inquest. As Greenwood later explained at the trial, his absence was due to the advice of his solicitor, Mr. Ludford.

Greenwood was arrested immediately after the Inquest on June 16th and charged with the murder of his wife. Further evidence was collected by the police before the Police Court proceedings which commenced on July 3rd and lasted for three days. Evidence was given by the foreman of the firm which supplied Eureka weedkiller to the accused, by the railway employee who delivered the parcel to Rumsey House on May 2nd and by a jeweller who had sold Greenwood a diamond ring in July 1919, presumably earmarked for his new wife. He was able to identify the receipt for £55 for its purchase.

The evidence of Webster and Willcox was heard in greater detail than at the Inquest. The physical and chemical nature of Eureka weedkiller was dealt with, a pink powder the colour of which would be destroyed by the digestive juices in the stomach. It would not appreciably affect the taste or colour of wine or tea if added in a dangerous amount. Webster gave a demonstration of arsenical mirrors in court to illustrate the Marsh-Berzelius test as if he was addressing students in a chemistry class, explaining that his analyses were confirmed by "controls", and by other analytical methods arriving at the same conclusions. Willcox, the last witness at this inquiry, described the effect of arsenic on the human body when given by the mouth as was evident in this case. Of special importance was his opinion that he was unable positively to exclude heart disease at the post mortem examination; that fatal cases of arsenical poisoning had occurred in which less than 2 grains (usually considered to be a fatal dose) had been given; that diarrhoea and vomiting would have eliminated at least half of the dose given. He was forced to admit to Greenwood's solicitor the possible administration of the fatal dose in wine, but refused to state that he considered it was given at lunch time but more likely in the late afternoon or evening. With regard to the "suffocating" pains over the heart complained of by Mrs. Greenwood, he thought they were more likely to have been caused by irritation of the stomach.

After the conclusion of proceedings, Willcox congratulated Ludford privately on the masterly manner in which he had dealt with the difficult points arising out of the medical evidence. Greenwood was committed for trial at Carmarthen Assizes. Counsel for the Crown was to be Sir Edward Marlay Samson, the Attorney-General. Less than three weeks before the trial he wrote to Willcox to request his wish for a consultation explaining that he had been so ill that his own doctor had kept him in bed for a week. Accordingly the meeting, attended by Mr. Wilfred Lewis, Sir Edward's colleague, and Mr. Seward Pearce the Deputy D.P.P., was held on October 21st lasting three hours. The lawyers had a crammed tuition course on arsenical poisoning like students preparing for their examination. But they also closely examined all possible questions that might be put by their rival counsel, Sir Edward Marshall Hall. A full summary of essential points was sent to both lawyers in good time before the trial commenced on November 2nd. At the police court proceedings Willcox had been cross examined by Ludford as to the probable total arsenic content in the body of deceased compared with that of Miss Barrow in the trial of *Rex* v *Seddon*. Ludford had indicated that Willcox's estimate of one grain was less than a fatal dose. Willcox was able to anticipate and warn counsel that this point would again arise at the trial. In comparison with the *Seddon* case, the amounts of arsenic in the liver, spleen and kidneys of Mrs. Greenwood amounted to three-quarters of that found in the same organs of Miss Barrow (10·1 mgs compared with 13·47 mgs). These figures were conclusive evidence that death in the case of Mrs. Greenwood resulted from acute arsenical poisoning, death no doubt being caused by heart failure due to vomiting, diarrhoea and dehydration. The total arsenic in the viscera amounted to 18 mgs. The muscles must have contained, taking the *Seddon* case analysis as a basis for calculation, 50 mgs of arsenic bringing the total arsenic to 68 mgs excluding any that might have been found in other organs and the skin. His estimate was that at least 2 grains of arsenic must have been taken by Mrs. Greenwood within 24 hours of death; this would be a fatal dose in a woman who was, according to Dr. Griffiths, considered to have been in a delicate state of health for several months before her death.

Anticipating the forthcoming trial, Marshall Hall interviewed the prisoner and said to his confidential clerk, Ernest Harvey, "I cannot make up my mind whether to call Greenwood. I am afraid he will make a bad witness and everything will turn on the evidence of his daughter and the cross examination of Webster and Willcox". This turned out to be partially accurate, though he was wrong about Greenwood, who proved an able and confident witness.

The trial at Carmarthen, commencing on November 2nd and lasting exactly seven days, was a memorable event which attracted so many visitors from far and wide that hotel accommodation was booked up some time beforehand, and the Guildhall was too small to accommodate so many members of the public. It was held before Mr. Justice Shearman. Marshall Hall was also unwell during the trial and alluded to the fact in court; this accounted for the fact that he left the court immediately after his final speech. He stayed at the Ivy Bush Hotel as did Willcox, whose medical attention he received during the course of the trial. The members of the jury were so carefully guarded that they were even forbidden from attending church on the Sunday.

Willcox arrived the night before the trial in time for a final consultation with Marlay Samson. After each day's proceedings they met again to discuss the day's events. Considering the customary necessity of an Assize Court Judge to keep aloof from outside contacts during the course of a trial of this nature, Willcox regarded it as a tribute to his reputation for absolute integrity and fairness that he was invited, and accepted the invitation, to dine with the Judge on the fourth evening of the trial.

Greenwood, who had already been in prison for ten weeks, had to be carefully guarded from hostile crowds on his arrival at court, so great was the local animosity towards him. He proved to be a good witness, cool and unruffled, countering his cross-examination with confidence and courage.

The trial was unusually complicated by contradictory evidence of witnesses. Dr. Griffiths and Nurse Jones disagreed about the times of his visits to Mrs. Greenwood during her final illness and the delay in his attendance during the night. The maids disagreed with Irene Greenwood concerning the wine drunk by the family at lunch, described as port by the maid and burgundy by Irene. Dr. Griffiths proved an unsatisfactory witness and was forced to admit having altered his testimony concerning the tablets which he had prescribed. At the Magistrates Court he had sworn that he had given two morphine pills (amounting to a poisonous dose of one grain of morphine) whereas later he insisted they were opium pills containing 1/40th grain of morphine in each pill—a relatively harmless dose. The truth of his revised statement was supported by Webster's analysis, which excluded the possibility of morphine poisoning. Nevertheless, the discrepancy and carelessness in his earlier evidence was fully exploited later by Marshall Hall's clever suggestion that a doctor who was careless in one instance might be dangerously so a second time, by confusing Fowler's solution with a bismuth mixture.

As might be expected in a trial in Wales in which many witnesses were called, there was some confusion over surnames shared by different witnesses. There were four Jones, three Morrises and three Griffiths.

In opening the case for the prosecution Marlay Samson presented the alleged motive for the crime the desire of the accused to marry Miss Gladys Jones, having carried on a clandestine friendship with her for a long period. Nineteen days after Mrs. Greenwood's death he had ordered a diamond ring from a London firm, for which he paid £55. The day before her death, the caretaker of Greenwood's office, at which he was said to have met Miss Jones frequently, had found a partially burnt letter in the grate in Miss Jones's handwriting in which she read the words "It will be nice when I am your wife". On September 24th he notified the Registrar of Llanelly of his intention to marry Miss Jones which he did on October 1st—three and a half months after his first wife's death. At the end of March he had ordered 10 gallons of Eureka weedkiller, which had been duly delivered. Greenwood did not gain financially by his wife's death; on the contrary it was true that she was a woman of comparative wealth at that time, having an annual income of between £700 and £900 which helped to enable the family to live in a comparatively affluent style with several maids, a cook and a full time and a part-time gardener.

Mrs. Greenwood's sister, Miss Bowater, also lived in the household and contributed to the expenses of its upkeep. Greenwood was not the main beneficiary of his wife's Will.

When first interviewed by the police superintendent on October 24th, Greenwood suggested that his wife's death was caused by the opium pills which he alleged as being "too strong". He had suggested this theory to the Vicar, who was a family friend, and the alternative theory of suicide which the Vicar hotly denied. The pills had certainly been taken within about half an hour of death. Greenwood cleverly suggested that the diarrhoea was caused by gooseberry tart eaten at lunch, but it was eaten by the rest of the family and the domestic staff without any ill effect.

Perhaps Marlay Samson dealt too long with the theory of the wine as vehicle of the poison. Miss Phillips had related how one day Mrs. Greenwood had complained that the burgundy was bitter. It had been shown that the weedkiller in solution in water gave a pink colour, but would not discolour red wine or alter its flavour; half a teaspoonful in a bottle of wine would give a fatal dose in each glass. Yet he did not exclude the theory that the poison could well have been added to the medicine, tea or brandy taken between 1.30 p.m. and midnight—as suggested by Willcox. In fact Nurse Jones referred to the burning sensation in Mrs. Greenwood's throat after her dose of bismuth mixture prescribed by Dr. Griffiths.

The maid, Hannah Williams, whose evidence pointed to the wine as the vehicle for the poison, was severely dealt with in cross examination. She stoutly insisted that she had put out the port wine on the table for the family lunch, wine glasses for Mr. and Mrs. Greenwood and water for Irene and the little boy, and had herself poured out port wine for Mrs. Greenwood alone; and at the evening meal the bottle of port had disappeared. She had noticed that Greenwood was occupied in the china pantry for fifteen minutes before lunch commenced. Marshall Hall suggested that she had been cajoled by the police to make such statements, working himself up to such a pitch as almost to lose his temper with the witness. The Judge intervened to soothe him down and to order him to stop bullying a witness, but he made no attempt at apology. No wonder she was a "poor little frightened thing", as he described her in his final speech.

Webster's evidence was confined to the analytical facts of the case, the total arsenic found in his specimens being slightly more than a quarter of a grain. No trace of morphine was found, but had one grain been given he would have expected to find traces in the remains for ten months after death. Again, he demonstrated bottles of port wine with and without Eureka weedkiller in solution, to show there was no noticeable difference in colour. Again the standard arsenical mirrors were compared with those from the case in question and handed round for judge and jury to examine.

Willcox's evidence was taken on the afternoon of the third day and on the morning of the fourth. He dealt with the post-mortem findings and the interpretation of Webster's analysis showing the probability that a fatal dose of arsenic was taken between 1 p.m. and 6 p.m., judging by the arsenic found in the stomach, intestines and other organs, allowing for the arsenic lost by vomiting and diarrhoea; that death was due to heart failure resulting from a dose of arsenic probably of the order of $\frac{3}{4}$ to 1 grain. There had been no evidence from the post mortem that the kidney function had failed during life. He ruled out of court the possibility of accidental poisoning by inhalation of arsenical fumes from weedkiller sprayed on the garden paths, and of accidental spraying of the gooseberries in the tart eaten by the whole household.

On the 4th day Marshall Hall startled the court by a fresh line of attack, a new theory for the ingestion of poison. He suddenly produced two bottles for all to see, obtained from a local chemist. He asked Willcox to look at them and compare the colour.

"One contains Fowler's solution of arsenic, the other a standard bismuth mixture. Both were kept in Dr. Griffith's surgery and he stated that he gave this lady a dose of four teaspoonsful of this mixture".

"Yes".

"If, by some unfortunate mistake, he gave her the same amount of Fowler's solution you would have got all the arsenic you found, or more?"

"Yes".

"And there is practically no distinction in colour between the mixture and the solution of arsenic?"

"No".

Having previously suggested to Dr. Griffiths that he might have prescribed the wrong pills, Marshall Hall recalled the unfortunate doctor for a further attack which lasted only a few moments.

"Do you keep all your solutions and drugs in your surgery?"

"Yes".

"Please understand I am making no suggestion, but is it possible that by an accident you might have dispensed Fowler's solution of arsenic instead of the bismuth mixture?"

"Quite impossible".

Thus there was exposed to the jury yet another theory for the possible means of ingestion of poison. Moreover, the discrepancy of the evidence of the doctor and Nurse Jones concerning the times of the last two visits of the doctor to his patient may have cast doubts on the accuracy of the doctor's testimony in the eyes of the jury.

Marshall Hall must have found it difficult to procure two medical witnesses to refute the evidence of Webster and Willcox in support of the defence. Dr. Toogood, toxicologist to the L.C.C., admitted that he had had no experience of analytical chemistry and on only one occasion had been concerned with a death from arsenical poisoning, admitting that he had "only a nodding acquaintance with chemistry". His opinion was that death was due to morphine pills given in mistake for opium pills, following gastro-enteritis due to gooseberry tart. He was forced by Marlay

Samson to give his opinion that arsenic found its way into the body of Mrs. Greenwood by inhalation of poison from the weedkiller spread on the garden paths—a theory which to any jury must have seemed absurd.

The defence received even less support from Dr. William Griffiths of Swansea, who also agreed that death was due to morphine poisoning. But with astonishing confidence he claimed that as much as $2\frac{1}{2}$ grains of arsenic could be present in the human body without deleterious effect upon the health of the individual, another claim which no other medical opinion could possibly accept.

The last witness called by Marshall Hall was his trump card. Miss Irene Greenwood, aged twenty-one, proved an excellent witness. She could remember everything that the family ate and drank on that Sunday at lunch and supper eighteen months ago, for the simple reason that her mother died the following night. Her father had whisky and soda, her brother water, her mother and herself Burgundy, not port wine as the maid had testified. She had drunk wine from a small red tumbler used as a wine glass. She always drank Burgundy on Sundays and several times a week. Again, she had Burgundy with her supper from the same bottle as at lunch.

Irene had never been asked by the police to make any statement. Nor had she been summoned to the Inquest or the Magistrates court. Why was this so? A probable explanation was that the police were most unwilling to embarrass or upset her feelings after her bereavement at a time when her mother's mysterious death, the subject of local gossip, must already have caused her considerable emotional distress. Or was her absence at the inquest due to the advice of her solicitor? This question was objected to in Court by her defence counsel and ruled out of order by the Judge. Yet it was an important point, for had she given evidence at the Inquest the charge of murder against her father might have been avoided.

Throughout the trial so much contradictory evidence had centred round the wine drunk by the family that Marshall Hall in his closing speech entirely ignored any reference to the prosecution's other theories as to the means of administration of arsenic, for example in tea or medicine or brandy as the prosecution had suggested. Using Irene's evidence as his strongest weapon to exclude wine as the means of administration, he reiterated his theory of accidental poisoning by Fowler's solution of arsenic. He ended his speech on an emotional and dramatic level, alluding to the figure of Justice holding the scales, and to medical science. "Science can do a great deal. These men with their mirrors, multipliers and milli-grams, can tell to the ten-thousandth part of a grain the constituents of the human body. Science has enabled us to talk from here to thousands of miles away without intervening wires of communication. Science has enabled us to kill tens of thousands by obnoxious gases and to blow Carmarthen to pieces with one little explosive. But science cannot do one thing; to find the vital spark which converts insensate clay into a living being. Once the life is gone out of a man by a jury's verdict or any other cause, life is at an end and no power of science can replace it ... Upon your verdict depends the reputation of the children".

The Judge's summing up must have been a difficult task, occupying the whole morning of the seventh day; it was unswervingly fair but slightly directed towards an acquittal. The jury retired at 1.20 p.m. and at 3.53 p.m. returned to Court. Asked by the Clerk whether guilty or not guilty the foreman replied "Not guilty". The verdict proved a popular one in Court, as the cheering was immediately suppressed by the Judge. The hostility towards the prisoner at the start of the trial, both in and out of Court, seemed to have faded at last. The Press shared in this jubilation the following day, but a leading article in *The Times* attacked the prosecution for bungling the case. Had the full verdict been read out in Court, which the Judge forbade, the attitude of the writer might have been quite different. When the foreman was asked whether "guilty" or "not guilty" he was not allowed to make any qualified statement. He handed the Jury's written statement to the Judge, but the Judge refused permission for this to be read out or to be disclosed either to the police or the D.P.P. and Home Office. It was not until after Greenwood's death in 1929 that the full verdict was published, hence the Press attack on Sir Edward Marlay Samson was quite unjustified and grossly unfair. The prosecuting counsel and medical experts were naturally keen to learn the content of the Jury's full verdict after the trial. Willcox's correspondence after the trial is of historical interest and is here published for the first time.

"Director of Public Prosecutions,

Whitehall.

December 22nd, 1920.

Dear Dr. Willcox,

I had an opportunity of speaking to Shearman J. yesterday about the Greenwood case and mentioned the importance of preventing the verdict, being used as a kind of precedent in which the jury negatived that arsenic was the cause of death. The judge then showed me in confidence the papers which the foreman of the jury had handed in at the end of the trial. All I can say about it (in the circumstances) is that it does not quite bear out Marlay Samson's recollection of its contents. It is not nearly so definite as his version and was a great deal longer and more argumentative. I asked the judge if I might say to you that you could use it in any scientific account you might write of the case. He said that the comment was a private and confidential communication from the foreman and that, even if it were not, he would be strongly adverse to its purport or contents being made public as he did not think anything should be disclosed, except the verdict and the reasoning by which the result was arrived at. I am afraid, therefore, that I cannot do more—unless you can suggest anything.

Yours very truly,

A. H. Bodkin."

December 27, 1920.

"Dear Sir Archibald,

Many thanks for your letter re the Greenwood case. I think it will be better to let the matter rest in view of what you say. I should, of course, be most unwilling to do anything against the Judge's wishes. I am glad that you have seen Sir Montague Shearman and learned his wishes on the subject which I shall strictly conform to.

Yours sincerely,

W. H. Willcox."

"Leigh House,
Eaton Gate,
S.W.1.   December 27th, 1920.

Dear Willcox,

I had a talk with Bodkin last week and discussed the Kidwelly case. I understand that you wanted to add the case to your museum of precedents. My suggestions are only those of a layman, but I think you will find it difficult to classify it. I know from a conversation I had with the foreman of the jury (a scientific Chemist engaged on smelting work) that he at any rate had some doubt whether the dose given on the Sunday was itself a fatal dose. But anyway the case was very interesting. It may perhaps have occurred to you—the theory of cumulative poisoning in smaller doses spread over a period. There were indications of that here and there in the non-medical evidence.

I enclose a letter, one of the many effusions I received. I tore most of them up as they were distracting, but I kept this. Perhaps you know the writer. I don't want it. It was a pleasure to meet you again, at Carmarthen.

Yours sincerely,

Montague Shearman."

"40 Welbeck Street,
London,
W.1.   January 6th 1921.

Dear Sir Montague,

Very many thanks for your kind letter. I was interested in the views of the jury, but will not make any allusion to these in any of my writings. I quite agree with you that it would be very undesirable and I think that the case was as interesting as, and from the scientific point of view must be classified with, the Seddon and Maybrick cases. Indeed, it has something between the two. There was no evidence for the fatal dose taken in the Greenwood case—no doubt full doses of poison had been taken in the previous few days. I have no doubt about arsenic being the cause of death and appreciate that the jury have not. I do not think that any other verdict was possible from the whole of the evidence given. I should like to say that I considered the case was conducted most perfectly in every way by yourself. I return Mr. Stevenson's letter. How much a Judge must be irritated by the various effusions he gets from the general public!

Yours sincerely,

William Willcox."

"12 Richmond Road,
Swansea.   January 5th, 1921.

Dear Willcox,

   I hope you were able to get the information you wanted as to the verdict
in Rex v Greenwood. Bodkin (the D.P.P.) told me that he would ask
Shearman J to let you see the paper. I travelled yesterday with the Under
Sheriff. He told me that the foreman was very vexed at their finding being
suppressed as they took so much trouble to come to that conclusion. Everybody I have met in South Wales seems satisfied as to who administered
the poison and the finding of the jury is now commonly known in S. Wales.*
I am glad to say I am really better and have had no return of the acute
pain and trouble. I am writing to Lane (a doctor in Wales) to say I would
like to have the treatment he administered in the spring, as I can be quite
free of work for a month then and it is a better time to be out of doors and
to improve ones general health.

                  With kind wishes for the New Year,

                          Yours very sincerely,

                               E. Marlay Samson."

* My collection of the Under Sheriff's information to me of the contents of the statement
handed to him by the foreman of the jury, and passed from him to Mr. Justice Shearman at the end of the trial, read as follows:—

"We are convinced that Mabel Greenwood died of Arsenical poisoning, but are
not convinced as to who administered it".

"40 Welbeck Street,
London, W.1.   January 6th, 1921.

Dear Sir Marlay Samson,

   Many thanks for your letter. I am glad to hear that you are better. I
saw Sir Archibald Bodkin (D.P.P.) with reference to the Greenwood case.
He saw the Judge from whom I have heard personally. They both think it
inadvisable for any publication to be made of the written verdict of the
jury, so under the circumstances I shall never allude to this in any of my
writings. I am most obliged to you, however, for telling me of it. I am
glad to hear that you are going to have a course of treatment under Ernest
Lane which, I am sure, will do good.

                  With kind regards and best wishes for the New Year.

                          Yours sincerely,

                               William Willcox."

"Raven Hotel,
Shrewsbury.   January 9th, 1921.

Dear Willcox,

Many thanks for your letter. I am very sorry that it was decided not to make public the jury's findings. I suppose Shearman J thinks that, as he did not do so at the time, it would be too late to do so now. It is very unfortunate and contrary to the jury's wish and from our own point of view leaves undecided the question of supreme interest.

I note that at the trial of Adelaide Bartlett* (1886) the jury gave a similar verdict. You may recall the case though it is an old one . . .

With kind regards,
Yours sincerely,
E. Marlay Samson."

* The verdict was almost identical. She was charged with poisoning her husband with chloroform. The jury added that they considered that grave suspicion was attached to the prisoner. (The Trial of Adelaide Bartlett, by Sir John Hall, Notable British Trials Series).

The full report of the verdict must have leaked out from members of the jury during the period of eight years until Greenwood's death, but the Judge successfully concealed it. According to the best traditions of English Law, an acquitted prisoner must be discharged free from any stigma of guilt to save him from further burden of punishment and to protect his family and relatives from all unnecessary hurt and embarrassment. The Judge was merely completing his duty to the prisoner with the correct courtesy of the law. The full complete verdict was released in 1929.

"We are satisfied on the evidence in this case that a dangerous dose of arsenic was administered to Mabel Greenwood on Sunday, June 15th, 1919, but we are not satisfied that this was the immediate cause of death. The evidence before us is insufficient and does not conclusively satisfy us as to how, and by whom, the arsenic was administered. We therefore return a verdict of 'Not Guilty'. (The trial of Harold Greenwood, by Miss Winifred Duke, Notable British Trials Series, 1930).

Poor Greenwood had already been in prison for four and a half months before the trial. As a result of it his career as a solicitor was ruined, and he lived in obscurity under the name of A. R. Pilkington at Ross-on-Wye. Those who believed that he was guilty of giving arsenic to his wife and that capital punishment is wrong could therefore rest assured that he had been sufficiently punished for his crime. Those who had believed in his innocence must always regard his fate as a cruel one, the sequence of the inquest verdict leading to his arrest and trial.

Even after the death of Greenwood, and of Sir Montague Shearman in 1930, Willcox kept his promise never to disclose his inmost feelings either in public or to his friends; in his addresses he carefully avoided any allusion to the legal aspects of the case though he did from time to time comment on the scientific aspects of the analysis. There is no doubt that he shared the Judge's opinion that Mrs. Greenwood was the victim of cumulative poisoning over a long period. The medical history of the case is strongly suggestive. There was little evidence that she had ever had symptoms of heart disease, shortness of breath, angina or failure of the heart; on the other hand, impaired appetite, weight loss, debility, a tendency to faintness and recurrent attacks of gastro-enteritis which had always, according to her doctor's account, cleared up until the last attack on the final Sunday. A clear picture of chronic arsenical poisoning. But cumulative poisoning could not have been proved by the Crown in court because no specimens of hair or nails or skin were kept for analysis—an oversight which was afterwards regretted. Neither Webster nor Willcox had known about the exhumation until it was completed. As a result of this case the custom arose whereby Home Office pathologists were summoned to attend exhumations in person, in order to ensure that all relevant material was retained for investigation.

Mrs. Yseult Bridges, who has studied the Greenwood case in great detail, has commented on the part played by Irene Greenwood in securing her father's acquittal:—"If she had given evidence at the inquest as she did at the trial the course of the trial might have been quite different. At the time of the inquest the prosecution had not yet based their case on the theory that the poison had been administered in the wine drunk at lunch. The extraordinary blunder on the part of the authorities concerned in ignoring Irene's existence during the investigations and proceedings allowed the defence to produce her at the last moment, like a rabbit out of a hat, to demolish the prosecution's case by swearing that she too had drunk of the same wine. If this evidence had been given at the inquest the prosecution would have suggested another and more probable medium of administration of the poison, such as medicine or brandy."

Willcox left in his files a short hand-written note, the source of which is quite obscure. At a sale at Rumsey House, a vase in the Hall was sold. This contained a broken packet of greyish powder. The curate who bought the vase emptied the contents into the fire causing a violet flame. Some of the powder at the bottom of the vase was sent by the Chief Constable to Webster who found a high percentage of arsenic in it.

Was this the Eureka Weedkiller? The complete truth of the Greenwood mystery will always remain obscure. Its uncertainties add to the interest of Medico-Legal history.

References

The Life of Sir Edward Marshall Hall, by Edward Marjoribanks, 1929.
The Trial of Harold Greenwood by Winifred Duke, Notable British Trials Series, 1930.
The Trial of Adelaide Bartlett, by Sir John Hall, Notable British Trials Series, 1886.

Chapter 16

Arsenical Poisoning at Tregonissey—(1922)
(*Rex* v. *Black*)

The publicity of the Greenwood trial had scarcely faded by the time the attention of the press was directed to the obscure Cornish village of Tregonissey following the mysterious death of Mrs. Annie Black on November 11th, 1921—a year and two days after the verdict in the Greenwood trial. Her death, like that of Mrs. Greenwood, aroused suspicion among the neighbours. But, more important in the light of subsequent events, Dr. Andrew, her doctor, refused to sign a death certificate and reported to the coroner. Whereas the drama of the Greenwood case was linked with the exhumation of the remains nine months after burial, in this case immediate investigation yielded results more accurately and quickly. The evidence of witnesses was more trustworthy, being dependent on memories of recent events. The trial at Bodmin of Edward Black for the murder of his wife by administration of arsenic lasted only two days, but it deserves detailed study and interest on account of the medical evidence, of which Willcox contributed a major share, and the drama of events which preceded it.

Edward and Annie Black were married in 1914, the latter being eighteen years older than her husband, their ages being 36 and 54 at the time of the events. Marion, aged 17, the step-daughter of Edward, lived with them above their confectioner's shop at Tregonissey, near St. Austell. The shop was owned by Mrs. Black before her marriage. Until his marriage Black had been employed in the clay pits, but subsequently became, like Seddon, an insurance company agent. But in spite of advancing himself in the social hierarchy he still retained the friendship of several old friends who appeared as witnesses at his trial. It was very curious that he was dismissed from his post by the insurance company during the period of Mrs. Black's fatal illness—on November 3rd, 1921.

Black claimed that his wife had had indigestion for several years, but her tragic final illness commenced on October 31st as gastro-enteritis which was incapacitating, first thought to be of the epidemic variety prevalent in Cornwall at that time. The illness persisted for eleven days, fluctuating in severity from day to day, vomiting and diarrhoea being its features. During the last three days these symptoms subsided, but she became, generally speaking, weaker. Dr. Andrew, no doubt remembering the case of Mrs. Greenwood, suspected poisoning. Having informed the coroner, he attended the post-mortem and was confirmed in his suspicion on finding no sign of any other disease. The inquest of November 14th was three times adjourned and would have been completed earlier but for a most strange series of events. Black's disappearance from his home at the climax of his wife's illness on November 8th led to great press publicity and the publication of his photograph in several daily papers. He was traced to a temperance hotel in Liverpool. By an extraordinary co-incidence he was arrested on November 21st by a Liverpool detective while in the act of committing suicide by cutting his throat, was rushed to hospital for treatment, and had recovered sufficiently for him to be brought to the final session of the inquest at St. Austell on January 5th. He was subsequently charged with the murder of his wife by the adminis-tration of arsenic.

Meanwhile, on November 16th a hamper arrived at St. Mary's Labora-tory containing certain organs removed from the body of Mrs. Black by the pathologist, Dr. Gilchrist, at the post-mortem examination.

On completion of Webster's analyses and their joint consultation, Willcox was requested to submit full reports to the Director of Public Prosecutions, Sir Archibald Bodkin, after considering Webster's results, the coroner's depositions and police statements. Following up his report, Willcox consulted Bodkin on January 18th before departing with John Webster for St. Austell late at night, in order to attend the Police Court proceedings, and to consult the Chief Constable, Colonel Prothero Smith, and Mr. Vivian Thomas, Solicitor acting for the Crown. At the inquiry Willcox expressed the opinion that Mrs Black's illness was caused by an irritant poison such as arsenic. The post-mortem findings showed no evid-ence of death from natural disease, nor any naked-eye abnormality in any of her organs.

Webster's analyses showed arsenic in all the viscera amounting to 1/17th of a grain in the whole body. Though present in appreciable amounts in all the organs (the greatest concentration being in the liver to the extent of 1.53 mgs.) the total amount in the body was considerably less than the customarily considered fatal single dose of two grains. The explanation of the small total quantity of arsenic was shown by the clinical history of "vomiting and diarrhoea" causing the excretion of large amounts of arsenic before death. Willcox had to explain why Mrs. Black had died three days after Black left his wife, in the light of the evidence of those nursing the patient that definite improvement occurred after his departure. Willcox attributed this anomaly to the presence of diseased kidneys in a debilitated patient, the microscopical examination showing that the kidneys were not only damaged by the poison itself but had previously been abnormal, probably for many years. "The small amount of arsenic in the body led me to think", he concluded, "that in addition to arsenical poisoning another factor played a part, namely, debility of the patient resulting from defective kidney function, though death would not have occurred unless arsenic had been administered."

The trial at Bodmin Assizes took place on February 2nd, 1922, before Mr. Justice Rowlatt, Mr. Holman Gregory and Mr. H. L. Murphy for the Crown, and Mr. J. L. Pratt for the Defence. The details of the tragic illness of deceased, and of Black's arrest were features of the trial. Its short duration was due to the damning evidence of the prosecution, though no satisfactory motive for the crime was ever postulated. No witnesses were produced to lend any weight to the power of the defence. Even Marshall Hall, with his superb oratorical powers, would have been unable to sway the jury towards an acquittal.

The chemist and an assistant were able to recognise Black as a customer at their shop at St. Austell where he purchased two ounces of arsenic, coloured with indigo, on October 29th. On a previous visit Black had ordered certain household goods to be sent to his home; and he had been known as a member of the local church choir. Closely questioned about his purchase of arsenic, Black insisted that it was recommended as the best agent for killing rats, but his daughter in her evidence denied that their shop and home were in fact infested with rats, or that any attempt had been made to eradicate the pest. Several witnesses identified his signature in the poison book; the superintendent of the insurance company had seen many of his signatures on business documents, and was familiar with it. In spite of this, Black, the last witness, denied that it was his, but claimed it was an imitation of his own. The arsenic purchased would have been enough to provide nearly five hundred fatal doses, each being enough to cover a threepenny bit.

Mrs. Black was taken ill on October 31st following her breakfast of tea and bread and butter, the tea being poured out by the accused. Severe vomiting and diarrhoea followed the meal, and necessitated the doctor's visit later in the morning. Mrs. Black was well known to the village folk, who came to like her at their visits to the shop. During the illness she was nursed by several friends by day and night, though Black, himself in close attendance, insisted on administering the doctor's bismuth mixture. Three men and two women friends spent nights in the house to support Black in the care of his wife, but there was no professional nurse. Had she been admitted to hospital the tragic end to her illness would certainly have been avoided. Almost invariably the patient complained of a burning sensation of the throat after taking the medicine. She was heard by several witnesses to complain to her husband that the burning occurred only after he administered medicine. On one occasion she swore she would take no further doses, though Black insisted that she must. Several doses given by her friends caused no retching or vomiting. On the third day of the illness Black had told several neighbours that his wife was gravely ill and unlikely to recover, though the doctor at that stage had expressed no serious anxiety. He insisted that her heart was seriously diseased. On November 3rd Black was dismissed from his post in the insurance company.

A detective of the Liverpool police described how he went in search of Black at a Liverpool temperance hotel on November 21st at midnight, forced the door of his room on the third floor, and entered the room in darkness. He found the prisoner sitting, fully clothed, on the side of the bed, with both hands to his throat. Blood streamed from his hands and a pocket knife fell to the floor. His life was saved by prompt removal to hospital. Pronounced fit to travel on December 30th, he travelled back to St. Austell with a police escort. After his disappearance and Mrs. Black's death the local and national press prominently displayed the news, his photograph appearing in several papers. Warrants had been issued for his arrest on false pretences charges; the inquest and post-mortem news added further drama to the case.

The letter which the local butcher received from Black, written just before his attempted suicide, was identified in court and read out, a tragic and dramatic document which brought tears to the eyes of several people there:—

"Dear Joe,
No doubt this letter will give you a shock, but I have always looked to you as a pal, and being the last letter I shall ever write in this world kindly forgive me for sending it to you. Joe, I am heart broken and can't stand it any longer, so now I am going to Annie. God bless her; she will forgive me if nobody else will. So farewell to all my friends I never thought you would have kicked me when I was down, but never mind old friend you can't hurt a dead man, and the people who are telling such horrible lies about me will have their day. For remember 'Vengeance is mine said the Lord. I will repay.' and don't forget the devil is not so black as he is painted. Well, Joe, for one thing, I can't understand. For God's sake why doesn't Dr. Andrew tell the others the state of Annie's heart, the same what he told it to me. Ask him to be a man and not a cad. What does he mean by suggesting arsenic. My God, Joe, you know me better than that. I made the greatest mistake of my life when I came away. What made me do it I can't say, but we all make mistakes, old friend, and now I am about to pay a big price for mine; so good-bye all. Kiss Marion for me, look after her, and ask her if she will forgive me, Tell her to be a good girl, and Heaven will bless her, and Annie, and Grannie, and I will be watching for her, for the time comes when there will be no more deaths, neither sighing nor weeping, for God shall wipe away all tears from their eyes. Remember me to all my friends, if I have any left, and oh, my God, how I should like to clasp you all by the hand, but that is forbidden now. Well Joe, you can do what you like with this letter, but it is my wish that you read it to all, and those in particular who are trying to brand me. I don't know where this letter will be posted from. A friend is going to post it for me, but one thing is sure, my body won't be found in England as I am already several hundreds of miles away. Now, kind friend, break the news gently to Marion, and tell her I won't trouble her any more. So now farewell to you from a heart broken miserable man whom I hope God will forgive (signed) Ted Black."

[Then followed at the end of the letter about 60 crosses marked "For Marion."]

Webster and Willcox, who had travelled from London on the midnight train to Bodmin, were present throughout the trial. Their evidence was an elaboration of that given at the police court proceedings. Webster gave a detailed account of the amount of arsenic estimated in the whole body (1/6 grain) together with the analysis of the main organs and the high content (1.53 mgs) in the liver. The minute traces of arsenic in the remains of the medicine in the bottles collected by the police were, he considered, insufficient to cause harm to the patient and might well have been due to impurities in the bismuth content. He had specially preserved the kidneys for microscopical examination for Willcox. In a cup of tea or in the medicine arsenic could have escaped detection even though it was coloured with indigo. He was extensively cross-examined about the Marsh test and the production of arsenical mirrors, samples of which were handed round in court. He did not agree that arsenic was retained in the body indefinitely. That was not the case, as it was excreted fairly quickly, though in chronic poisoning some remained in the hair and nails.

Willcox's evidence was both an extension of that of Webster and its interpretation to the illness and death of Mrs. Black. He described how arsenic affects the body both by its action as an irritant poison in the stomach and intestines, and by its effect after absorption as a protoplasmic poison to the organs, the brain, heart, liver and kidneys, as he considered was the case here. Death may therefore be delayed for days or even weeks after a dose which might be much less than the normal fatal single dose— usually considered to be two grains. He considered that a large dose had been taken early in the illness or at its onset on October 31st. Vomiting and diarrhoea would have accounted for the loss of a considerable amount. His microscopical examination of the kidneys had shown evidence of previous damage to the kidneys, and there was recent change due to the effects of the poison on the cells. Death in this case was due to failure of the kidneys (uraemia) consequent on the effects of arsenic, the diarrhoea in this case being due to this cause. The improvement of symptoms in the last three days of life was due to removal of the irritant cause of poisoning during this period, though death was due to failure of kidney function, the effect of the protoplasmic poison. He considered that the burning sensation in the throat was due to irritation by arsenic, and was probably correctly connected by the patient with the taking of the medicine.

The evidence of all witnesses in the case was consistent with the guilt of the prisoner. There was no contradictory evidence as in the Greenwood trial, except for that of Black himself, the last witness to appear. Black had been interested in first aid. In the search of his house the police had discovered a Red Cross Instruction book with a page turned down, dealing with arsenic and other poisons. It was an exhibit, but Black denied all knowledge of its existence in his home since the war ended. He also denied the signature in the poisons register as being his own. Counsel for the defence could do little more than stress the absence of motive for the alleged crime, claiming that the illness was due to a severe form of gastro-enteritis.

Before the judge summed up, the foreman of the jury requested to see two cups of tea, one with and the other without arsenic. Webster was instructed to prepare this, but was unable to obtain any arsenic in Bodmin. He had to motor to Wadebridge to obtain it, while the Judge made his address. The jury then retired, taking the cups of tea and other exhibits with them.

The Judge dealt at length with the course of the illness and the scientific evidence. "You have had a very great deal of scientific evidence, the best that can be got. Sir William Willcox and Mr. Webster are among the most eminent gentlemen in the kingdom that could give it. To persons like you and me, who are not medical men, or chemists, their arguments and conclusions were sometimes difficult to follow and criticise, and you have to take a certain amount for granted because it is difficult for us to realise the minute particles of stuff which produce the important results you get in chemistry. Broadly speaking, I think Dr. Willcox made the case intelligible to you, but it is for you to be satisfied in your minds." The case, he went on, was one of circumstantial evidence, because no one saw the poison given. Then he went on to discuss the strong circumstantial evidence, but the question of motive was never satisfactorily cleared up.

After 45 minutes the jury returned a verdict of guilty, after which Black was sentenced to death.

Black's appeal was rejected by the Court of Criminal Appeal on March 6th, and he was executed on March 24th 1922.

Several aspects of the case remain obscure. Why was a plea of insanity not made on his behalf? At the present time this would certainly have been successful. His letter to the local butcher before his attempted suicide provided evidence which could have been construed as evidence of a psychotic personality. Likewise, his attempted suicide itself. Or was this due to pangs of a guilty conscience or fear of detection? If so, perhaps it was unfortunate that his suicide was prevented at the last moment. Why did Black need to murder his wife? No other woman was known to be the object of his affection—or was it for her money and her sweet shop? She certainly ran this herself with success, and was probably of more value to him, financially, alive than dead, even though they had been known to quarrel about money, according to her daughter. The answers to these questions are still a mystery.

Reference

"Poison Mysteries in History, Romance and Crime", by C. J. S. Thompson, The Scientific Press, 1923.

Chapter 17

Arsenic in Chocolates and Scones—(1922)
(*Rex* v. *Armstrong*)

From the point of view of hospital work and medical practice 1921 must have been one of his busiest years, judging by his diaries of the post-war decade. In November the preliminary stages of the Black investigations were well under way, leading up to the trial of Edward Black at Bodmin in February. On December 23rd, Willcox was preparing to relax for the Christmas festivities, and was engaged in sending off his Christmas cards with his secretary, when he was telephoned by Sir Archibald Bodkin, Director of Public Prosecutions, requesting a consultation on Christmas Eve. Bodkin was "squeezed in" during a spare hour in the afternoon at Welbeck Street. When Bodkin started talking about a second solicitor suspected to be a criminal poisoner, he could hardly believe his ears, for the case was initially so reminiscent of the Greenwood case, yet more complex than that. The interview was prolonged as long as possible, his patient being kept waiting for fifteen minutes. Their consultation was postponed and continued on Boxing Day. Willcox always spent Christmas Day with his family at home, and often hunted with the Cottesmore for the Boxing Day meet. But this idea was abandoned. Instead, they had a three-hour discussion of documents Bodkin brought with him—depositions, police statements, the long report of the Chief Inspector Aldred Crutchett of Scotland Yard and an up-to-date summary of the investigations of a case more complex than any Willcox had ever encountered.

"What about it?" asked Bodkin, getting ready to depart.—"Mrs. Armstrong undoubtedly died of acute arsenical poisoning".

"Will you report fully in writing?"

He spent Boxing Day composing a report which enabled Bodkin to decide to arrest Armstrong on a charge of murdering his wife by administration of arsenic. This report was later handed to Armstrong's Defence Counsel. Armstrong was arrested on New Year's Eve and at Willcox's suggestion Bernard Spilsbury was instructed to carry out the exhumation and post-mortem of Mrs. Armstrong, which he did on January 2nd. So it was that Willcox then had on his plate at the same time two trials for murder by arsenic, Black and Armstrong. The evidence pointed to almost certain proof of attempted murder by Armstrong of his rival solicitor, Oswald Martin, and of strong suspicion that he had successfully murdered his wife nine months previously in the same way.

Herbert Armstrong, M.A. of Cambridge, was a solicitor of many years standing, fifty-three years of age, having qualified in 1895, the sole proprietor of the firm of Cheese & Armstrong of Hay, Breconshire, a firm which he had joined in 1906. A keen Territorial before the War, he had served in the Royal Engineers until his demobilisation in 1919 with the rank of Major. In September 1919 he returned to pick up the threads of his practice single-handed. A small man of five feet six inches, he was somewhat self-important, though popular in the district, in his position of Clerk to the Justices in Radnorshire, Herefordshire and Breconshire. His home in Cusop, where he lived with his wife and three children, was near Hay, a pleasant town in an agricultural district on the river Wye and near the Welsh border.

In July 1919 Oswald Martin, who had been wounded serving in France as a private in the London Scottish, joined R. T. Griffiths of Hay, the rival firm of solicitors whose office was situated on the opposite side of the street. The firm became known as Griffiths & Martin, but Griffiths was in poor health and died in November 1920. Martin married in June 1921 the daughter of the local chemist, Mr. John Davies. The wedding at Cusop was attended by Mr. and Mrs. Armstrong.

About eight weeks after his return, Armstrong invited Martin to tea. Although he had been aware that Armstrong was jealous of him as a younger man and a professional rival, Martin accepted the invitation. The visit was a success; he met and liked Mrs. Armstrong, staying about two hours with them.

At the end of 1919 a small estate was sold at Brecon, Armstrong acting for the vendor. The sale should have been completed by February 1920, but for some obscure reason the sale was delayed by Armstrong in spite of the repeated entreaties of the purchasers, for whom Martin acted. In fact the sale was never completed though a deposit of £500 had been duly paid. Martin gave formal notice to Armstrong that, unless the business was completed by October 20th, 1921 he had instructions from his clients to rescind the contract which he formally did on that date. Under pressure on the phone, Armstrong agreed to interview the clients of Martin, attempting to persuade them to hold their hands for two weeks—but the request was refused. As Armstrong refused to return the deposit money representing 10% of the purchase price of the property, Martin threatened on December 5th to take legal proceedings against Armstrong unless the deposit was repaid.

Martin's Illness

After repeated requests, Martin agreed to visit Armstrong on October 26th at tea time. At 5 o'clock both had tea and buttered scones, Armstrong handing his rival a scone with his fingers with an "excuse fingers" apology. Though surprised at the time, Martin ate the scone, afterwards taking bread and butter and two cups of tea. He was subsequently quite seriously ill, feeling sick at 7.30, eating no supper. He vomited repeatedly throughout the night, diarrhoea commencing in the early morning. Dr. Hincks diagnosed this as a bilious attack, as any doctor would at the first visit. His patient had fully recovered by November 1st 1921 when he resumed work.

The Amateur Detective

Though no suspicion arose in the mind of the highly respectable and much-loved doctor, Martin's father-in-law John Davies, the local chemist, carried out one of the cleverest investigations of amateur crime detection on record. He had sufficient medical knowledge to suspect that his son-in-law had been poisoned, but more significantly, was alarmed when he recalled his sale of half a pound of arsenic to Armstrong in 1919. The sale of this poison had actually aroused his suspicion at the time of Mrs. Armstrong's death on February 22nd, 1921, but at the time he had, as he thought wisely, not mentioned it to anybody. Davies now inquired of the doctor the nature of Martin's illness. On being informed it was a bilious attack he replied: "Are you sure he has not been poisoned? I must put you on your guard because it is always easy to be wise after the event". Davies then visited his sick son-in-law himself, correctly (as it turned out) diagnosed arsenical poisoning, warning Martin and his own daughter against taking anything given or sent to them by Armstrong.

The Poisoned Chocolates

He then learnt that they had received by post from an anonymous donor a box of Fuller's chocolates on September 20th. They had produced these to offer to several guests at a small dinner party in October, following which Martin's sister-in-law had been ill the following night. They had noticed that the box had been opened and the ribbon re-tied. The postmark on the cover was too faint to be read.

Examining the remaining chocolates, Davies found that two of them in the top layer had been tampered with; the ends had been removed and white powder inserted. His suspicion was fully confirmed. After discussion with the doctor, to whom suspicion was strongly conveyed, it was arranged that every effort should be made to prove the accuracy of their deductions; that the chocolates had been sent by Armstrong, and that Martin had been poisoned after taking tea with Armstrong. At this stage Dr. Thomas Hincks carried on investigations. He visited Martin on Sunday, October 30th before his full recovery. He imparted his suspicion to his patient and collected a sample of urine. The chocolates and urine were dispatched to the Home Office analyst John Webster, who found that the urine contained 1/33rd of a grain of arsenic in seventeen ounces. Two of the chocolates had been opened and filled with about two grains of arsenious oxide in each. There was still no proof that Armstrong had sent the chocolates, nevertheless suspicion was strong enough.

While out riding his horse one day Hincks had a sudden inspiration. It suddenly dawned on him that the symptoms of his former patient, the late Mrs. Armstrong, were exactly consistent with those to be expected in arsenical poisoning. He had read reports of the Greenwood trial in the papers. The terminal phase of Mrs. Armstrong's illness was almost exactly the same as that of Mrs. Greenwood. His only doubt was about the mental breakdown which afflicted Mrs. Armstrong some weeks before her death. Some of his records of her illness were admittedly incomplete but most of the gaps in his notes could be filled in from his vivid memory of her tragic illness. He was convinced that Mrs. Armstrong must have died from arsenical poisonings that he had acted wrongly in signing her death certificate in February 1921. Davies, the chemist, had records of the sale to Armstrong of arsenic in pure form, or as a weed-killer in June 1919, May and August 1920, and in January 1921.

Dr. Hincks, a man of great professional integrity and discretion, was in an embarrassing predicament such as is rarely encountered by any doctor in the course of a career in practice because Armstrong was himself under his care and treatment for venereal disease, said to have been recently acquired. He was faced with the necessity, or otherwise, of reporting to the police his suspicion that his patient Armstrong had nine months previously poisoned his wife with arsenic. If he failed to report it he would both in his own conscience and in the eyes of Martin and Davies be guilty of neglect of his public duty as a medical man. Yet, if he did so, it would be tantamount to a confession that he had made a mistake when he had signed a death certificate for Mrs. Armstrong stating that she had died from natural causes. Wisely and courageously he decided to act. Legal proceedings were set in motion when he wrote to the Home Office on November 2nd. Later, he was summoned to an interview with the Chief Constable of Hereford in the presence of a representative of the Director of Public prosecutions. Hincks told them that he regarded Armstrong as being mentally abnormal, clever and well-read, and that he kept a revolver at the side of his bed and was probably a homicidal maniac. "If he gets to know about the police inquiries he might murder himself, his children and me" he said.

Willcox Reports

Willcox considered that the illness of Martin's sister-in-law following the eating of a chocolate was consistent with arsenical poisoning. In the case of Martin himself, the urine passed on the 4th day indicated that a possible fatal dose of arsenic had been taken on October 26th, the development of symptoms suggesting that the poison had been taken in solid form, nausea commencing two hours, and vomiting four hours, after eating the scones.

Mrs. Armstrong, he continued, had been attended by Dr. Hincks for rheumatic symptoms from May to August 1919. She then began to have bilious attacks. A year later she developed insomnia and delusions of guilt and inferiority. She was certified and admitted to a mental hospital in August 1920. On admission she was vomiting and seriously ill. She developed peripheral neuritis affecting her four limbs, but this had so much improved by December 12th that she could walk unaided, her general health and mental condition having also improved. Under pressure from Armstrong the doctors allowed her to return home on January 22nd, 1921. But she soon became seriously ill again, the neuritis returned and she began to suffer from vomiting, diarrhoea and weight loss. These symptoms were all consistent with subacute arsenical poisoning. Arsenic had certainly been administered during the last six days of her life; Willcox was certain that arsenic would be found on analysis of her organs.

On the basis of this report Bodkin arranged for Armstrong to be arrested on a charge of the attempted murder of Martin. This occurred in his office at Hay on December 31st. On searching his pockets a small white folded packet containing a white crystalline powder was found. On analysis by Webster it was found to contain between three and four grains of white arsenic. Another brown paper packet contained grey powder, arsenic mixed with charcoal.

The Exhumation

Dr. Bernard Spilsbury carried out his gruesome task on January 2nd, 1922, in Cusop Churchyard. He had left London by train in the morning in very cold weather when snow lay in the streets of Hereford. The grave was opened at 6.30 p.m. and the body removed to a nearby unheated cottage in the presence of the undertaker, who identified the body, and two detectives. Spilsbury was remarkably quick at post-mortem work. He found no evidence of any gross disease likely to have caused death. Removing the main organs, he caught an evening train home, bringing to St. Mary's the containers with the organs for Webster to analyse. He phoned Willcox before retiring to bed and discussed the result.

Webster's preliminary tests showed that there was at least two grains of arsenic in both liver and kidneys, thus confirming Willcox's opinion that a poisonous dose had been administered in the last few days of life. The tests were completed within twenty four hours.

In a two hour meeting at Welbeck Street on February 12th, Spilsbury described the well preserved state of the body, particularly that of the internal organs. The liver and kidneys showed characteristic changes due to metallic poisoning. They both agreed that the mental symptoms were most probably due to arsenic acting on the brain (encephalopathy). Their conclusions were expressed in Willcox's second report. In half of the large intestine Webster found 37.6 mgs of arsenic which indicated that over two grains were probably taken within twenty four hours of death. The presence of over two grains in the liver meant that more than this amount was taken during the last six days. The arsenic found in the hair and nails suggested that doses had been taken before Mrs. Armstrong's admission to hospital.

The Magistrates' Court

On January 19th Willcox gave evidence at the police court proceedings in the Black case on the same day as Armstrong was charged with the murder of his wife. A few days later Armstrong faced a similar ordeal at Hay on the double charge of murder and attempted murder of Martin. At the little court at Hay where Armstrong had so often appeared in his capacity of Clerk his place was taken by eighty-year-old Mr. C. Phillips to whom the prisoner kindly offered his help. Armstrong was well known in the district and was actually a churchwarden of his church. The hearing of a double charge was bound to be lengthy; in fact it was spread over four separate days, while Webster's analyses were proceeding. On January 5th the medical evidence commenced with the appearance of the Medical Superintendent of the mental hospital who described the physical and mental condition of Mrs. Armstrong on admission. For more than half the day Dr. Thomas Hincks gave evidence. Having completed his testimony concerning the illnesses of Martin and Mrs. Armstrong he was confronted by a most unpleasant and rare predicament such as seldom falls to the lot of any doctor during the course of a career in practice. Asked to describe the illness of the prisoner who had been a year ago under his care and treatment, the doctor refused to disclose professional and confidential information. Counsel for the Director of Public Prosecutions, Mr. St. John Michelthwaite, claimed that privilege for a medical man could not be upheld. He quoted the case of *Garner* v *Garner* of 1920 in which Mr. Justice McCardie ruled against privilege being extended to a medical man in Court. Hincks was then ordered to proceed. Hincks had no alternative but to obey and in doing so acted perfectly correctly. He disclosed that Armstrong had been treated by him for venereal disease contracted while his wife was in hospital. On one occasion while he was having an injection Armstrong asked "By the way, doctor, what is a fatal dose of arsenic?" Witness answered "Two or three grains". Armstrong then asked "Wouldn't one be enough?". Hincks had been amused but surprised.

A few days before going to Hay, Spilsbury had another discussion with Willcox at Welbeck Street. Both were so busy that they met on Sunday for two hours. They set out for Hay with Webster on Thursday, February 16th. The following and final day was entirely taken up with these witnesses; Spilsbury, Webster and Willcox in that order.

Spilsbury described how the remains were unusually well preserved ten months after burial, especially the liver, kidneys, uterus and intestines. The condition was mummification rather than putrefaction. There was no sign of natural disease, but fatty changes consistent with poisoning of the liver and kidneys by arsenic. He had conveyed sixteen jars from Cusop to St. Mary's Hospital for Webster to analyse the contents.

John Webster said that two of the remaining chocolates in the box each contained over two grains of arsenic while thirty others were untouched. The total arsenic estimated in the body of Mrs. Armstrong was over three grains, the largest amount ever found in his long analytical experience. The powder found in a packet in Armstrong's pocket contained over three and three-quarters of a grain.

Though Webster's evidence was shorter than that of his colleagues it displayed the enormous amount of laboratory work in connection with the case. Everyone in court, but particularly Willcox who had been an analyst himself, marvelled that he and Roche Lynch had managed to complete the work in so short a time as two weeks. They had certainly done more hard work than anyone else concerned with the case. Apart from the organs, they had investigated numerous bottles for poisons, some containing homeopathic medicines and others arsenical weed-killers.

Willcox claimed with certainty that a fatal dose of arsenic had been taken within twenty-four hours of death, his opinion being based on Webster's analysis of the arsenical content of the small and large intestines. Likewise, a similar amount had been taken shortly before Mrs. Armstrong's admission to hospital, judging by her symptoms and the arsenic analysed in the nails and hair. He said that for a doctor in practice the diagnosis of arsenical poisoning was notoriously difficult during life, when no cause of suspicion existed, as the symptoms so closely resembled those of natural disease and food poisoning; it was for this reason that arsenical poisoning had been as common and had become even fashionable. While Dr. Hincks had been mistaken, as he had frankly admitted, in supposing and certifying death as due to natural causes, his certificate had otherwise been accurate. It was a mistake any good doctor could be forgiven for making. Lastly, Martin's illness had undoubtedly been caused by taking arsenic at teatime and probably in a dose of two grains at least.

The Trial of H. R. Armstrong

Armstrong was committed for trial for the murder of his wife at Hereford Assizes before Mr. Justice Darling on April 3rd. The trial ended on the tenth day.

The Attorney-General, Sir Ernest Pollock, K.C., (later Lord Hanworth), appeared for the Crown, assisted by Mr. C. F. Vachell, K.C., and Mr. St. John Michelthwaite. Defence Counsel was Sir Henry Curtis Bennett, K.C., assisted by Mr. S. Bosanquet, K.C.

It was the last trial for murder at which Lord Darling, then aged seventy-three, presided before his retirement after twenty-five years as a judge. But he had lost none of his power of controlling the proceedings; his repeated interjections to clarify points of detail in the evidence showed the intense interest he took in this tedious task. He afterwards described it as his most interesting experience as a Judge. Both this and the Seddon trial were the longest Willcox ever attended. In this case he sat through the trial from the second day to the end, taking copious notes, evidently enjoying the spirited, yet studiously courteous, battle between opposing counsel. The temper and nervous tension Marshall Hall had displayed in Greenwood's defence and his bullying of witnesses were strikingly absent here. It is worth comparing the similarities and differences between the setting of the two tragedies and trials.

Major Armstrong, as he liked to be called, was fifty-three and his wife forty-eight at the time of her death, whereas Greenwood was forty-six and his wife forty-eight. Both men were rather unsuccessful solicitors in small country towns some sixty miles apart—certainly from the point of view of material success. Both lived somewhat beyond their financial means and incomes. The Greenwoods had four children, the Armstrongs three. Both wives were in ill health for several months before they died. Mrs. Armstrong had taken homeopathic medicines, Mrs. Greenwood more orthodox remedies, but Mrs. Armstrong was more clearly neurotic, —a fact which was a help for the defence. In both cases the doctors failed to diagnose arsenical poisoning at the deaths of their respective patients, the diagnosis being made after exhumation. But suspicion of foul play arose in quite different ways. Local gossip, coupled with a too hasty second marriage, led to Greenwood's arrest. Mrs. Armstrong's death from arsenical poisoning would never have been brought to light had not her husband attempted to poison his rival solicitor eight months later. There was no local gossip, but Dr. Hincks and the local chemist played their parts as amateur detectives to make amends for the doctor's initial error at the time of Mrs. Armstrong's death. The medical evidence was the predominant feature of both trials. Both Greenwood and Armstrong were good witnesses, unruffled and composed throughout their ordeal. But here the resemblances cease. Greenwood was an easy-going man, a good mixer and popular with women. Armstrong was conceited, calculating, yet stupidly tactless. The alleged motives were different in the two cases.

While the Attorney-General opened the case for the prosecution on April 3rd, the first day of the trial, Willcox, Spilsbury and Webster travelled together by train to Hereford. They stayed at the same hotel as the lawyers acting for the Crown. There they all met together for two hours after dinner, the representative of the D.P.P.—Mr. Paling—being present. A firm believer in meticulous preparation before a contest in court, Willcox was the dominant figure in the group, discussing the details of the case with his colleagues and the likely arguments the defence would use in opposition,—like a general preparing on the eve of an important battle. It was specially necessary that the evidence of each medical witness should be complementary and consistent, the expression of the truth as each saw it.

During the opening session Curtis Bennett argued that, as the Defence admitted at the outset that Mrs. Armstrong's death was caused by arsenical poisoning, the evidence of Martin's illness should be inadmissible as it would prejudice the jury. But the Judge ruled that, as the Defence argued that her death was due to suicide the evidence would be admissible. This decision meant that the trial would be longer than Curtis Bennett had hoped.

The Attorney-General opened by describing Mrs. Armstrong's illness and the evidence together with the opinions of Webster, Spilsbury and Willcox that as more than three and a half grains of arsenic had been found in the exhumed remains ten months after burial, and in view of the distribution of the arsenic in the organs, over two grains must have been administered within twenty-four hours of death.

Mrs. Armstrong's Will had been made in June 1917 bequeathing £50 per annum to her husband until 1933 and thereafter £100 per annum, the remainder (apart from certain minor bequests) to her children.

A new Will had been made out in Armstrong's handwriting on July 8th, 1920, bequeathing all her property to her husband, appointing him sole executor,—the children being excluded. The Will was witnessed by two of the household maids, but not in the presence of the testatrix according to law. The gross value of the estate was £2,419, net value £2,278.

Colonel W. H. Willcox, 1916.

(From "Loyalties" by Sir Arnold Wilson. Oxford University Press, 1930.)

Lt.-General Sir Stanley Maude, Army Commander, Mesopotamia, 1916–1917.

Harold Greenwood

(From The Trial of Harold Greenwood by Winifred Duke.
William Hodge & Co. Ltd.)

Mrs. Armstrong

(From Notable British Trials Series, The Trial of
Mrs. Armstrong by Filson Young. William Hodge &
Co. Ltd.)

Sir Archibald Bodkin, Director of Public
Prosecutions.

Dr. W. R. Hadwen giving evidence at Gloucester Assizes, 1924.

(By permission of the Daily Mirror, 1925.)

On his hunter "Waddy", 1926.

After presiding at the Medical Conference on Fasting and Dietetics, at Bridge of Allan, May 30th 1933. With Sir Humphry Rolleston, Lord Horder and Sir Henry Lunn (l. to r.).

Armstrong had made many purchases of arsenic supposedly for weed killing for his fairly extensive garden, his principal enemy being the dandelions, according to the prisoner's evidence given later in the trial in answer to questions by the Judge. These purchases had all been from Mr. Davies, the local chemist and father-in-law of Martin; solid and liquid weed-killers and pure arsenic between June 1919 and January 11th, 1921, the date of the last recorded purchase.

Turning to the treatment of Mrs. Armstrong in the mental hospital, the accused had pressed the Superintendent, Dr. Townsend, for her release before he deemed it medically advisable, by suggesting that, as her delusions had cleared away, she would be much happier in her own home. He succeeded in obtaining her release from hospital and psychiatric supervision. Exactly a calendar month later Mrs. Armstrong died—on February 22nd. She became so seriously ill during the last six days of her life that she lost the use of her limbs and was unable to get out of bed, evidence of some importance in contradicting the possibility of a suicidal dose of arsenic being accessible to the patient within a few days of death.

Turning to Martin's illness, the Attorney-General alluded to the correct diagnosis made by Dr. Hincks and proved by his investigation of the urine, and he also referred to the finding of arsenic in Armstrong's pocket on his arrest and to the several sources of supply in his house. He had had frequent opportunities to administer poison to his wife; some three months after his wife's death he had unsuccessfully proposed marriage to a lady of long acquaintance—(subsequent evidence in the trial did not indicate that this was a strong motive).

The three medical experts who appeared on the sixth day all agreed that a fatal dose must have been taken within twenty four hours of death, apart from repeated doses over a considerable period.

Webster's evidence was of great technical detail. He had found in the parts of the body examined three and a half grains of arsenic—a record amount in Webster's whole experience of twenty two years as an analyst in more than three hundred cases. A similar amount was found in the packet found in the prisoner's pocket on arrest, and an appreciable quantity in four bottles taken from the prisoner's house. Webster brought no arsenical mirrors, but instead merely a small tube which contained an equivalent amount of arsenic as was found in the exhumed remains.

Spilsbury and Willcox gave evidence of approximately equal duration; the former dealt mainly with the facts already mentioned, and the latter with their interpretation at the bedside.

Willcox considered that all the symptoms before and after treatment in hospital were indicative of arsenical poisoning though the earlier rheumatic symptoms of 1919 were not so caused. Due to the cessation of administration of arsenic in hospital, symptoms of neuritis cleared up; but they returned after the patient came home, presumably due to further doses of the poison. The whole illness was such that suicide could be ruled out of court.

The principal witness for the Defence was Dr. F. S. Toogood, Medical Superintendent of Lewisham Hospital and pathologist to the L.C.C. He played a similar role to that in the Greenwood trial. He considered that the illness of Mrs. Armstrong was attributable to indigestion due to gall-stones which Spilsbury had discovered in the body. The term "auto-intoxication" was used by him to explain the peripheral neuritis in life and the albumin in the urine. This term, which has fallen into unjustifiable disuse, used to be applied to the metabolic and chemical changes that occur during the course of natural diseases such as diabetes, failure of kidney function (uraemia) due to nephritis and other diseases of the kidney, and in heart failure. Together with his colleague Dr. Ainslie, he argued that the patient had auto-intoxication from gallstones and rheumatoid arthritis, though he ignored the fact that the patient had no previous complaint of joint disorders. They criticised Spilsbury's failure in investigate the joints microscopically. To be consistent with the suicide theory he postulated that arsenic was taken not later than February 16th—six days before death, at a time when Mrs. Armstrong could have procured the arsenic for self destruction. But Toogood's greatest difficulty was the explanation of Martin's illness. Having admitted the accuracy of Webster's analysis, how could the excretion of arsenic in the urine be explained? He made various suggestions. Firstly, with regard to impure bismuth, contaminated as it sometimes was with traces of arsenic. Dr. Hincks had prescribed bismuth mixture, but according to the British Pharmacopeia there would have been required more than seven thousand grains (one pound) of bismuth to yield the amount of arsenic that was found in the urine. Secondly, that Davies, a trained pharmacist, had dispatched the urine specimen in an unclean bottle, or used a cork con-taminated with arsenic. And thirdly, that as the bottle may have pre-viously contained peroxide of hydrogen, traces of arsenic could have remained over from this source. Toogood's colleague Dr. W. Ainslie went further by suggesting that the contents of the bottle might have absorbed arsenic from the glass itself. But these were theories of despair which Curtis Bennett did not pursue in his final speech.

Whereas Marshall Hall when defending Greenwood scored a point by indicating that the prosecution had not proved the administration of poison by the prisoner to his wife, in this trial Curtis Bennett did not attack the prosecution on these lines. His defence rested entirely on the theory of suicide, supported by one of the nurses who quoted a casual remark made by Mrs. Armstrong: "Would it be possible to kill oneself by jumping out of the attic window?".

The Attorney-General, replying on behalf of the Crown, claimed that the case depended on circumstantial evidence. The prosecution had endeavoured to be fair to the prisoner. He doubted if in history the pois-oned cup had ever been seen to be poisoned, and when administered had been known to have been. Poisoners would always with subtlety endeavour to cover up things that were sinister. Would the jury seriously believe Armstrong's evidence that he carefully made up twenty little packets of arsenic to kill dandelions on his lawn and have one ready in his pocket at his arrest?

After forty eight minutes, the jury found Armstrong guilty on the charge of wilfully murdering his wife and sentence of death was passed.

To Sir Henry Curtis Bennett, recalling the Greenwood trial, this was a disappointment and a surprise. Nevertheless, he fought for his client to the end. The case came to the Court of Criminal Appeal on May 11th, 1922, before the Lord Chief Justice, Mr. Justice Avory, and Mr. Justice Shearman, who had been the judge at the Greenwood trial. The hearing lasted five days and the twelve hour speech of Curtis Bennett was the longest of his career. But the appeal was dismissed. Two months after Edward Black was executed at Exeter, Armstrong suffered a similar fate at Hereford.

After the trial Willcox was asked by a doctor why a defence of insanity was not applied and an acquittal obtained by application of the McNaghten rules? He replied that he had considered and actually suggested to defence counsel that Armstrong might have suffered from General Paralysis of the Insane. But in the absence of confirmatory laboratory and clinical evidence of the disease while he was in hospital, they were not satisfied with the evidence of insanity; and in 1922 a successful plea on these grounds would have meant life imprisonment. Therefore they preferred to make a bold bid for victory. No doubt in the present permissive state of the law he would be acquitted on grounds of mental ill health and undergo a comparatively short term of treatment in a mental hospital.

The Armstrong trial was one of the best examples of the way in which the testimony of three expert witnesses—Webster, Spilsbury and Willcox in that order—was complimentary and invariably consistent throughout. The evidence of Webster dealt with facts and findings, that of Spilsbury with findings and their interpretation, while that of Willcox was of the interpretation and opinion of the facts applied to the whole truth concerning the illnesses of the victims as seen through the eyes of a practising physician.

Speaking of the Armstrong trial in his address to the Medico-legal Society in July 1922, Willcox referred to the variation of the way in which symptoms ensue after taking arsenic as a poison. "If the stomach contains food, or if food is taken within a few minutes of the poison, the onset is delayed. In the case of Martin, the poison was no doubt taken either in tea or scones or bread and butter. There was a delay of one and a half hours before the occurrence of nausea, nearly four hours before the onset of vomiting and over eight hours before diarrhoea". And to the Harveian Society in 1923, he expressed the opinion that the selection of arsenic by Black and Armstrong for use as a poison was prompted by the sensational success of its use in the case of Mrs. Greenwood in 1920.

Armstrong's chocolates were one of the macabre relics of criminal history which were shown regularly to students at St. Mary's attending lectures on Forensic Medicine. Periodically Willcox would take them with him to brighten up the interest at lectures and addresses on poisoning as for example when he addressed the Oxford University Junior Scientific Club in 1926. But at the end of twenty-five years, about six years after

Willcox's death, they had become so crumbled that they were finally destroyed by Roche Lynch.

References

"The Trial of H. R. Armstrong", by Filson Young 1922, Notable British Trials Series.
"Poison Mysteries in History, Romance and Crime", by C. J. S. Thompson, The Scientific Press, 1923.

Chapter 18

Tragedies of Diphtheria—1924
(Rex v. Hadwen et alii)

Before the First World War Willcox's name had become so closely connected with unnatural deaths, particularly those due to drugs and poison, that his evidence in court in other forensic spheres, though of great interest, tended to be quickly forgotten. Yet in the cases to be described his opinion was sought in such a way that he appeared to be in the position of a spokesman of medical opinion on behalf of the profession and a representative in court of orthodox medical practice and knowledge as taught in the medical schools. Of infectious diseases, diphtheria was one of the most serious of those which at that time were common; but the reason that it became of legal importance lay in the circumstances that it was not uncommonly a cause of sudden and unexpected death from heart failure in children. At this period Willcox gave expert evidence in court on two occasions in cases of alleged neglect in treatment. Diphtheria achieved status as a disease in 1883 and 1884 when it was described by Klebs and Loeffler, the mortality rate then being over 30%, though this was markedly reduced following the introduction of antitoxin treatment by Von Behring in 1890. This treatment was used on a wide scale from 1895 onwards with such success that by 1912 the mortality was 6.2%, and 5.1% in children between the ages of five and ten, being even less than this in cases treated in the first two days of the illness.

The case of *Rex v Jewell* in 1913 was almost a repetition of a tragedy, similar to that of the Chisholm child in 1906, and again the parents of seven-year-old Norah were Christian Scientists and therefore disbelievers in the value of orthodox medical treatment, though they had in this case already summoned and paid for Christian Science treatment from an expert before the child's death. There was no anxiety until July 13th when the child collapsed and quickly became moribund. By the time Dr. Andrew Bell arrived she was already dead. The Coroner was informed and a post-mortem showed no throat ulceration but enlarged glands in the neck and ulceration of the external genital organs from which diphtheria bacilli were cultured; they were also cultured from the throat swabs after death. At the Inquest held by Mr. George Cohen at Hornsey on August 1st, Benjamin Jewell, builder and decorator, and his wife stated that they believed that the child had mumps which was known to have affected the school which Norah attended. The triviality of the throat infection and the enlarged neck glands might have excused them as laymen for making this mistake. They were fully aware of the legal necessity for calling qualified medical aid in the case of any serious illness in their children but they had good reason for having faith in Christian

Science treatment by reason of its recent success in the case of their other child whom they had considered had had an attack of mumps. Willcox's evidence covered all aspects of the illness up to Norah's death on the twelfth day. His criticism of the parents' treatment centered round their failure to summon medical aid even though they felt sure the diagnosis was mumps. From the depositions of the inquest it seemed that the verdict of manslaughter against the father was a harsh one. Nevertheless, he was charged by order of the Director of Public Prosecutions, Sir Charles Matthews. The charge was quickly disposed of at the trial at the Central Criminal Court, presided over by Mr. Justice Rowlatt on September 8th, Bodkin and Clarke Hall appearing for the Prosecution and Kingsbury and Curtis Bennett for the Defence. Following the evidence of Dr. Bell and Dr. Johnstone, Medical Officer of Health, and during Willcox's evidence the Judge closed the case by directing the Jury to find a verdict of Not Guilty in view of insufficient evidence that the father thought that his child was seriously ill. The parents had already suffered sufficient punishment by the death of their child and the anxiety sustained by their trial.

The sudden death of a schoolboy, Howard Watson, in 1914 was a more serious matter because he was a boarder at a school kept by Mrs. Latham. At the inquest held on October 27th, suspicion of considerable neglect was found. No doctor had seen the child until after his death at the school. Nor had his parents been aware of the nature of his illness. The Medical Officer of Health had notified Mrs. Latham in June that one of her day pupils was suffering from diphtheria and again of another day pupil during the school holidays in August. Following Howard's death he fully investigated all the children at the school, having obtained positive results from throat swabs from Howard's throat after death and from one pupil whom he classified as a diphtheria "carrier" not suffering from active disease. In spite of Howard's death Dr. Bridger, the school doctor, informed the M.O.H. of a further case of diphtheria in the school whom he had not been requested to visit until three days after the onset of the illness.

Howard died suddenly and unexpectedly on the 15th day of the illness, the post-mortem showing ample signs of diphtheria with heart involvement. Willcox and his senior colleague at St. Mary's Hospital, Sir John Broadbent, were consulted by the D.P.P. with a request to produce a joint report on all the evidence. Broadbent was a noted specialist in infectious diseases serving on the staff of the London Fever Hospital. Their joint report, from all the evidence which followed the verdict of manslaughter against Mrs. Latham at the inquest, resulted in her trial at Chelmsford Assizes on February 3rd, 1915 but before this date a Conference was attended by Matthews with Richard Muir, Dr. Bridger, Dr. Pugh and Willcox on November 11th. Further meetings of Muir and Willcox took place on several occasions until December 22nd. The opinion of all the doctors, the general practitioner, the M.O.H., Broadbent, and Willcox, was that the symptoms of the patient, the difficulty in his breathing and swallowing, the nasal discharge and foetor on the tenth day of the illness should have caused Mrs. Latham to seek medical advice at an early stage, in which case the life of the boy might well have been saved by antitoxin treatment. They considered that the earlier treatment had been commenced the more likely it would have been to be successful. In the case of a school headmistress it was specially important that medical advice should have been sought whether or not she believed the child suffered from diphtheria. The success of the defence at the trial relied on the evidence that Mrs. Latham was ignorant of the fact that the deceased was seriously ill or suffered from diphtheria but considered the child had mumps. She was acquitted on all charges.

Rex v. *Hadwen*

Nowadays diphtheria is so uncommon that comparatively few doctors at present in practice in Britain have ever encountered a case, thanks to its prevention by inoculation in children. But until the Second World War every doctor in practice was on the lookout for it whenever he encountered a patient with a sore throat. Indeed he carried in his medical bag several throat swabs to investigate any suspicious sore throat.

The Hadwen trial at Gloucester in 1924 aroused exceptional publicity far beyond Gloucester both among the public and in the medical profession to which the case probably did a great deal of harm. In his whole career this was the only trial in which Willcox gave evidence for the Crown in a charge of manslaughter against a doctor. There was an inevitable clash of opinion between orthodox medical opinion and that of an experienced and senior practitioner who openly defied the teaching and belief of almost every qualified doctor in practice. The case raised the issue of the duty and obligation of a doctor to his patients according to the law and professional ethics imposed on him under the disciplinary code of the General Medical Council. The duel between Willcox and Sir Edward Marshall Hall recalled to mind the earlier one in the Seddon trial of 1912, but this case was in no way comparable because Marshall Hall won an unexpected and astonishing victory after a battle in which defeat at first seemed inevitable and fortune played a great part in the outcome. It is surprising that in his biography of Marshall Hall Marjoribanks omitted any mention of it, for Marshall Hall, the son of a doctor, was probably endowed with knowledge of medical practice to a greater degree than any other counsel then in practice. And this was a case in which he defended the right of a doctor to complete freedom in his unorthodox method of treatment even though that was likely to involve a breach in his relationship with the General Medical Council which nowadays would very probably expose him to disciplinary punishment by that body, or at any rate a claim for damages in a Court of Law.

The principal figure in the story, Dr. Walter Hadwen, was an important citizen in Gloucester, a Justice of the Peace and Chairman of the Medical Panel Committee. He held the degree of M.D. of St. Andrews, M.R.C.S., L.R.C.P., and had been in practice for many years in the town. But, more significant, he was a prominent anti-vivisectionist, being President of the British Union for the Abolition of Vivisection under whose auspices was published monthly the British Anti-Vivisection magazine called the Abolitionist. He was also a well-known opponent of vaccination but in this respect he was not alone in the profession as there has always been a considerable body of authoritative medical opinion of high repute against the policy of vaccination as a compulsory procedure. As a consequence Dr. Hadwen had a considerable following both in Gloucester and throughout the country although he had had clashes of opinion, as Marshall Hall exposed at the trial, with several of his medical colleagues in practice in the city of Gloucester.

Nellie Burnham was a ten-year-old girl in a family of four children living with their mother, the father being in America at the time of the tragedy. She was the third child in the family to suffer from sore throat being taken ill on July 30th. Leonard aged 14 and Gladys aged 4 had already been attended by Dr. Hadwen since July 19th and the remaining and oldest, Hilda aged 18, was taken ill after the death of Nellie. The Burnhams were members of a "Club" of which Dr. Hadwen was the "Club Doctor". He was called to see Nellie on August 1st, making subsequent visits on the 4th, 6th and 9th August. On the evening of the 9th the child's uncle telephoned Dr. Hadwen to say that the mother and he were not satisfied with his treatment of the child and had decided, as she was so seriously ill, to call in another doctor. This was accordingly arranged with Dr. Hadwen's consent, after which Dr. Ellis saw the child on the night of the same day, finding her gravely ill with no hope of recovery, the diagnosis being obviously severe diphtheria. She died at 1.0 a.m. on August 10th. With the mother's willing consent the Coroner was informed, a post-mortem conducted and the Inquest held on August 13th and 14th, was completed on September 12th resulting in a verdict, in which 9 out of 12 jurors concurred, that the cause of death was "diphtheria and pneumonia caused or contributed to by the failure of Dr. Hadwen to use competent skill and sufficient attention". The Coroner interpreting this probably quite correctly as a verdict of manslaughter committed Dr. Hadwen for trial. The latter appeared before the Bench of which he was a member; an adjournment being procured, bail was granted. A further adjournment was imposed by the Director of Public Prosecutions, A. H. Bodkin, pending further investigations, including a report from Willcox on the evidence obtained from the coroner's depositions and other information.

In his request for a full report the D.P.P. directed Willcox's attention to questions of medical ethics and particularly to the circumstance, afterwards taken up by the Defence in a big way, that unfortunately Dr. Hadwen had not been invited to attend the post-mortem—a point which turned out to be of major significance at the trial. He was reminded of three judicial statements as to the responsibility of medical men, the most relevant in the present case being that of *Rex* v *Spiller* as follows:—

"Any person who is a qualified medical practitioner who professes to deal with the life and health of others is bound to have competent skill to perform the task he holds himself out to perform and bound to treat his patients with care, attention and assiduity and if a patient dies for want thereof he is guilty of manslaughter".

Willcox based his opinion on the illnesses of the children on their case histories, the evidence of relatives and a neighbour who saw the child during the illness of Nellie, the evidence of Dr. Ellis, and Dr. Washbourn's account of the post-mortem. There was no doubt that the illness was diphtheria, that Hilda and Gladys were proved in hospital to have it and that the post-mortem was conclusive. He was highly critical of the handling of the illness, the cursory and inadequate examination of the patient and the failure to investigate. He concluded that Dr. Hadwen's care of the case and his views on the treatment and diagnosis of Diphtheria

"were entirely contrary to all accepted views regarding Diphtheria.... any medical practitioner holding views such as those expressed by Dr. Hadwen at the inquest is bound to fail in the diagnosis of this serious disease and by so doing not only is the life of the patient seriously endangered but also the health of the public likewise, as failure to diagnose means failure of isolation of patents who will spread the disease to others, as in this case".

On the evening before the case in the Magistrates' Court commenced Willcox was present at a conference with Prosecution Counsel Mr. St. J. Michelthwaite and Mr. Saywell at which Dr. Ellis, Dr. Washbourn, the Pathologist, and Dr. Berry, the Medical Officer of Health, were present.

The trial at Gloucester Assizes commenced on October 27th and lasted three days. It was of such interest to the medical profession that *The Lancet* published a 65-page supplement on November 8th of which medical evidence occupied nearly 27 pages and that of Willcox $10\frac{3}{4}$ pages. It was presided over by Mr. Justice (Sir Montague) Lush; Mr. C. F. Vachell led for the Crown, defending Counsel being Sir Edward Marshall Hall, helped by Mr. A. F. Clements. Dr. Ellis withstood the attack of Marshall Hall extremely well, yielding no ground on the firmness of his immediate diagnosis of diphtheria when he saw the child, the smell of her breath, the extensive throat membrane and the result of the swab. But the greater part of his cross-examination was centred on the acrimonious correspondence, both private and in the local press, between him and Dr. Hadwen which had taken place the previous year as a result of which he tendered his resignation from the panel committee. During a small outbreak of smallpox the previous year Dr. Hadwen had launched in the local press a campaign against the policy of vaccination at which his medical colleagues considered they had been maligned. Marshall Hall cleverly exposed this correspondence to the full in such a way as to demonstrate to the jury the animosity of the witness to the accused and the possible bias of his evidence. Dr. Washbourn considered the post-mortem findings showed undoubted diphtheria of the throat with involvement of the right lung. Closely questioned as to why he had not invited Dr. Hadwen to the post-mortem his valid reason was given that the Deputy Coroner, also present, had expressed the opinion that this step was unnecessary. An attempt was made to make him admit that the pneumonia had been caused by a chill caused by the patient walking downstairs barefooted resulting in a fresh infection of the lung during the course of the illness, but here again the medical evidence stood firm. Dr. Ronald Berry, the M.O.H. and superintendent of the Isolation Hospital, spoke of the children Hilda and Gladys who were proved in August to have diphtheria while under his own care in hospital. Berry was then attacked by Marshall Hall on the value of antitoxin treatment. Marshall Hall had learned of a case of Berry's in which antitoxin had been apparently unsuccessful. Sir Edward (handing to witness a name on a slip of paper): "Do you know that case which I will call A.B.?"—Witness: "Yes".

"Antitoxin was given on September 12th and over a month later the child was returned home as cured?"—"Yes".

"Five days later was the child found to be suffering from Diphtheria and afterwards her brother?"—"Yes".

"The child was taken back to hospital?"—"Yes".

"That is a strong instance of failure of antitoxin?"—"Not a bit. The child became re-infected".

"It was a fresh attack?"—"Yes".

"She was a very unlucky child?"—"Yes".

In this way Marshall Hall had cleverly cast doubts in the minds of the Jury on the fallibility of antitoxin.

Sir William Willcox's evidence lasted three hours, far longer than any other witness and was about one sixth of the total time of the trial. Questioned about his qualifications, he explained that he had had experience of diphtheria before the war as a physician, during the war as a military physician and, more recently, in his position as a physician to the London Fever Hospital. It might be thought that the whole subject could have been dealt with in 15 or 20 minutes but no aspect of diagnosis and treatment of the disease and the illness in question was omitted in the light of advances in treatment since antitoxin was first used in 1895. He had wisely come to Court armed with the relevant statistics showing the decline in mortality of the disease from 389 per million in 1893 to 71 per million in 1923. He stressed the importance of bacteriological diagnosis, daily visiting by the doctor and the early use of antitoxin. He strongly supported Washbourn's view that pneumonia in this case was diphtheritic and unrelated to a "chill" said to have been contracted during the course of the illness. Marshall Hall then digressed to discuss Hadwen's view on the value of vaccination against smallpox.

Sir Edward: "Don't you think that a medical man to go about in an epidemic of smallpox, who persistently declines to be vaccinated, must have an honest belief in what he thinks regarding vaccination?"

Willcox: "I should think so".

"There is a strong feeling amongst many doctors and the public against vaccination?"—"Yes".

He considered Hadwen's failure to diagnose, and give antitoxin, was wilful neglect. "It was his bounden duty to give it". He assured the Judge that the earlier it was given the more favourable the outcome.

To cases given it by the second or third day the mortality was reduced to about 3% compared with 30% in the untreated disease.

Marshall Hall carefully and cleverly avoided giving Willcox any opportunity of giving his opinion on the duty of a qualified doctor to his patients in accordance with the ethical code of the General Medical Council knowing what its probable damaging effect to his cause would be in the eyes of the Jury.

Dr. Hadwen's evidence must have astonished and amused those doctors who read or heard it in court. His views were entirely opposed to all orthodox views of the medical profession held by teachers in the medical schools, of whom Willcox was an example. He honestly believed that antitoxin was useless and "highly dangerous" though no explanation of the danger was given. He had never used it himself nor did he consider that others should do so but that "everyone must act according to his conscience before God"; nor did he allow "any of his patients suffering from diphtheria to be treated with antitoxin by any other medical man". "As president of the largest anti-vivisection society in the world", he continued "I urge other people to follow in the line I myself pursue". He sidetracked the value of statistics as indicating the declining mortality by comparing the treatment to the obsolete fashion of bleeding of former times. He did not believe in the bacterial cause of diphtheria (which had been discovered by Klebs of Zurich in 1883, and Loeffler of Prussia in 1884), claiming that the bacteria were the result and not the cause of the disease, nor did he believe in the germ theory of disease at all.

The Judge: "Do you think the whole medical profession has gone wrong in teaching the importance of bacterial cultivation?"—"I consider so".

"You still say the child did not die from diphtheria?"—"Certainly—the child never had a symptom of diphtheria".

This answer produced an outburst of clapping from the public which caused the Judge to warn the Court that it would be cleared if it occurred again. He might well have asked Dr. Hadwen on what grounds he would ever diagnose diphtheria because Hadwen had previously admitted that in the past he had at times done so.

Sir Edward in his peroration was brief and probably more effective for being so. He had called no witnesses for the defence as he would thereby have sacrificed his right to make the final speech before the judge's summing up. Claiming that her death was caused by a chill resulting in pneumonia contracted by the child going downstairs barefooted to get a cup of water, he asked the jury to believe they could not be "reasonably satisfied that there was wilful or culpable neglect. There had been no evidence to show that Dr. Hadwen was the sole doctor in England holding the same views about diphtheria." Drawing the minds of the Jury away from the tragedy of Nellie Burnham he then dealt with his old antagonist. "The case for the Prosecution was dependent almost entirely upon the evidence given by that most eminent man, Sir William Willcox, for whom he (counsel) had the greatest regard. But he was not in a position, however great his position might be, to come down and say there was an absolute rule of practice by all qualified men that on suspicion of diphtheria they must take a swab and inject antitoxin. He (Counsel) submitted with the greatest confidence that it would be a terrible day for this country for the medical practitioners as well as for the people who were their patients, if any such broad principle of law was laid down." "It was most unfortunate", he ended up with dramatic effect, "that the doctor called in to take Dr. Hadwen's place had been a bitter opponent in the preceding year. Had Dr. Hadwen been allowed to be present at the post-mortem many of the questions left in doubt would have been definitely and finally cleared up. It was little less than a public scandal that the Coroner should not have given Dr. Hadwen an opportunity of being present or even of being represented there."

This last point was referred to again at the conclusion of the Judge's summing up which was well balanced and fair, but not sufficiently conclusive in favour of a conviction. They, the jury, were not there, he argued, to say whether Dr. Hadwen's views were those of a wise medical man or not. Who could tell what would have happened to the patient assuming that all proper care had been taken? The disease might still have proved fatal. The Crown must prove that in all probability if care had been shown, the child would have recovered. There were many cases of negligence where death had been caused in which a person might have to pay damages but he would not be indicted for manslaughter. "I don't pass judgment on Dr. Hadwen" he concluded "but I say that a doctor may get his mind into such a state of prejudice and his judgment so blinded that he would rather sacrifice his patients than his prejudice. If such a doctor was so prejudiced that he is unwilling to avail himself of the discoveries of the profession I can understand a jury saying that he is guilty of wilful neglect".

After an absence of 20 minutes the jury recorded their verdict of "Not guilty"—received with loud cheering and handclapping which again received severe reproof from the judge. Suddenly acclaimed as a public hero, Dr. Hadwen had to be escorted by police through the excited cheering crowds of over 5,000 admirers. It was certainly a great triumph for Hadwen and Marshall Hall who had won their case against formidable medical opposition without even needing to call the medical experts in support of the Defence, who were ready and prepared to give evidence.

In considering the Prosecution's defeat it is only fair to point out that the Defence relied upon two factors in the case that arose by sheer chance. Firstly, it was by a curious chance that Mrs. Burnham chose to call Dr. Ellis in place of Dr. Hadwen to see her child on August 9th. If she had called any other doctor in the town Marshall Hall would have been unable to expose to the jury that his animosity of the previous year had probably caused him to be a biased witness—a point that was used to the full by the defence. But neither Willcox nor many others considered this to be true. Secondly, the omission by the Coroner to extend to Dr. Hadwen an invitation to the post-mortem was a curious chance happening and did not occur through any evil intention. Willcox afterwards did not consider this should have had any influence on the course of the trial though in fact it certainly did. Marshall Hall had merely to exploit these two lucky events to show the Jury that Dr. Hadwen had been treated with discourtesy—as it might have been construed by an ordinary observer. It was a trial the like of which would never occur again.

Dr. Hadwen published his comments in *The Abolitionist* of December 1st. He criticised the Coroner's Jury and the Grand Jury at the Magistrates Court; the latter had acted as a rubber stamp. "Proceedings of this nature in which responsibility is calmly delegated to other shoulders render such magisterial and grand jury functions a sheer waste of time. There is something radically wrong in the administration of English law which allows such a farce to continue while the 'prisoner' is called upon to suffer months of nervous strain and anxiety with an increasing drain on his purse. . . . The verdict has clearly shown that a conspiracy to ruin a fully qualified medical man who declines to bow down to a modern medical fashion would not be tolerated in an English Court of Law; that twelve independent men and women in the City of Gloucester (all of whom with one exception were unknown to me) can come to a unanimous decision that liberty of conscience thought and action are still the prerogative and right of every honest and intelligent Englishman and that no medical hierarchy any more than an ecclesiastical (or say a 'a religious') one will be permitted to override these principles".

A long article on the trial in the same edition by Miss Beatrice Kidd cited Sir William Willcox as Dr. Hadwen's chief opponent—he was given the honour of a separate column, "A Home Office expert sent down to ruin our President if the feat was humanly possible . . . he appeared to accept all the statements of the Burnham family and showed no sign of having considered Dr. Hadwen's own testimony . . . his evidence was really less important than that of any other person called because he had never seen Nellie Burnham either alive or dead. He is a licensed vivisector holding the worst certificates B. and E.E. enabling him to operate on cats and dogs and to keep them alive after mutilation. He was not likely to entertain any particularly friendly feeling towards the leading protagonist of anti-vivisection and his bias was unmistakeable". This was a cruel attack on Willcox, who had never mutilated cats and dogs, whose fondness for horses and dogs was well known. Such an attack would have been more aptly applied, if at all, to certain experimental physiologists engaged in whole-time research. Willcox had by now become a martyr in place of Dr. Hadwen. He made no reply to any attacks on him.

A public meeting was held on November 12th in the Shire Hall which could not contain those who had queued up. Dr. Hadwen was presented with a cheque to cover his legal expenses. The meeting ended on a religious note with the well-known hymn "Praise God from whom all blessings flow". But no prayers were offered for Mrs. Burnham and her family. The British Union for the Abolition of Vivisection held a similar meeting at Queen's Hall, London, on February 6th, 1925, at which Willcox was again the principal object of attack and which was fully reported. Many distinguished members were present; but John Galsworthy, Margaret Bondfield, Ellen Wilkinson and Bernard Shaw were unable to be present. One wonders what kind of address Shaw might have made.

This famous trial was not the first clash between the antivivisectionists and medical scientists. As early as 1892 Sir Victor Horsley (Lyons, 1966) was one of the chief speakers at a debate at the Church Congress at Folkestone on the subject "Do the interests of mankind require experiments on living animals, and if so, to what extent are they justified?" After this indecisive and heated debate there followed an acrimonious correspondence in *The Times* between Horsley and Miss Frances Cobbe, the founder of the National Antivivisection Society, on her book "Nine Circles". In 1903 the Hon. Stephen Coleridge was sued for libel by Professor W. M. Bayliss of University College Hospital after his speech at the Annual General Meeting of the Antivivisection Society, the plaintiff being awarded £2,000 damages. In 1907 the Royal Commission on vivisection commenced work. Horsley gave extensive evidence before the commission which formulated in 1912 the first regulations concerning licences for vivisection.

Diary of Mrs. Burnham's Household

July 19th. Leonard ill (aged 14).

20th. Leonard sore throat, breath offensive, bloody discharge from nose.

21st, 22nd, 23rd and 26th. Dr. Hadwen saw Leonard.

27th. Leonard recovered and ambulant.

28th. Gladys ill (aged 4). Seen by Dr. Hadwen.

29th. Gladys seen by Dr. Hadwen (breath offensive).

30th. Nellie ill (aged 10).

31st. Nellie sore throat.

August 1st. Nellie seen by Dr. Hadwen. Ulceration of throat. Three minutes, no light.

4th. Nellie discharge from nose and throat (neighbour's evidence). Seen by Dr. Hadwen.

6th. Nellie seen by Dr. Hadwen.

7th. Nellie, nasal discharge (Uncle's evidence) Nellie walked downstairs.

8th. Nellie vomited twice (mother's evidence).

9th. Nellie seen by Dr. Ellis. Diphtheria diagnosed. Vomited several times.

10th. Nellie died.

11th. Hilda admitted to hospital—diphtheria.

12th. Gladys admitted to hospital—proved diphtheria.

References

The Lancet Supplement, November 8th 1924.
"The Life of Sir Victor Horsley", by J. B. Lyons (Peter Dawney), 1966.

Chapter 19

Medical Witness—1920–1933

Income Tax Evasion

The devotion he gave to patients, and the efforts he made on their behalf in the cause of justice, were illustrated by Willcox's struggle in an unusual role from June 1920 until the next year on behalf of defending counsel, Sir Richard Muir, acting for A. H. Bradbury charged with income tax frauds. Willcox examined the patient on several occasions and gave strong supporting evidence for the defence at the Magistrates' Court, the trial at Winchester and at the Court of Appeal presided over by the Lord Chancellor. Though the accused was ill throughout these events, the defence lost the fight on his behalf at all stages in a struggle which Willcox considered, from the extenuating circumstances alone, ought to have been won.

Bradbury was a director of the coal merchant firm of A. H. Bradbury and Sons, whose Head Office was in London and registered office in Southampton. With his co-director Bryder he was charged before the magistrates at Southampton on June 11th for conspiring to evade income tax by declaring false returns. The day before the case came to court Bradbury was examined by Willcox and Dr. Frost, his personal doctor; a joint report was to the effect that he suffered from high blood pressure with kidney disease and chronic bronchitis. In spite of this the case lasted nine days and he was committed for trial at Winchester Assizes on July 12th, Bryder being acquitted on all charges. Willcox again saw him before the trial and a similar report stressed that his state of health was serious. He was convicted at Winchester and sentenced to two years imprisonment, in spite of Muir's efforts and Willcox's pleas for mitigation of sentence. It appeared that Bradbury had been under the care of Dr. Frost since 1907. Owing to his ill health the managing director of the firm had dealt with the income tax affairs of the firm and the personal tax of the accused. It transpired that there was a large margin of discrepancy between his actual personal income returned and that which he actually received from the firm, of which Bradbury claimed ignorance. Pleas of ill health and consequent inability to be held responsible for the mistakes of the Managing Director were unsuccessful at the trial. Willcox saw the patient again on October 7th; his health was worse and his heart affected. The Appeal, held next day, was unsuccessful; his sentence was not reduced to less than two years in the second division. Until the last few moments of the summing up it was hoped that at least a reduction of six months would be granted in view of the reparation that had been made and the assistance the accused had given to the authorities. The Court considered it was so bad a case that they were unable to do this in as much as he had been found guilty on all the fourteen counts, each of which could have carried a sentence of two years hard labour. Bradbury was imprisoned at Winchester and later at Wormwood Scrubs. The poor man had already been punished enough through financial worry and the expense of litigation. While awaiting the appeal he had written to Willcox describing attacks of increasing angina and chronic bronchitis:—"With regard to what I mentioned (Oct 7th) about my nerves, it must be remembered what I have gone through largely owing to Edlin's (the managing director) folly. An invalid living at Bournemouth, I have had to stand two trials, seen our splendid business brought nearly to the edge of ruin and our name dragged in the dirt, my home wrecked, and my wife and my children's future socially ruined. It has cost me already over £10,000 to defend these actions and, as you know, although entirely innocent, owing to the action of the judge at Winchester, I was sentenced to two years imprisonment for doing things which I knew nothing whatever about. Consequently, you may imagine the state in which even a strong man's nerves would be, suffering under awful injustice as I am". Willcox wrote to the prison doctor at Winchester in November stressing the gravity of his state of health and his poor outlook, a heart attack (coronary thrombosis) or stroke being likely at any time. The Judge had ordered that Bradbury be placed in the infirmary at Winchester and it was only by Willcox's special request that he was permitted to wear his own dressing gown and underclothing. In January 1921 Willcox interviewed Sir Ernley Blackwell, Legal Adviser to the Home Office, and Sir Edward Troup, urging his release from Wormwood Scrubs on medical grounds. Though his efforts were unavailing, his prognosis was accurate for Bradbury died in prison later, but meanwhile Willcox's final approach in writing took the form of a stern reproof.

"February 5th, 1921.   40 Welbeck Street, W.1.
Dear Sir Ernley Blackwell,

You will remember my calling to see you and Sir Edward Troup on January 22nd, concerning the prisoner Bradbury serving sentence at Wormwood Scrubs. I was rung up tonight by the M.O. of the prison saying that Bradbury was unconscious and suffering from a cerebral (brain) haemorrhage, which he considered was due to the mental disturbance caused by his long confinement. Should he recover from this attack (which is doubtful) I am most strongly of the opinion that immediate release is his only chance of survival. A second attack will certainly follow unless he has the necessary quietude which his removal home would ensure. The urgency of the case has compelled me to write to you personally. I anticipated that this complication would arise in Bradbury's case in view of the very serious arterial disease from which he is suffering.

Yours sincerely,

W. H. Willcox."

Sir Richard Muir's biographer, Sidney Felstead, commented (1927) on Muir's view that the result of the case was a "disgraceful miscarriage of justice. The defendant was a dying man and, even in the face of strong evidence from Sir William Willcox to that effect, the judge sentenced the prisoner to the maximum term of two years . . . a most severe punishment, because it meant confinement in a cell with only an hour's exercise a day." What affected the mind of the judge, Muir facetiously observed, was the fact that, in consequence of the frauds, the judge might have to pay a fraction of a penny extra income tax; though he was known to have been wealthy he was reputed to be the meanest man on the Bench. Sir Richard fought the sentence up to the bitter end but failed to obtain any mitigation at the Court of Criminal Appeal where the learned judges told him that, if his client was in the bad state suggested by Sir William Willcox, then the Home Secretary could order the release of the prisoner whenever his health demanded it. A good example of "passing the buck". This was finally done too late, for Willcox proved correct. After spending over six months in prison poor Bradbury passed away at Wormwood Scrubs whilst the order for his release was lying at the Home Office waiting to be despatched to the Prison Governor.

His resignation from the post of Analyst to the Home Office meant that Willcox could devote more time to his hospital work and practice; less time was spent at inquest attendances than was the case before the war. His medico-legal work became far wider in scope, being more often concerned with living problems than dead certainties, to quote a saying of a famous surgeon. He often became involved in litigation connected with non-fatal illnesses; claims for damages and compensation cases figure prominently in these. His reputation for well-balanced impartiality and freedom from bigotry of any kind lent added weight to his opinion and testimony as the years passed. Some of the cases dealt with between 1921 and 1930 will be described, in which his influence in the Law resulted sometimes in success, but often in failure. But at the same time as the medico-legal work was going on, his practice grew, sometimes more than he would have wished. The work of a consulting physician in practice, being necessarily private and confidential, cannot be exposed to public view, yet during those years the individual care of patients gave him more anxiety than appearances in courts of law. His absence from London for more than a few days often led to accumulation of patients. This was well shown during the Armstrong trial (1922) which kept him away at Hereford for ten days. He arrived in London at 3.30 a.m., got a few hours sleep, and had thirteen consultations on that day, although in the normal course of events five or six would have been the usual number on days when there were no hospital engagements. Some of these patients, many of whom were well-known persons in all walks of life, required detailed care in nursing homes. Often, interruption of his holiday in the New Forest was called for by doctors who particularly required his attendance on patients. One of these patients was King Feisal of Iraq who came to England for medical treatment for amoebic dysentery in August 1925. His health had been seriously impaired as a result of the hardship endured during four years in military campaigns in Syria before being crowned King. He remained under treatment until November, when he departed to Aix-les-Bains for convalescence.

Coroners and Death Certification

In 1908 Willcox had been one of the medical members, together with Sir Malcolm Morris, of the Departmental Committee to enquire into the law in relation to the functions of the coroner and to make amendments to the Coroners' Act of 1887. Among the recommendations were changes whereby the coroner could cancel the inquest in cases in which he was satisfied that death was natural, if the post-mortem findings justified such a procedure. The jury were no longer required to inspect the body, except at the coroner's discretion. The fees to medical men were raised to a fairer level, and for the first time the disqualification for medical officers in hospital from receiving fees was removed. The coroner, in the case of death during anaesthesia, was excused the duty of holding an inquest if he was satisfied that due care and skill had been used, though of course such deaths still had to be reported to him. Again, in 1923 Willcox was a member of the Committee to consider death and cremation certification. A few months earlier, at a meeting of cremation authorities at Guildhall, he had criticised the system of certification as an insufficient safeguard against homicide by poisons. The Committee formulated the present day death and cremation certificate brought into use by the Coroner's Law and Death Certification (Amendment) Bill, passed through Parliament in 1923, which came into force in January 1924. The fees payable to the doctors were clarified; for a report by a medical practitioner to the coroner, half a guinea; for attendance at an inquest, one guinea; and for a post-mortem, two guineas. The 1968 schedule approved by the B.M.A. for corresponding work is one and a half guineas, four guineas, and five guineas, respectively.

Was Chlorine the cause of Death?

Four months before the Armstrong trial commenced at Hereford, Willcox had attended an inquest in that town concerning the death of a foreman miller at the Hereford Steam Flour Mills. The request came from the firm of Henry Simon Ltd. which had installed the chlorination plant, to protect the firm from litigation which might have arisen should the verdict have been critical of the efficiency or danger of the plant. The active agent employed in the flour maturing process was chemically pure chlorine gas, electrically produced. The maturing process of the flour, as carried out at that time, consisted in acidifying the flour so as to improve its gluten content and eradicate its yellow colour. The cylinders of chlorine and the control plant at the Mill were of the latest type; the former were fitted with the safest type of valve, and the latter was considered foolproof. Two months before Leach's death a defective gas cylinder had been supplied.

Leach, who had many years before suffered from asthma, first became ill in mid-May 1921 with recurrent bronchitis and asthma, which did not incapacitate him until October 4th. From then on he did not leave his house. Though the evidence at the inquest showed that he had been exposed to fumes of the gas from the leaking cylinder for only two days at the beginning of August, both he and his wife later claimed that the illness was caused by chlorine gas. His doctor had been consulted on August 24th; he called in a heart specialist who diagnosed asthma and heart failure. In view of the claims of the patient and his wife, his death on November 18th was reported to the coroner. The post-mortem, carried out by the doctor and Dr. T. H. Oliver, showed heart failure due to disease of the heart muscle, but how far was chlorine gas responsible? Dr. Oliver considered that death, though due to heart failure, was accelerated by exposure to chlorine. Willcox expressed, at the resumed inquest, his firm belief, based on his experience of chlorine in gas warfare at the Dardanelles, that chlorine would have had an immediate serious effect on the patient, whereas in this case there was no immediate incapacity, nor was the millwright working in the same atmosphere adversely affected. The removal of the victim from exposure to such a low concentration in the mill would cause such effects to cease. The post-mortem findings showed dilatation of both sides of the heart, and diseased coronary arteries, which he considered was alone the cause of death. The verdict was death due to natural causes, with a rider that chlorine might have accelerated death. The Hereford papers made a special feature of Willcox's evidence, a headline reading "Suggestions of fatal chlorine gas disposed of at inquest". The Home Office factory inspector agreed with the verdict. In this case Willcox acted as an unbiased referee in arriving at a decision in the face of conflicting evidence.

Sometimes Willcox's opinion was instrumental in solving a legal conundrum without the necessity of litigation. During his career he must have saved an enormous amount of expenditure in courts of law, however much the barristers' pockets may have suffered in the process. The case of H. J. Bailey was such a case.

Willcox was approached by the Registrar of the Institute of Chemistry to report on the cause of his death—was it attributable to hydrogen sulphide, or not? If the answer was "yes", then his widow would be entitled to a full widow's pension. Bailey was an inspector of factories, under the Alkali Works Regulations Act, in Wales and part of Yorkshire. On April 4th, 1929, he inspected the Silkstone Chemical Works at Barnsley, and was taken ill soon after inspecting a tank; two workmen had already suffered from exposure to gas after cleaning a tank. The following day he was seen by a doctor, but carried on working for a week, completing his tour on April 16th. He died from a brain haemorrhage about six hours after arriving home. Post-mortem investigation showed no evidence of an ordinary source of brain haemorrhage, but the organs, particularly the liver, showed evidence of toxic changes. Considering the history of the illness there was no doubt death was consistent with hydrogen sulphide poisoning contracted on April 4th. With the help of Willcox's report, Bailey's widow was awarded a pension of £133 per annum and a gratuity to the children, following the application by the Ministry of Health to the Treasury—an award which was deemed "a most gratifying result" by the ministry officials.

The Bleaching of Flour

In September 1924 Willcox was approached by the National Association of Millers to advise regarding the use of bleaching and "improving" methods of millers in preparation of flour for bakers of bread. His evidence in the case of *Hutchinson* v. *Flour Oxidising Co.* in the Chancery Court in 1909, and a similar case in 1912 in support of the methods in current use, showed that his opinion and research experience mentioned in a previous chapter, would again be a valuable support at the Departmental Committee to be held at the Ministry of Health "to enquire whether and to what extent the practice of treating flour with chemical substances is objectionable on grounds of health, and whether it is desirable in the interests of public health that the practice should be prohibited or restricted, and in the latter case what restriction should be imposed". This inquiry was a prolonged affair and had arisen as a result of attacks in the press on the current methods of treatment of flour by millers throughout the country. In his evidence at the inquiry in March 1925, Willcox's opinion was unchanged—that the current methods in use were still quite safe, so long as the use of nitrites and chlorine was carried out with care, and subject to Government inspection. During the inquiry, further animal experiments were designed by Willcox and Roche Lynch, and carried into effect by Roche Lynch on a more elaborate scale than had been done in 1909—the results being substantially the same. It was apparent that, in order to produce at all times of the year a flour having the uniform appearance and baking properties demanded by the bakers and the public, one or other method of treatment in use at the time was desirable.

Willcox's kindness and sympathy for patients was often extended after death to their widows and other dependent relatives. His struggles for those suffering hardship became widely known, for he often lent the weight of his authority in support. Two examples will be quoted here.

A doctor who had been in practice in Leicestershire before the First War was well known to Willcox professionally. He died in 1923 of pneumonia, possibly caught from a patient. As a result of four years' service in France, he returned home so debilitated that Willcox considered him unfit to return to his practice, but had succeeded in getting him a post at the Ministry of Pensions. Further endeavours were made by him to obtain for the widow a generous pension at her appeal, heard before the tribunal in 1925, which failed in spite of Willcox's report that the doctor's death had been indirectly caused by the debility resulting from military service at the front.

The other case was that of a dentist who had served in the Army Dental Corps since 1916, at first in France, later in England since 1920. He served a statutory period of three years in China, submitting his intention to resign at the end of the period. He was court-martialled in Hong Kong for appearing late on duty and being unfit for duty owing to excessive drinking. The sentence of dismissal from the service was not upheld by the G.O.C., but referred to the War Office. But the sentence was confirmed and promulgated by the War Office in November 1925. Willcox's report to his solicitor was made after studying all the relevant documents and evidence before the court martial. The medical history revealed successive periods of ill health attributable to attacks of malaria and influenza requiring hospital admission on several occasions. Willcox's report was instrumental in persuading the War Office to rescind the findings of the court martial, thus saving the honour and reputation of the dentist; and his lawyer's plan to submit an appeal to the King was no longer required.

The year 1927 began on a sad note with the unexpected deaths, both from influenzal pneumonia, of two great figures in the medico-legal world whose loss left a great gap in Willcox's life. First, the Senior Home Office Analyst, John Webster, with whom he had been associated ever since the day when they trained as analysts together at Guy's under Stevenson. They had co-operated in many complicated investigations, notably those to do with the trials of Seddon, Greenwood, Black and Armstrong. As an expert chemist, not medically qualified, Webster preferred his work in the laboratory to the duties of an expert witness and for years escaped unwanted publicity more successfully than any of his medico-legal colleagues. In his obituary in *The Times* Willcox wrote of his brilliant analytical technique, his musical talents as an organist, and of "his shy and retiring disposition. The publicity of many causes célèbre did not appeal to him at all. He was one of the most loyal and charming colleagues".

Within a month Willcox's old friend and antagonist Sir Edward Marshall Hall died likewise from influenzal pneumonia. He had been grossly overworked for a long period and had fought against the illness, unaware how lethal it could be at a time in history when there were no antibiotics. He was a tired man, worn out by his own success. Willcox had been cross-examined by him for the last time about two weeks before, at a police court in Wales, in the case of a boy accidentally killed by electrocution by a wire fence surrounding land owned by defendants for whom Marshall Hall appeared, a case in which the relatives of the deceased boy launched a prosecution for manslaughter. Willcox was made to admit that, as death was caused by the electric current of so low a voltage as was used here, it was a very exceptional occurrence indeed; but unexpectedness in electric shock was a very important factor. Sir Edward commented "It is like funk in a case of an influenza epidemic, is it not? It probably kills more people than influenza itself." The casual comment was remarkable, in view of the sequel. They never met again, for Willcox did not attend him in his final illness. His death brought back vivid memories of their association in so many notable trials since 1911—Seddon, Alabaster, G. J. Smith of the "Brides in the Bath" case, Greenwood and Hadwen. Marshall Hall had been the most formidable advocate in his time at the Bar. Willcox had suffered the loss of an antagonist whose challenge had always been stimulating and enjoyable, a friend beyond the confines of the Law.

Suspected Arsenical Poisoning

Arsenical poisoning had become quite a common topic of conversation at the period following the Greenwood, Armstrong and Black trials in the 1920's. Perhaps it was no surprise to Willcox that he should from time to time be consulted for his opinion in cases of suspicious deaths as to whether arsenical poisoning was the cause; often these requests came, not from coroners or doctors, but from relatives of the deceased. Nevertheless, these cases were often difficult to handle, especially the elderly psychical widow who consulted him in 1928, suspicious that she was being poisoned by various people including her daughter, who did her shopping out of pure kindness. She had many delusions of persecution; even after Roche Lynch's negative report of the analysis of her urine for poisons was read to her she continued to pester Willcox's secretary, Miss Hutcheson, for further appointments which were firmly and politely refused.

The following year a lengthy committee meeting was held at Welbeck Street concerning the illness and death of a wealthy middle-aged business-man who died after a long illness of a puzzling kind. The brother of the deceased developed suspicions that he had been poisoned by his wife, noting that his condition had often relapsed when he was visited by her. He also suspected her of poisoning her father-in-law the previous year. Willcox was asked, and agreed, to act as chairman of a committee to investigate the whole illness. All the doctors who attended the deceased for a period of several years were present, including Lord Dawson of Penn; Dr. W. J. Adie, and Dr. (later Sir) Gordon Holmes, the distinguished neurologists; Dr. Porter Phillips and Dr. J. C. Woods, psychiatrists, Dr. Eidenow and Dr. Snowman, the patient's general practitioner. There was unanimous agreement that the illness was a physical one secondary to melancholia and mental depression, with no evidence of death due to poisoning.

The difficulty which doctors encounter in deciding whether death is natural or otherwise arose in the strange case of 53 year-old Mrs. Llewellyn in 1928. Acute arsenical poisoning simulates natural disease so closely that certainty can only be arrived at with the help of the analyst; even then expert opinion is often required before homicidal poisoning becomes a matter of genuine suspicion in the eyes of the law. These cases present features simulating gastro-enteritis, neuritis and even mental derangement. In his address to the students at Cambridge in 1925 Willcox taught that many cases of arsenical poisoning escaped recognition during life and that victims were buried, a death certificate having been signed certifying natural disease.

By a curious and interesting chance Mrs. Llewellyn's death occurred only a few miles away from Greenwood's home. She and her second husband, whom she had married in 1925, lived at Llanelly in Carmarthenshire. She died on June 13th, 1928, after four days of an illness closely resembling gastro-enteritis. But her doctor, Dr. T. R. Davies, no doubt familiar with the Armstrong and Greenwood cases in Wales several years before, had already suspected arsenical poisoning as early as April, when he was unable to understand why she had had repeated attacks of gastro-enteritis since the end of the previous year. By a curious chance he had been a student at St. Mary's Hospital and a "clerk" of Willcox's firm; which explains perhaps how he came to be on the look-out for examples of arsenical poisoning. The patient had developed rheumatoid arthritis in May 1926 and came under his care in July. The doctor's careful survey of symptoms in April caused him to arrange an analysis of urine for arsenic by the county analyst; the finding of arsenic to the extent of 0.6 mg per litre confirmed his suspicion. Her somewhat unexpected death naturally and correctly caused him to report the death to the coroner as a case of suspected arsenical poisoning. He was ordered to carry out a post-mortem examination which was also attended by the deceased's stepson Dr. Llewellyn, a doctor in practice some miles distant.

Mrs. Llewellyn had become crippled with arthritis and confined to her home for some weeks; she also suffered from long standing kidney trouble. The changes found in the organs were, he considered, consistent with arsenical poisoning. But the heart and kidneys were also seriously diseased, and the condition of dropsy was obvious. He carefully preserved specimens for analysis, including peritoneal (ascitic) fluid. The amount of arsenic analysed in the organs and the fluid was so small (0.9 mg), almost infinitesimal, that arsenic as a cause of death in a patient with advanced heart and kidney trouble was a matter of doubt in the mind of the coroner, though not in the opinion of Dr. Davies, who firmly believed all along that arsenical poisoning had occurred. No doubt his suspicions were confirmed by other circumstances. Mrs. Llewellyn had taken out a Life Assurance Policy for £500 in 1926, her medical examination having been conducted by himself. There had been some discord and unpleasantness among her relatives, her son and daughter having strongly opposed their mother's second marriage.

The inquest on June 15th, 1928 revealed that she was fond of fish, of which she consumed more than an average amount, likewise of stout. Dr. Scholberg, senior pathologist of Cardiff, considered that death was due to natural causes. There was no doubt in his mind that the small amount of arsenic found was taken in the food or drink she had consumed; small amounts of arsenic were sometimes found in the urine of healthy persons for this reason, and certain fish contained an appreciable amount of arsenic. The inquest was adjourned pending further enquiries.

Willcox was frequently consulted by doctors in doubt in cases of suspected poisoning and other cases with obscure features. A few days after the trial of Mrs. Pace ended (July 11th) he received a letter from Dr. Davies seeking advice concerning details of the analyses and their significance. Willcox replied briefly, sending him reprints of his writings on the subject. By another interesting chance, the solicitor acting for the brothers of Mrs. Llewellyn was Mr. Ludford, well known to Willcox as Greenwood's solicitor in 1920. After the second adjournment of the inquest pending further analyses of the organs. Willcox was consulted by Dr. Davies and Mr. Ludford at Welbeck Street. Willcox's report to the coroner led to the final stage of the inquiry and completion of the inquest at

Llanelly, which resulted in a verdict of death from natural causes. The report supported the opinion of Scholberg to the effect that certain fish and other articles of food, such as glucose in beer, had been shown to contain sufficient arsenic to account for arsenic in the urine as great as was found in the case of Mrs. Llewellyn's specimen taken in April. If a fatal dose of arsenic had been taken four days before death, he would have expected much more arsenic to have been found in the body than was the case here; the analysis of the peritoneal fluid would likewise have revealed a greater amount, whereas it was, in fact infinitesimal. The arsenic analysed could all be account for by the food eaten and by the stout and other drinks taken. He considered the case of historical importance as being the first in his experience in which the occurrence of arsenic in ordinary food and drink had aroused problems of medico-legal importance. Willcox was fortunate in that he was not summoned to the inquest, for his report brought little satisfaction to the brothers and sister of Mrs. Llewellyn. The sister protested in court that she knew her sister had been poisoned. But even if this opinion was correct, Willcox, having little knowledge of the circumstantial evidence, nevertheless was well aware that there was clearly insufficient evidence to justify a verdict of death from arsenical poisoning, or to justify advising the Director of Public Prosecutions to launch a prosecution with any hope of success, at any rate on the scientific evidence.

" The Well of Loneliness "

The Director of Public Prosecutions, Sir Archibald Bodkin, sought Willcox's advice on an unusual subject in November 1928; it was the only occasion he agreed to report an opinion on public morality. He would have been the last person to make any official public statements on such subjects unless specifically asked to do so, unless the subject was of medical importance, as was clearly the case here. The well-known novel by a famous author, Miss Radcliffe Hall, had been published earlier in the year, being widely reviewed in the press, including *The Daily Telegraph*, *The Times* and its Literary Supplement. In the form of fiction it was a plea for the toleration of Lesbianism by an authoress who was herself an invert. Had she been an unknown authoress the publicity might have been avoided; the novel certainly would not have sold so successfully on the Continent as it did.

The book had been condemned by the Chief Magistrate, Sir Charles Biron, at Bow Street on November 9th, 1928, as "indecent, obscene and corruptive", under the Obscene Publications Act of 1857. The Senior Treasury Counsel Eustace Fulton appeared for the Director of Public Prosecutions, while Norman Birkett was leading Counsel for Jonathan Cape Ltd. the publishers.

The Act of 1857 provided procedure whereby the police were authorised to search for and seize obscene literature; and then in due course, subject to the magistrates' decision, the objectionable literature could be destroyed. Norman Birkett was allowed to produce only one of forty witnesses he had lined up to give evidence in spite of his submission—Mr. Desmond McCarthy. But the Chief Magistrate ruled their evidence as inadmissible in law and closed the hearing by declaring that the book was an obscene libel and would tend to corrupt those into whose hands it would fall. The order for seized copies to be destroyed was then made. Twenty guineas costs were awarded against each of the two defendants.

Willcox was not only asked for his opinion by the Director of Public Prosecutions, Sir Archibald Bodkin, but was requested to submit names of other medical authorities suitable to appear with him at the Appeal at the Quarter Sessions concluded on December 14th. The whole subject of Lesbianism was of medical concern. "I do not desire that the proceedings", wrote Bodkin, "which I regard as of extreme public importance, should be of the character of a literary debate, but I want to be able to call some gentlemen of undoubted experience and position who can inform the Court of the results to those unfortunate women who have proclivities towards Lesbianism, or those women who indulge in them, results which are destructive morally, physically and mentally."

Willcox suggested seeking the opinion of Sir Farquhar Buzzard, the distinguished neurologist, who had just been appointed Regius Professor of Medicine at Oxford. Buzzard took a keen interest and gave his opinion privately to Bodkin, but declined the invitation to appear at the Appeal. This was at the time of King George V's serious illness. He was naturally reluctant, as a doctor known to have attended the King, to appear in Court in a case of that nature with all its attendant publicity. Another suggested expert, a well known psychiatrist, declined the offer for the simple reason that he had attended the authoress professionally. Eventually four medical experts were lined up to give evidence at the Appeal—Willcox, Dr. Maurice Wright, and Dr. Leatham Birley (psychiatrists) and Miss Lilian Barker, governor of Borstal Institution for Girls. Rudyard Kipling, whom Bodkin consulted as a literary expert, was more vehement in condemnation of the book than the medical experts. "Poisonous, pernicious and damnable" were the adjectives he applied to the book. "Have those who propose to allow the circulation of the book any daughter of their own, and would they like them to read and discuss the book? It is not a scientific subject for those genuinely desirous to study the subject, but a novel to be widely circulated . . . The book is not a romance dealing with 'affinity of souls' or any such rubbish."

Willcox read the book from cover to cover, making numerous annotations. He allowed his own children to read it, but they were perhaps still too young to comprehend the nature of sex aberrations or to appreciate the vice in its pages. His report was a personal one, not prompted by any outside influence or consultation with his colleagues in accordance with his usual practice before appearing in court. It is worth quoting, as it was not only brief but the only official evidence of its kind which he submitted in his whole career. "In my opinion there is no doubt that the book is obscene, indecent and unfit for publication in this country. It advocates the toleration and social recognition of a form of vice known as Lesbianism practised by inverts. The description of this practice, written in carefully veiled language in good literary style, can leave no doubt whatever as to its meaning. It is a form of unnatural vice known for thousands of years and fully described in medico-legal works. It is well known to have debasing effects on those practising it, of a mental, physical and moral character. It leads to nervous instability and in some cases to suicide. If widespread, it becomes a danger to a nation. It is antisocial. If practised by a partner of a normal marriage it usually leads to the unhappiness of the normal union, and often to the dissolution of the marriage. Its practice would corrupt a pure friendship. The publication of the book would involve risk of its being read by large numbers of innocent people who might, out of pure curiosity, be led to discuss openly, and even practise, this form of vice. There would be a danger that readers would become addicts to an unnatural vice though they were not themselves inverts. The book advocates the social recognition of inverts and the vice they practise. On these counts it is a most dangerous publication which would result in Lesbianism becoming more common in this country than it is. If publication be permitted on legal authority, the country would be flooded with other works of an obscene and indecent character. It would be a social and national disaster."

The other witnesses mentioned above gave evidence of a more detailed and technical kind, but their conclusions were almost exactly similar.

The decision of the Magistrate at Bow Street was upheld at the Appeal at Quarter Sessions where the Chairman, Sir Robert Wallace, described the book as "most dangerous and corrupting". It was a notable defeat for Birkett. Nor did he forget it easily, for in 1959, thirty years later, he moved the second reading of the Obscene Publications Bill in the House of Lords with success, supported by the opinions of a large body of authoritative literary experts, one of several changes in the law which the Bill contained being the right of authors and publishers to give evidence in Court on the ground that they were defending their literature against the charge of obscenity (Life of Lord Birkett of Ulverston p. 584). Another change in the law has been the sanction by both Houses of Parliament of publication of any kind of literature for a permissive society *provided it is deemed to be of sufficient literary merit.*

Alcohol and Motoring

The dangers of alcoholism to the individual health and the community were often expressed in Willcox's addresses and lectures. He was a member of the B.M.A. Committee on Drunkenness in 1926, and became President of the Society of Inebriety, though himself a moderate consumer of both spirits and wines. But he had the broadest possible outlook on the use of alcohol to the healthy individual and did not advocate prohibition or abstention to his friends, his patients or his own family. But between the two world wars there was far less traffic on the roads than now, the speed of traffic was slower, fatal accidents much rarer, and the standard of driving higher, though driving tests had not yet been established. Where non-fatal accidents occurred he was often eager to search for extenuating circumstances in an accused individual before assuming he was drunk in charge of a car. Such was the case of a 34-year-old man charged at Bow Street following an accident on New Year's Eve in 1925. Though the policeman involved and the police surgeon considered him drunk, Sir James Purves Stewart, the distinguished neurologist, saw him at the Police Station in the early hours; he already knew him as a patient whom he had treated for a nervous breakdown in 1922; he attributed his symptoms to his nervous condition, coupled with his poor eyesight and the mental "shock" occasioned by the accident. This opinon was supported by that of Willcox. The man had had a distinguished war career in the Canadian Army in France as a private soldier, and was gassed at Ypres. He gained rapid promotion to sergeant-major and finally to colonel, served on the Somme and was wounded. He later returned to duty, was awarded the M.C. and Croix de Guerre, being wounded and gassed a second time. It was no doubt his excellent record, and his state of mental ill-health following his distinguished service that got him off the charge of being drunk in charge of a car, though he was fined £10 with £15 costs for driving to the danger of the public and disqualified from driving from twelve months.

More serious was the case in November 1928 which brought Willcox to the Old Bailey to give evidence for the prosecution of Cecil Kent on a charge of drunkenness while in charge of a car. A pedestrian might easily have been killed, and Kent convicted of manslaughter had he died. As it was he was admitted to hospital unconscious with a broken leg.

Evidence was produced to show that Kent's driving had been seen to be extremely erratic. His counsel, Sir Henry Curtis Bennett, based his unsuccessful defence on the fact that, not only had Kent been in the habit of taking medinal for some time, but the accident followed soon after a dose had been taken. Willcox's opinion was to the effect that "if medinal was taken after a certain amount of alcohol it would tend to accentuate the symptoms of alcoholism such as unsteadiness of gait and thickness of speech, but it would not be the cause of these symptoms."

Willcox's next appearance at the Old Bailey, on January 21st, 1931, was in defence of a thirty-one-year-old Captain R.A. committed for trial on charges of manslaughter and of being drunk in charge of a car. The accident was complicated by being a double one. The victim, a schoolmistress, had already been knocked down and seriously injured by a motor cycle near Woolwich Barracks, an ambulance had been summoned and first aid was being administered in the roadway alongside the parked ambulance. The captain, unable to see the injured woman lying in the road among a crowd of onlookers, accidentally struck the victim, dragging her a distance of several yards, causing further injuries, fractured ribs and collarbone. The Captain passed his test for drunkenness with flying colours, the local doctor later being praised by Willcox in his testimony for the very thorough examination of the accused. The captain had been able to walk steadily for twenty minutes to the police station. He admitted having dined well with his parents at Epsom, taking a whisky before dinner, two tots with the meal, and a glass of port afterwards. The evidence of witnesses, and Willcox's opinion, indicated that the most serious injuries were almost certainly due to the first accident and were themselves likely to be fatal. In his evidence Willcox was given the opportunity of saying that he considered it dangerous to treat a patient on the road at night and that the second accident should never have been allowed to occur. With this view both judge and jury agreed. The accused was found not guilty. The jury's rider was that there was negligence on the part of the ambulance authorities and that steps should be taken to prevent similar occurrences in the future.

Criminal Abortion

The trial of a female abortionist "Dr." Hannah Brown and her male associate Bacon in 1928 was memorable in several respects. It was the last case in which Willcox gave evidence in court in a case of criminal abortion. He had of course given evidence in many cases of this kind, particularly before the war. Two cases, those of *Rex* v *Lowry* (1906) and *Rex* v. *W. O. Smith* (1910) were almost exactly similar and resulted in convictions. The case was reported to the Home Office by Dr. Marie Stopes, famous for her birth control clinics. It was the last case in which Sir Travers Humphreys as Treasury Counsel appeared before he was made a judge on the retirement of Lord Avory. He had received news of his promotion during the course of the proceedings, was allow but ed to complete his part in the trial. Willcox was his last witness in the trial which occupied four days at intervals between January 31st and February 16th, 1928. "You were truly in at the death", Travers Humphreys wrote to him on February 20th, "as you were the last witness I ever called. In fact I knew of my approaching severance from the Bar and came down on Thursday to the C.C.C. in order to have a good finish up." The expert medical evidence was conclusive here.

Bodkin, as Director of Public Prosecutions, had consulted Willcox at the end of June after receiving the report of Roche Lynch concerning the nature of the "remedies" advertised for women, Travers Humphreys requiring Willcox's opinion on the dangers of the remedies, aloes and quinine, in the doses used. Mechanical agents being also part of the treatment, the opinion of the well-known gynaecologist Malcolm Donaldson was also obtained. Willcox and Roche Lynch entirely agreed that the doses used for women in pregnancy would be dangerous, and especially in conjunction with the mechanical methods employed, they were likely to terminate pregnancy; and here they were intentionally given for this purpose "The case is not a strong one" Willcox wrote to Bodkin, "but some years ago I had two cases (1906 and 1910) very similar to this, in which convictions were obtained. Opinion seems to have altered somewhat in recent years on the question of abortion; in fact some of the leading gynaecologists hold what are, I think, distinctly illegal views, to judge from what they say at medical society meetings." The three experts gave evidence at the South London Police Court before Christmas, and at the Old Bailey in February, when Curtis Bennett defended. Willcox was the last witness called by Treasury Counsel in his last case at the Bar, which ended in a memorable victory.

In support of a Surgeon

Generally speaking the public have always been appreciative of the potential skill of the surgeon in life saving emergency operations. But this is not always the case. Sometimes a surgeon has been expected to sacrifice his fee on the grounds that the patient or relative considers the operation has been performed unnecessarily or he may even be sued for damages even though a little medical knowledge would indicate that the operation was not only necessary but even life-saving. Willcox attended such a case in March 1930 when he was called into consultation by a West End doctor to see a seven-year-old girl suffering from tonsillitis complicated by double mastoid infection. A distinguished ear surgeon successfully operated on the mastoids and the girl made an excellent recovery after rather a stormy illness, in the days before antibiotics had been dreamed of. Nevertheless, the patient's father not only resented payment of the surgeon's fee but planned to counterclaim for damages of a sum of over £200 for the expenses involved in the operation on the grounds that it was totally unnecessary. The surgeon, with Willcox's support, successfully called the bluff of the patient's father. Willcox's firmly expressed opinion was to the effect that, had the operation not been performed, the child would have developed an abscess of the brain and died; the parents should have been grateful for the prompt precautions which saved the life of the child. Unable to find any medical authority to support the plaintiff's cause, the solicitors had to abandon litigation planned to take place in the King's Bench Division. Though Willcox's own small fee was sacrificed the surgeon was certainly paid the account for his fee as originally submitted.

Sometimes absurd claims for damages for negligence are initiated or encouraged by tactless remarks uttered by doctors to patients. Willcox successfully prevented litigation in 1933 when acting for a medical protection society in support of a dentist against a claim for negligent treatment. The woman patient had been encouraged to sue the dentist by the ill-conceived theory of two doctors and a specialist that certain symptoms, suffered more than two weeks after her dental extractions, were caused by cocaine poisoning. Willcox reported that the harmless preparation novocaine was very rarely toxic and that it could not possibly have accounted for symptoms after so long an interval; that it was highly likely that her trouble had been caused by infection at the root of her extracted teeth; and that the dentist's treatment had undoubtedly been carried out "in a careful and competent manner with correct judgment in the procedure".

References

"Sir Richard Muir—A Memoir of a Public Prosecutor" by Sidney Felstead—1927 (John Lane—The Bodley Head Ltd., London).
"Norman Birkett—The Life of Lord Birkett of Ulverston", by H. Montgomery Hyde (Hamish Hamilton) 1964.
"The Life of Sir Edward Marshall Hall", by Edward Marjoribanks 1929.

Chapter 20

Arsenic in Sheep dip—1928
(*Rex* v. *Pace*)

The difficulty which confronts coroners and police in investigating cases of death due to poisoning was illustrated in the case of the quarryman and sheep farmer, Harry Pace, aged thirty-six, who died in a remote part of the Forest of Dean on January 10th, 1928. The suspicion of unnatural death being reported to the coroner by Pace's brother, Inspector Alan Bent of Gloucester Constabulary conducted enquiries, and early in March Chief Inspector Cornish of Scotland Yard was summoned to help the local police.

On March 22nd Willcox's help was sought by Sir Archibald Bodkin, Director of Public Prosecutions, to try to solve what was still a mysterious death, "in a matter which, I am sure, will be of as considerable interest to you as it is of difficulty to us", to use his own words. After studying the reports of Bent and Cornish, the post-mortem findings and the results of the analyses, was he satisfied that death was due to arsenical poisoning? Was suicide a possibility? Could arsenic have been absorbed through the skin in the process of sheep dipping, which he carried out daily according to Ministry of Agriculture regulations? Bodkin had meanwhile instructed the coroner to avoid calling any scientific witnesses until Willcox's opinion on all these points had been given.

Pace was employed as a quarryman near Coleford in the Forest of Dean. His home was Fetter Hill Farm in a remote part of the forest. He was a keen amateur sheep farmer who spent much of his spare time tending his sheep, which numbered seventy or eighty at the time of his illness. Like other country folk, he was allowed free grazing for his sheep in the forest. He had always been a healthy and strong man, the father of five children. His wife, aged thirty-eight, had had ten pregnancies, including several miscarriages and several children who died in infancy.

His illness commenced in July 1927 after dipping some lambs in a tub used for the purpose, situated outside the farmhouse door. Abdominal pain, diarrhoea and "burning pain in the throat" were notable symptoms. He became confined to his home, nursed by his wife. Though visited by relatives, his wife did not permit anyone else to assist in his nursing care. Even after the visit of Dr. du Pré his mother was suspicious enough of the cause of the illness to request a further opinion. A joint consultation was arranged with Dr. Nanda, as a result of which he was admitted to Gloucester Royal Infirmary on August 19th. By this time he had already developed symptoms of neuritis in his hands and feet, so that he was unable to walk and at first, even to feed himself. Treatment in hospital was, to a great extent, beneficial. His digestive system improved so well that it was normal when he left hospital, but his neuritis was slow to improve. Pace was not an easy patient. Always a man proud of his health, he resented being in hospital, became depressed and discharged himself home on October 26th. The hospital doctor's diagnosis was arsenical poisoning, with neuritis, resulting from ingestion of sheep dip. He regained the power in his legs and returned to work, but in December his symptoms returned. On Christmas Day he was mentally ill and became violent, threatening to murder his wife, and children, with a razor, having struck his wife with a pair of tongs. His symptoms of diarrhoea, vomiting and neuritis returned, and he died on January 10th after considerable suffering. The doctor certified death as due to influenza, anuria (kidney failure) and peripheral neuritis. But by this time his brothers and two sisters were so suspicious that his death was unnatural that they met together and decided to inform the coroner, with the consent of Dr. du Pré.

The post-mortem indicated toxic changes in the organs, the kidneys, heart and liver being sufficiently damaged to cause death. The organs were studied by Professor Walker Hall, pathologist at Bristol, the analysis for poisons being conducted by Dr. R. Ellis, the County Analyst for Gloucestershire. The findings were indicative of arsenical poisoning, each organ containing appreciable amounts of arsenic, as much as 3.6 grains (more than a fatal dose) in the liver, and one grain in the kidney. The total quantity in the organs amounted to over 9 grains. No other cause of death was considered possible by these experts. Arsenic was present to the extent of 20% in the sheep dip found in the house. The only discrepancy in the opinions of these two experts related to the times at which the poison was likely to have been taken, points of detail of such legal importance that Bodkin passed on this problem to Willcox.

Chief Inspector Cornish entered into the case on March 7th with great zest and industry. Within ten days of his arrival he had interviewed thirty-seven witnesses, taken statements and submitted a lengthy report of fifty pages to Bodkin. The statements included those of ten relatives, four doctors who had attended Pace, Walker Hall, Ellis, Dr. Carson who had conducted the post-mortem, several friends of the Pace family and the local chemist who had sold the sheepdip to Mrs. Pace.

According to Cornish, Pace was unquestionably a remarkable man. He never associated with other men more than necessary, and when passing people whom he knew quite well would hang his head and take no notice; he was said to have an erratic temper. The evidence of cruelty to his wife, as mentioned in her statement, received support from the statements of the children, corroborated by the fact that she had at one time taken out a summons against him for cruelty at Coleford Police Court. This was the suggested motive for foul play, coupled with the evidence that Mrs. Pace had had illicit affairs with other men, in support of circumstantial evidence justifying a charge against Mrs. Pace of homicidal poisoning of her husband. There was proof in the Poisons Register at the chemist's shop in Coleford that Mrs. Pace had purchased two packets of Battle's sheep dip on July 22nd.

Among substances found at the farmhouse were medicine bottles, eye drops, bottles of liniment and packets of sheep dip in powder form. One of the bottles contained arsenic and was considered by Dr. Ellis to be an aqueous solution of sheep dip from which the sulphur had been extracted.

After a week of careful study and thought, Willcox submitted his report on March 23rd. He considered that the post-mortem findings were indicative and typical of arsenical poisoning; the analyses showed arsenic far in excess of a poisonous dose. Large amounts must have been taken more than three days before death and probably more than a fatal dose (two grains) within 24 hours of death. The illness in July 1927 suggested arsenical poisoning at that time. Neuritis was a typical feature of chronic or recurrent arsenical poisoning. The sheep dip, if mixed with water, would produce a colourless and strong solution of arsenic.

At the resumed inquest on May 9th and 10th preliminary evidence was taken from the local doctors, the hospital doctors and the pathologist. Meanwhile, Willcox was attending a Rheumatism congress at Bath. Arrangements for his attendance on May 14th, by request of the coroner, were made by Grace Hutcheson, his secretary, by careful alteration of his appointments at home. The coroner having expressed a wish to Bodkin for personal help with the technical aspects of the inquest, Mr. J. R. Paling was appointed to assist him. He and Willcox travelled to Gloucester on Sunday evening and stayed two nights at the Bell Hotel. The same evening a conference was held there at which Paling, Walker Hall and Ellis were present. Discussion centred round the possible routes by which Pace had acquired arsenic; an attempt was made to clarify the likely periods in the illness when arsenic had been administered. In this way the experts achieved considerable conformity of opinion which was necessary in the evidence required of them on the following morning—May 14th, the thirteenth day of the inquest.

Professor Walker Hall in his evidence said that there was no sign of natural disease in the organs, but signs in the stomach of irritant poisoning and changes in the liver, heart and kidneys indicating poisoning by arsenic. The last dose of arsenic must have been taken six to forty-eight hours before death, but arsenic must have passed into the liver for a period of three weeks or more before death. He excluded the possibility of absorption of such a quantity through the skin, in spite of certain statements on the subject expressed in Taylor's well-known text book of Toxicology— statements which could only be accepted with reservations. His simple experiment with a sample of blood taken five days after death was quoted. Kept at room temperature (60° F.) until May 4th, it showed no signs of putrefaction as would normal blood. This unusual finding was the effect of delayed putrefaction characteristic of arsenic.

Dr. R. Ellis gave evidence concerning the amount of arsenic found on analysis of the organs and of the sheep dip. One packet sent to him, according to the makers' instructions, had to be mixed with 20 gallons of water, making a solution of 2%, two grains in eighteen teaspoonsful being a fatal dose. He produced a bottle containing cornflour and milk.

"In this bottle there is cornflour and enough clear sheep dip solution to contain two grains", he said, handing the bottles to coroner and jury. In like manner he handed two separate bottles containing tea, one containing two grains of arsenic. These were possible ways by which the poison could be concealed for purposes of administration.

Willcox's evidence was received with intense interest and attention, lasting over an hour. He dealt with the interpretation of the findings of the pathologist and analyst, to the illness and death of Pace, his opinion being in agreement with their own. The amount of arsenic in the organs was over four times a fatal dose. Since the stomach contents were almost free of arsenic, probably none was taken during his last six hours of life. The finding of 4·7 grains in the intestines indicated that probably this amount was taken within forty-eight hours of death. The presence of 3·6 grains in the liver and 1 grain in the kidney indicated that arsenic had been taken earlier than forty-eight hours before death. The symptoms of the illness indicated repeated administration from July 24th to August 19th, 1927, when Pace was admitted to hospital. A large dose was certainly taken at the onset of the illness in July. Pace was again ill on Christmas Day when a dose must have been given, to explain the symptoms described by Dr. du Pré who visited him two days later. Several further doses had been given during the two weeks before death. Several other features of the illness were consistent and suggestive of arsenical poisoning, the rash on the armpits, slight jaundice, pigmentation of the skin, the redness of the throat and gullet, and the absence of putrefaction in the specimen of stored blood.

Ghosts of crime and tragedy of bygone years flitted through the court as Willcox recalled various poison dramas of the previous seventy years. Having agreed with a smile to the coroner's statement that his experience of the secret administration of arsenic was almost unique, he was asked to compare the analytical findings in this case with other cases of historical importance. The trial of Madeleine Smith in Glasgow in 1857 on a charge of poisoning her lover D'Angelier was a romantic story in itself, briefly referred to; the trial of Mrs. Maybrick in 1889 at which the evidence of Sir Thomas Stevenson, Willcox's chief of his early years, played a prominent part; and the trials at which he himself had appeared, those of Bingham (1911), Seddon (1912), and Armstrong (1922), were also recalled; and he might have mentioned Greenwood (1920) and Black (1922)—all cases of arsenical poisoning and trials for murder.

Mrs. Pace's solicitor, Mr. Trevor Wellington, cited the large amount of arsenic in Pace's remains to support a theory of suicide, yet there was no reasonable support for such a theory either on the grounds of scientific reasoning or of common sense. He also suggested that arsenic might have been taken as a contaminant of bismuth in medicine. Speaking quietly, Willcox mentioned that arsenic is allowable as a contaminant of bismuth to the extent of only two parts per million. If his death had been attributable to that cause, Pace would have to have taken a quarter of a ton of bismuth to account for the amount found in his body. He considered the last theory, that of absorption of arsenic through the skin, was quite impossible here. Even small amounts absorbed would require a large open wound which was not present in this case.

After the jury had returned a verdict that the deceased had met his death at Fetter Hill Farm by arsenical poisoning, Mrs. Pace, his widow, was arrested on the Coroner's warrant.

At the Magistrate's Court, Paling stated that he thought there was no doubt that the arsenic causing death had its origin in sheep dip. The day before the lamb dipping in July two packets had been bought, but neither of these packets had been used as two unopened packets were seen in the house in August; when the house was searched two days after the death of Pace, only one was found. The police had also discovered a bottle containing a dark liquid which on analysis was found to contain arsenic.

The Trial of Mrs. Pace

Beatrice Pace was committed for trial before Mr. Justice Horridge on July 2nd, 1928, at Gloucester Assizes. Few trials had elicited so much local interest and partisan feeling; the mystery of the case was well known in view of the numerous adjournments of an inquest which had lasted from January 16th to March 14th, all reported in the local and national newspapers. For Willcox it was another, and as it turned out to be, the last cause célèbre at which he appeared. He sat through the whole of the trial which lasted into the afternoon of the fifth day. His visit to Gloucester Assizes revived memories of the famous defence of Dr. Walter Hadwen by Sir Edward Marshall Hall in 1924 at which Willcox had appeared; several persons were present in Court who vividly recalled the occasion. In this case Norman Birkett, K.C., played a similar role to that of Marshall Hall but, as it turned out as the trial progressed, a far easier one. Birkett and Dr. Earengey defended Mrs. Pace. Counsel for the Crown was the Solicitor-General, Sir Frank Boyd-Merriman, K.C., assisted by Mr. St. J. Michelthwaite, who had appeared for the Crown in the Hadwen case in the same court in 1924.

In opening his case, the Solicitor-General said that there could be no doubt about the cause of Pace's death. There was found in the body of Pace nine-and-a-half grains of arsenic, over four times a fatal dose, in the main organs alone. Large amounts of arsenic in the form of sheep dip, bought for the legitimate purpose of dipping his lambs, were admittedly found in the house of deceased. Battle's sheep dip as used by Pace and purchased by his wife contained 2,800 grains of arsenic in one packet, equal to about 1,400 fatal doses. It also contained sulphur in the proportion of three parts to one. The sulphur, insoluble in water, could easily be filtered off. If the sheep dip had been swallowed in powder form large amounts of sulphur would have been found in the body, though this was not so here. Death by suicide could be positively excluded. Apart from the unlikelihood of a man repeatedly taking arsenic over a period of several months for this purpose, which would be absurd, instead of a large single dose to end his suffering, he could scarcely have thought it necessary to take the trouble to separate off the sulphur from the sheep dip if this had been his intention.

Mrs. Pace had made two statements to the police. "I don't think it possible for any person who had visited him to have given him any poison to take". In the second, she said "It is my view, and I am convinced, that my husband poisoned himself, and I don't think anyone else could have done it. If they had, I should have known."

Pace had for the first time been attended by his doctor in May 1927 for abdominal pain and diarrhoea. The night after dipping his lambs on July 23rd symptoms recurred more severely, his doctor again attending. Accordingly he asked his brother Leonard to complete the dipping of his lambs for him while he was in hospital in August. This was done with the use of other sheep dip owned by Leonard, the two packets purchased by Mrs. Pace remaining unused. Mrs. Pace had told the police that one packet had been used on July 23rd, whereas Leonard said he had seen two packets in the house in August.

During his time in hospital Pace improved much in health, his digestive system became normal, but the neuritis was slow to improve, so that he could scarcely stand up unaided when he returned home on October 24th, taking his own discharge. He was told by the hospital doctors that he was suffering from arsenical poisoning resulting from sheep dipping; that the neuritis would take two years to clear up. Actually by Christmas he could walk unaided.

An important incident occurred on Christmas Day, when Pace became violent, walked downstairs from his bed, struck his wife with a pair of tongs and threatened to murder his whole family with a razor. With the help of a neighbour he was calmed down and returned quietly to bed.

The Solicitor-General called seventeen witnesses of whom six were relatives of the deceased, three were friends or acquaintances, and eight were medical men.

Leslie, the eleven-year-old son of deceased, described how his father had asked him to bring to his bedroom the box in which sheep dipping materials were kept. He did so, and his father, after inspecting the box, asked him to put it away in a drawer of a chest, in the bedroom. Could Pace at that time, knowing he was suffering from arsenical poisoning, have suspected that sheep dip was being removed from the packet?

Mrs. Porter, mother of deceased, described how her son had complained two days before his death that water at his bedside tasted unpleasantly salty, and was grateful for fresh water from the tap to quench his thirst. Her offers of nursing help for her son had not been welcomed by Mrs. Pace, but she admitted that Mrs. Pace had cared for her son devotedly.

Birkett's most formidable witness, against whom he was quite powerless, was deceased's brother Elton. His were the most incriminating items of circumstantial evidence against the prisoner. He and his wife had often visited Pace during his illness. He claimed he had heard Mrs. Pace say she wished her husband was dead, she wished to be rid of him and could poison him. She resented their presence in the house. On one of their visits they found Mrs. Pace leaning over her husband saying "Harry, Harry, you are dying; we shan't see you much longer." It was at the request of Elton and his mother that Dr. Nanda was called into consultation, but Mrs. Pace had given them intentionally the wrong time for the consultation, in order to prevent them meeting the doctors at the house. Birkett failed to trip him up on any point of his evidence, and made no comment on the steps taken to inform the coroner and stop the funeral. "I can see now," the witness concluded, "that I had good cause for saying what I did.".

Dr. du Pré, Pace's doctor, stated that he had at no time prescribed arsenic in any form, but had treated him for gastritis when the patient attended his surgery in May 1927. He had been seriously ill again at the end of July, but improved markedly in hospital though the neuritis still prevented him from walking when he left hospital in October. When he became ill again at Christmas, Mrs. Pace walked to his surgery at night in thick snow to ask him to come to see her husband again. He thought she had nursed him with care and devotion. Seeing him after Christmas he thought he had influenza; he now knew he had made a mistake by certifying his death and now realised that Pace had died from arsenical poisoning.

Dr. Carson, pathologist, and Dr. Ellis, County Analyst, repeated the evidence submitted at the inquest, concerning the changes in the organs, the arsenic found in the body, and the arsenical content of Battle's sheep dip.

Dr. Carl Edwards, scientific representative of a firm which made sheep dip, said he had never known of a case of accidental arsenical poisoning through the skin in a human being. Sheep were often known to have died after dipping, but invariably death was due to accidental swallowing of the liquid.

Professor Walker Hall, describing the changes in the organs, considered that some of the changes in the heart and liver must have been caused two or three months before death, or even earlier. Changes might well have occurred in 1926 and 1927 when deceased had evidently had symptoms of pain and diarrhoea. The presence of arsenic in the bones was evidence of chronic poisoning. The fatty degeneration of the kidneys probably commenced shortly before death. The pigmentation and eczematous rash were consistent with, and in view of the analytical results, indicative of chronic arsenical poisoning. In cross examination, he admitted that his diagnosis of arsenical poisoning was delayed for three weeks pending the results of the analysis of arsenic. At post-mortem the changes were those consistent with many kinds of poison. Could death have been due to influenza, as Dr. du Pre had certified? The answer was emphatically negative. There was no cough or fever; the skin was cold and clammy, not hot, as in influenza. The "burning pain" in the throat is not a symptom, though there may be a sore throat at the onset of influenza; the illness does not last long, nor is peripheral neuritis a complication.

Having sat in court throughout the proceedings, Willcox was the last witness called by the Crown. His evidence on the fifth morning corresponded exactly to that given at the inquest, and his opinion to that of Walker Hall, and there was little more to be said. Both agreed that a large dose of arsenic had been taken between six and forty-eight hours of death, on Christmas Day and in repeated doses in the interval.

The climax of the trial had now arrived. It was an eagerly awaited clash between the fifty-eight-year-old analyst and physician, the most experienced authority in England on arsenical poisoning, and a forty-five-year-old barrister whose reputation was not yet established. To many it seemed that Birkett's case was hopeless; he called no medical witnesses for the defence. Dare he try and fight the expert on the scientific evidence, as Marshall Hall had done in the Seddon trial? In this predicament Birkett adopted the safest course open to him. He asked no questions concerning the medical or scientific facts of the case, but confined himself to simple questions which could only be answered by "yes" or "no". This was a well-known policy in the history of advocacy which had been exploited by Marshall Hall four years previously in this same Court at Gloucester against Willcox himself, at the trial of Dr. Hadwen. Willcox must have been reminded of that occasion now. Birkett questioned him solely on remote possible causes of death.

"Arsenic may find its way into the body through the mouth?"—"Yes".

"Sometimes through the skin?"—"If the skin is broken."

"You have from time to time referred to cases of accidental poisoning from certain preparations such as sheep dip, which contain arsenic?"—"Yes".

"Also, that there is a danger of suicidal death from this preparation?"—"Yes, there is, of course, a risk".

"There is a risk of chronic arsenical poisoning to those who carry out sheep dipping?"—"Yes".

"If the most perfect methods of cleanliness were not followed during the process, some of the arsenic might be absorbed when taking food?".—"Yes, if the person did not wash his hands, or if there were rashes on the hands."

Birkett asked no questions likely to reveal to the jury Willcox's opinion of his theory of suicidal poisoning to be proposed in his closing speech—which commenced after the luncheon interval.

He startled the Court by suggesting that the scientific evidence was as consistent with self administration of poison as with the theory of the prosecution, in open opposition to all the evidence of the scientific witnesses and to the simple principles of common sense. Probably never before had such an absurd theory been so successful in a trial of this kind; even the judge was taken in by it. "I agree", he said "with all the scientific evidence," (by that, he meant the scientific findings), "but the burden on the Crown is to exclude self administration, and that they have not done. There is the evidence of Dr. du Pré, that on every occasion he had observed the prisoner she had exhibited the demeanour of a devoted wife and nurse. Every wife in the country has the opportunity of administration of poison. If it is said that the prisoner alone prepared the food, that will not do. So far as the purchase of sheep dip is concerned, the quantity purchased in 1927 was the same as in the previous five years. The only evidence of possession was that in the sheep box known to Pace but unknown to his wife." He concluded by submitting to the judge that there was no case to go to the jury on the indictment.

Mr. Justice Horridge said that no case had been more thoroughly investigated, and no case could have been conducted with more scrupulous fairness. "My opinion is that it would not be safe to ask the jury to proceed further with it". He instructed the jury to return a formal verdict of "Not Guilty". This being done, Mrs. Pace was acquitted. The result was highly popular in the district, Birkett being greeted by shouting and clapping after the judge had retired. The case set the seal on his reputation as an advocate for the defence. He certainly showed skill in handling the final stages of the case, in spite of his absurd theory in which he could scarcely have believed inwardly himself.

The termination of any great trial always raises many "ifs" and "buts" in the minds of spectators, and this was such a case. What would have been the verdict if the jury had been allowed to express their own opinion? Why did the judge prevent this? The tragedy of the death and suffering of Pace had been forgotten in the applause which greeted Birkett at his success. Pace had been depicted as a blackguard, but was he really so? It seemed that he was mean by nature, but there was little evidence of evil brought out at the trial, except cruelty to his wife. But was not this caused by the effect of arsenic on his brain administered by other hands than his?

Willcox's private opinion was that the Judge's action was prompted by popular clamour in sympathy for a dejected widow with the care of children already rendered fatherless. He felt like Sir James Paget after the acquittal of Adelaide Bartlett on a charge of poisoning her husband with chloroform in 1886, when he said "Once it (the trial) was over, she should have told us, in the interests of science, how she did it."

Willcox had sat next to Walker Hall in court. The case resulted in a mutual friendship. Thereafter the professor would often be invited to stay at Welbeck Street on his visits to London. "I feel that I must once more thank you", he wrote to Willcox after the trial, "for your kindnesses and hospitality during the whole of last week. To be with you, and to be associated with you in the case, was to me a highly esteemed privilege and education. The experience I shall value time and again, but the memories I shall treasure almost daily. Carey Coombs (a Bristol physician) had prepared my mind for your kindliness of thought and action, but your consideration and courtesy were more than I ever expected."

The accuracy of the opinion expressed jointly at the inquest and trial by these two Crown experts concerning the timing of the final dose of poison given to Pace was later confirmed in some confidential documents submitted to Willcox in October 1928. The documents were carefully returned, but Willcox's notes are illuminating. Poisoning with arsenic had been repeated during a period of three years; the final dose of poison was given thirty-three-and-a-half hours before death. Sheep dip was used, mixed with butter and in cornflour, in beef sandwiches and in brandy. What he failed to note was that there was suspicion (not proof) of participation in the crime by hands other than those of Mrs. Pace.

References

"Norman Birkett—The Life of Lord Birkett of Ulverston" by H. Montgomery Hyde
(Hamish Hamilton) 1964).

"Poison Mysteries Unsolved", by C. J. S. Thompson (William Brendon & Son Ltd.)
1937.

"The Trial of Adelaide Bartlett" by Sir John Hall, Notable British Trials 1886.

"Acute Arsenical Poisoning." Discussion opened by Sir W. H. Willcox at the Medico-
Legal Society and addressed by Prof. I. Walker-Hall, May 23rd 1929. Transactions
of Medico-Legal Society, Vol. XXIII, 1929, p. 163.

Chapter 21

Lectures and Addresses and Rheumatic Diseases

Willcox was a slow and at times hesitant speaker in the witness box. This was due to his extreme care in the use of words in order that opposing counsel should not discover any discrepancies in his testimony; at the same time he was thinking of the next likely question ahead. After his death he was described as the most deliberate expert witness who had ever entered the witness box. In contrast was his fluency in delivering carefully prepared lectures and addresses. From 1920 onwards he became one of the most sought-after medical speakers both to learned societies and to lay organisations; his experience in courts of law had given him ample practice in explaining scientific facts to ordinary people, both to juries and lawyers. Some of his addresses are worthy of passing note. In 1922 and 1923 he addressed the Leicester Medical Society on Toxic Jaundice, the Suffolk Division of the B.M.A. on Poisoning at Ipswich, The Medical Society of London on Infection of the Teeth and Gums.

Speaking on Food Poisoning to the Provision and Canned Goods Trades Section of the London Chamber of Commerce in November 1922 he praised the system of good canning, claiming that tinned foods were probably even safer than fresh food. In support of this view he took as an example one of the greatest experiments in history, the feeding of millions of troops in the war. There had been only four cases of food poisoning resulting from tinned foods, three in France, one in Port Said; and these were probably the result of contamination by carriers after the opening of tinned food. He had never met an example of food poisoning from tinned food contaminated by the heavy metals tin, copper or lead.

Food preservation became a subject of such increasing commercial and medical importance after the First World War that Neville Chamberlain, Minister of Health, created a special committee to deal with the subject. Though Willcox was far too fully occupied to be on it, he suggested that Dr. A. P. Luff would be a more suitable member than himself, having been interested in the subject for over thirty years. As Luff had finally retired in 1919 from active practice, he had plenty of time to devote to this committee, which was constituted in 1923 with Luff as a medical member.

In January 1924 Willcox opened a discussion on Preservatives and Colouring Matter in Food at the Society of Public Analysts of which he had long been a member. There was a considerable variation in the views expressed by experts in the trade, and by several analysts including Roche Lynch.

In popular appeal arsenic was very much to the fore. It was because of the need for care in its use in industry and its danger to the public by reason of its easy accessibility that he considered it his duty to warn the medical and pharmaceutical professions on this subject. The address to the Medico-Legal Society in July 1922 was a wide survey of arsenic in homicidal, accidental and suicidal poisoning, and its use as an abortifacient. It was one of the oldest known poisons whose importance at that time overshadowed other known poisons in importance. Its preparations were easily accessible, and it provided symptoms simulating natural disease; being tasteless it could be introduced concealed into food or drink. His talk, though mainly scientific, made references and comments to historical examples—Madeleine Smith, Greenwood, Armstrong, Bingham and Black; and to the accident in Mesopotamia in 1916 when an outbreak among troops occurred from drinking water accidentally treated with sodium arsenite instead of alum for purposes of clarification. Whenever he spoke of arsenical poisoning he usually recalled the Madeleine Smith case; it was appropriate that his address at the B.M.A. Glasgow meeting in July 1922 was on "The Dangers to health arising from Industrial Preparations of Arsenic", for it was a window of a corner house in Blythwood Square from which Madeleine handed the fatal dose of arsenic to her lover L'Angelier in 1857. Like others interested in crime and poison, Willcox walked round the square as many others have done, merely to see the site of a former crime. The house still stands as it did, but is no longer privately owned by one family. He had studied the trial in detail, his book being heavily annotated. His address, given in non-technical style easily understood by the large audience, lay and medical, attracted headline news in the press. He strongly criticised the Poisons and Pharmacy Act of 1908 whereby sale restrictions in force since the Act of 1868 were removed; as a result, the public had been exposed to the dangers of poisoning by substances used as weedkillers, insecticides, fungicides, rat poisons, sheep dips, and antiseptics. He considered that during fourteen years a large number of fatal cases of accidental and suicidal poisoning had been attributable to that step, and in not a few instances of criminal poisoning (Seddon, Bingham, Greenwood, Armstrong and Black). As an example of poisoning on a large scale the Haslemere accident of April 1920 was quoted. During transit in a railway carriage a sack of sugar placed beside a leaky tin of weedkiller absorbed enough of the substance to cause acute arsenical poisoning in sixty people though fortunately there were no deaths, and the Ministry of Health took steps to prevent further accidents of that kind. The time had come, he considered, when something drastic should be done about the sale of such substances and their supervision. The first safeguard was to limit the sale to properly qualified and competent persons, registered pharmacists and selected persons with special licences to sell industrial and agricultural substances containing arsenic. He ended by calling for a resolution which was passed unanimously "that the sale of arsenical preparations in Section 2 of the 1908 Act should be limited to properly qualified and competent persons or qualified pharmacists, and that their sale should be limited to purchasers who have obtained a licence for the possession of these substances." Though the resolution was passed at the B.M.A. meeting no further steps were apparently taken. Willcox received a critical letter from the Horticultural

Trades Association who considered that the present regulations were sufficient and that his resolution would severely hurt the trade. The resolution was reported and supported by the *Glasgow Herald*, the Pharmaceutical Journals of England, Australia and New York, the *Shanghai Times*, the *Civil and Military Gazette of Lahore*, the *Lancet* and *British Medical Journal*. The *Pharmaceutical Journal* devoted a leading article in favour of the resolution.

Willcox was too dynamic a character to earn a reputation as a scholar, either in the classics or in medical history. But his Presidential Address in January 1923 to the Harveian Society on "The Relationship of Medicine and Toxicology" was a wide survey of medical history which always has an appeal to those interested in both subjects. His ability to compress much material into a few words written in an attractive style is perhaps better illustrated here than in any of his other papers; he was to a great extent prophetic in stressing the importance of the development of chemistry in the advance of medicine commencing in the last century and continuing rapidly today. Then he traced the history of criminal poisoning in which the analysts played a prominent part; of Palmer who used strychnine, Madeleine Smith, Dr. Pritchard who used antimony; Dr. Lamson who used aconitine to poison his nephew and was convicted as a result of Sir Thomas Stevenson's masterly analysis; Mrs. Maybrick, another of Stevenson's cases; Crippen; Seddon, Armstrong and Black, cases in which he had himself played a major role. He ended by describing a case seen by him only a few days previously.

A Government official had been ill in hospital for three weeks with abdominal symptoms but got better and returned to work. But he became ill again with symptoms of neuritis and peeling of the skin of his hands and feet. Analysis of hair by Roche Lynch showed a definite quantity of arsenic. On close questioning the patient disclosed that he had had a quarrel with his cook whom he sacked on the day after symptoms commenced. This case was quoted, along with others of special interest to the skin specialists whom he addressed at the Dermatological Society of London in 1926.

The history of Toxicology, when discussed by Willcox, always drew huge audiences, not that he was an outstanding orator, but crime has a strange fascination, especially to young listeners. It was on this theme that he lectured to the Listerian Society at King's College Hospital in January 1925, to the Cambridge University Medical Society a week later on "Interesting Cases of Fatal Poisoning" and in June 1926 to the Oxford University Junior Scientific Club on "Arsenical Poisoning". On this last occasion he exhibited Armstrong's chocolates, at that time only four years old.

His interests were by no means centred entirely around toxicology and forensic medicine. His work in the rheumatic disorders will be discussed later, but he took a keen interest in the treatment of diabetes, both before and after the discovery and early use of insulin in treatment. He came to know Dr. (later Sir Frederick) Banting personally when he came to England on visits. Details of early trials of insulin in the wards of St.

Mary's were described in the *Practitioner* issues of December 1923 and July 1924. Willcox was one of the first to point out the important part played by infection in bringing diabetes to light and its part in counteracting the action of insulin in diabetic subjects, views which have been universally accepted. They were described in his address to the Nottingham Medico-Chirurgical Society on November 5th 1925, illustrated by cases in his hospital wards, and to the Harveian Society on April 10th, 1924.

He addressed the Incorporated Association of Headmasters at the Guildhall in January 1924 on "The Health of Boys during School Age". He encouraged the public school authorities to continue to foster the development of character, habits of mind, intellectual ambition and physical fitness in such a way as to educate boys for leadership in all walks of life, while at the same time sports and games should be used to foster physical fitness as a primary object rather than for competitive purposes alone. His views on this subject were very much in line with those of Sanderson of Oundle School at which Gerald, John and Philip were educated. Oundle was at that time considered the leading school in scientific education. Sanderson discouraged competition between his school and other schools at sport and liked to turn boys loose at an early age in subjects in which they were most interested. In this respect Sanderson was ahead of his time.

He went on to discuss the health of schoolboys with regard to diet and ventilation; the importance of avoiding overcrowded dormitories, insisting that 80 square feet per boy must be the ideal to aim at, though not always attainable. By overcrowding infections were spread, and still are.

His address to the joint meeting of the Manchester Scientific Societies in 1924 attracted a packed audience of scientists and members of the Literary and Philosophical Societies and others interested in crime detection. It was reported prominently in the press with particular emphasis on the more sensational aspects of the Crippen and Seddon cases, even reaching the South African and Japanese Press. He dealt with the development of physics and chemistry as the basis of modern medical advances, the parents, as it were, of toxicology, which was so closely associated with crime detection. He traced the advances in the technique of poison analysis since the Palmer trial in 1855 when, before the technique for strychnine had been developed, the evidence was entirely circumstantial and based on the symptoms of the victim; the knowledge of arsenic and its detection since the days of Marsh, Berzelius, Orfila, Fresenius, von Babo, Stas, Pasteur, Thomas Stevenson, his own teacher in his early years, and of Thorpe, who originally devised the electrolytic method used in the Marsh-Berzelius technique. He ended by explaining the important part these developments played in courts of law and the duty of the medical witness in presenting evidence before judge and jury.

Litigation in cases involving medical knowledge was becoming so much more common and important in law at that time that the subject of "The Medical Witness" was discussed at a meeting of the Hunterian Society in November 1924. Mr. Justice Horridge opened the debate. He said the evidence of the medical witness was the handmaiden of justice, particularly in matters of Wills, Divorce, and compensation claims. The training of doctors was such that they were mostly very fair, though they should not go into court with preconceived ideas, nor conceal their ignorance when it is apparent. They should use language understood by lawyers and other ordinary folk. They should not, for example, describe a bruise as an echymosis.

Willcox, who was followed by Spilsbury, spoke of the privilege of giving evidence as to facts and as to the interpretation of them in clear and concise language. The facts should be accurately recorded beforehand. The witness's reputation depends on his evidence. The true function of the expert witness was to assist the court by his expert knowledge and experience. He was not there to win the case for any particular side. He should never be an ex-parte witness but must be free from bias. The responsibility was not lightly to be undertaken. He should be up to date in all matters relating to the subject in hand and if necessary must be prepared to conduct or arrange for experiments to be made during the course of a trial. He instanced the case of the "shampoo" case (carbon tetrachloride). He should try to see the case from the point of view of judge and counsel and assess their psychological approach. And in ending, he stressed the importance of the preliminary report so that counsel will know beforehand the evidence that he is likely to give.

Spilsbury's contribution was necessarily brief as there was little more to be said. But he advised the lawyers present that textbooks were often fallible and were often quoted out of context to confound medical witnesses. They were often out of date by the time the case came to court, a fact often overlooked by experts in the Law.

The Medico-Legal Society

Willcox became a member in 1906 on the recommendation of Pepper who had been a founder member at the birth of the society in 1901. On June 23rd, 1927, he became President following the seven year term of office of Lord Justice Atkin. In the preamble to his Presidential Address in October he said that the objects of the Society were the promotion of medico-legal knowledge among doctors and lawyers and its advancement in the cause of justice. The value of the meetings was enhanced by the joint discussions and mutual criticism. In law there should be no risk of inaccurate deductions from scientific investigation and all tests must be without flaw in cases where the question of innocence or guilt of an accused person was at stake. His subject "Recent Advances in Toxicology and Forensic Medicine" covered a wide field; blood stains in crime detection; advances in the technique of analysis for arsenic, alkaloids and other poisons; the toxic effect of organic arsenical compounds used in the treatment of syphilis and yaws, and of thallium, then used for ringworm of the scalp; and the dangers of barbiturates and carbon monoxide.

At the Annual Dinner, responding to the toast of the Society, he said during the course of his speech that there should be developed in London a centre for research in Forensic Medicine. This wish was fulfilled in 1935 at the birth of the Metropolitan Police Forensic Science Laboratory at Scotland Yard.

During his two year Presidency discussions covered a wide field of subjects in some of which he claimed no special knowledge, yet he never missed any meeting. Subjects of addresses included "drunkenness as defence of insanity in a trial for murder", "alcoholism in relation to criminal and civil responsibility", "the influence of childbirth in insanity and crime", "the medico-legal aspects of pain"; "the hair in forensic medicine" (Professor John Glaister), "juvenile delinquency", "fume diseases", "firearm injuries" (Professor Sydney Smith), "sterilisation of the unfit" (Lord Riddell), and "criminal abortion". He expressed his own view that abortion, unless sanctioned by reason of urgency for the sake of the mother's life or health, was anti-social and bound to harm the individual and society, though he felt bound to admit that he had noticed in the last twenty years a considerable modification of opinion in the profession, many experts having manifestly extended the medical indications for therapeutic abortion. The last meeting during his term of office was on acute arsenical poisoning; the main speaker, Professor Walker Hall, described his recent research on the experimental pathology in animals done at Cardiff, and on the disputed subject of possible absorption of arsenic through the skin, a subject which arose as a legal point in the case of Mrs. Pace's trial. In his introduction, Willcox alluded to the existence of arsenic in nature, its presence in many types of food in minute amounts, in fruit sprays and especially in certain types of fish, quoting the Llewellyn case as an example of this.

During his presidency Willcox conceived the idea of having a suitable Society Badge. The design was the inspiration of Lord Riddell who succeeded him as President. His suggestion for the motto was a saying of Seneca; "Involuta Veritas in alto latet" ("Truth lies wrapped up, hidden in the depths"). A beautiful badge was designed by Martin Travers, carrying this motto. It depicts a blindfolded damsel representing Truth being pulled out of a well of uncertainty by two hands, Medicine being one and the Law the other. A brilliant speaker and thinker, Lord Riddell had an exceptional knowledge of the medical profession and almost every social problem of the day.

On the subject of "The Doctor in the Law Courts" Willcox opened the discussion. He said that most doctors regarded Courts of Law with aversion for several reasons. Often kept waiting for lengthy periods at times when it was difficult to cope with the demands of practice, their evidence was criticised by lawyers, and often they suffered inconvenience and financial loss. The Society had done a great deal to relieve the doctor's fear of the law and lawyers in general, so that "the lions and the lambs can now sit down together". Every doctor in court must give evidence as to facts, but may be asked, and must be ready to give, his opinion even though he may not regard himself as an expert. His language must be such as to be readily understood by ordinary people, his evidence free from bias. The expert medical witness must be prepared to inform the court of current scientific opinions on the subject in question, and is well advised to consult with his medical colleagues on the side of the same litigant. Further, imagining himself in the position of opposing Counsel, he should endeavour to anticipate the question he is likely to be asked.

Lord Riddell, who followed, elaborated the position of the doctor in a court of law. While many witnesses are confined to dealing with facts, all witnesses skilled in a particular trade or profession are experts, and thus entitled, if they are asked, to express their opinions according to the legal maxim: "Cuilibet in sua arte perito est credendum" ("Whoso is skilled in his profession is to be believed").

At this stage of his career Willcox received a heavy correspondence from doctors and others seeking advice on drugs and poisons which he generously did his best to answer. Some of these queries concerned obscure poisons used by African natives, obtained from plants, a subject which even today has been little explored. He was sometimes forced to confess ignorance of certain plant poisons, but was able to refer the witness to authoritative articles or books on the subject in question. His friendship with Mr. C. J. S. Thompson and familiarity with his writings were helpful here.

Problems of drug toxicity are by no means new. Though the number of drugs in use in medical practice has immensely increased in recent years, and *pari passu* the complications of their employment, even in the 1920's the problem was becoming a source of concern. Willcox discussed this subject in the Harveian Lecture in March 1928. Speaking of barbiturates and the new Quinoline derivatives (the atophan group) used for gout, he said "It is unfortunate that the manufacturers of new drugs do not always take the medical profession into their confidence and often fail, when introducing a new drug, to give adequate advice regarding care and caution in its use". Since the Second World War, the advent of an immense number of new drugs has at least caused to be set up an elaborate organization to remedy these dangers and compel the manufacturers to initiate extensive scientific trials before drugs are allowed to be sold on the market.

The occurrence of dangerous liver poisoning from the atophan group of drugs was reported in correspondence to the B.M.J. in July and August 1926 to which Langdon Brown, Willcox and others contributed. Willcox had seen three cases quite recently, one of which was fatal. The occurrence of further cases during the next two or three years set the seal on the fate of those drugs in treatment. His work as physician and experience in toxicology brought such frequent opportunities for observing the effects of drugs on the liver that he came to be regarded as an authority on the subject. No account of his publications and lectures would be complete without reference to his two main addresses on this subject. His Lettsomian lectures on Jaundice, three in number, to the Medical Society of London in 1919, dealt with jaundice due to chemical poisons, jaundice complicating other disorders, catarrhal jaundice (now termed infective hepatitis), and jaundice caused by spirochaetes; all his personal experience was condensed and linked with the current knowledge of that period. The three Lumleian lectures to the Royal College of Physicians in 1931 on

Toxic Jaundice formed an equally exhaustive account of infections, and numerous poisons and drugs known at the time to affect the liver. To these there would now need to be added new groups of drugs. Reprinted from the *Lancet* of July, the lectures formed a valuable monograph, illustrated by coloured photo-micrographs, which was fully comprehensive at that time. Its study could materially assist any student through his examinations, if he was lucky enough to be questioned on the subject, and is still a valuable and interesting work of reference for physicians, surgeons, anaesthetists, general practitioners and specialists in industrial diseases, and toxicology. Special attention was drawn to delayed effects from drugs and poisons, notably chloroform and allied substances, arsenical compounds used in syphilis, alcohol and the quinoline (atrophan) group used for gout. His new phrase "hypohepatism", indicating failure of liver function, later fell into disuse and was never replaced; and the "toxiphylatic" function of the liver to defend the body from assault by poisons might fail and result in death of the liver cells and of the patient. A like result could of course complicate hepatitis of obscure causation, now considered to be due to virus infection. The disorder hitherto known as "Acute Yellow Atrophy" was now brought into line and shown to be merely the end result of acute liver failure due to infection or poisons or drugs.

The thesis, illustrated by numerous personal cases, explained how cirrhosis would commence and sufficient regeneration of liver cells occur to allow survival of function notwithstanding irreparable damage. His experience and knowledge were clarified in such a simple style that he could be readily understood by any interested student. The lectures were an example of a painstaking effort for medical education and of his belief that if a task is to be undertaken it must be done thoroughly and well.

When the B.M.A. celebrated its centenary in 1932 during the Presidency of Lord Dawson, Willcox was elected President of the section of Forensic Medicine. In his opening address on July 28th, to the section on recent developments in the subject, he showed his customary interest and desire to keep the subject abreast of the advances occurring at that time when it was apparent that the days were past when the medico-legal expert could be expected to appear as an expert in almost every speciality, as had been his position in relation to the Home Office before the Great War. He considered that in no other branch of medical science had greater advances been made in the last twenty years and that it was especially in the sphere of analytical chemistry, microchemical techniques, investigation of blood stains and groups, and of firearm injuries for medico-legal purposes that further advances were most likely to occur.

At that time he had been a member of the B.M.A. for over twenty-five years and, as he indicated, considering the first professional chair in the subject had been established a hundred and thirty years earlier at Edinburgh, it was high time for the establishment of a similar chair at London University and for the creation of a medico-legal institute in London as a centre for research and postgraduate studies.

The Rheumatic Diseases

When he became physician to the in-patients at St. Mary's in 1919 Willcox regarded his duties to the hospital and its students as his foremost concern and interest. Among his patients he encountered disorders of wide variety. But it was not purely by chance that he soon came to acquire more than an average physician's experience in the rheumatic diseases which embraced the complications of rheumatic fever, a disease very common at that time, and chronic forms of rheumatism and arthritis which were distinctly of a different nature and were becoming commoner year by year. Several of his senior colleagues had gained great reputations in the subject of juvenile rheumatism, notably his former teachers W. B. Cheadle (1835–1910) and David Lees (1846–1915), whom Willcox had served as house physician. Then there was F. J. Poynton (1869–1943), St. Mary's-trained, who later became physician to Great Ormond Street and University College Hospitals. Poynton, who had written extensively on rheumatic fever, published in 1913 the conclusions of his researches with Alexander Paine in which they claimed to have discovered the presence of haemolytic streptococci in the joints of patients, which when transmitted to rabbits by injection into the joints produced changes typical of the disease; though this research could not be successfully repeated by others it nevertheless deserved credit denied to it by some authorities.

But it was the career of A. P. Luff (1855–1938) that most closely fore-shadowed and influenced Willcox. Their careers bore a striking resemblance. Both men commenced their training without influence and in somewhat impecunious circumstances. Both were expert chemists who came to be trained by Sir Thomas Stevenson as analysts, achieving Home Office appointments, and both became interested in what nowadays is termed Rheumatology. Luff had become a noted authority on chronic arthritis and particularly gout; his writing on these subjects gained for him such a large practice in Queen Anne Street that he retired as early as 1913— before the age of sixty; he was the author of a Manual of Chemistry for Medical Students and a textbook on Forensic Medicine and Toxicology in two volumes. So it was that Luff and Willcox were probably the only two physicians of their time who were regarded as experts at the same time in Toxicology, Medical Jurisprudence and Rheumatology—a rare combination of specialities. In a sense, therefore, it may be said that after the Great War the mantle of Luff had fallen on Willcox for he had acquired from Luff an interest in rheumatic diseases, and many patients, both in hospital and in practice, passed on to him when his senior colleague retired. Between 1920 and 1935 Willcox delivered many addresses on various aspects of the subject to learned societies, while at the same period Reginald Miller became a recognised authority on juvenile rheumatism.

Willcox's teaching was based on personal experience in the wards of St. Mary's and on the results of detailed investigation and treatment carried out in co-operation with the hospital laboratories and physiotherapy department. He was one of the first doctors in England to appreciate the importance of the rheumatic diseases as a national problem affecting labour and the efficiency of industry. In 1936 he became a Co-Founder of the Empire Rheumatism Council, now called "The Arthritis and Rheumatism Council for Research in Great Britain and the Commonwealth".

Focal Infection

Willcox was not content merely to carry on treating his hospital patients by customary and routine methods. Essentially an individualist, he examined every patient with meticulous care, searching for any possible cause of an illness. The cause of Rheumatic Fever was well established as being due to streptococcal infection while it was already commonly held that Rheumatoid Arthritis arose in a similar way, though no bacteria had been discovered in the joints of these patients. The work of Pasteur and Lister had focused attention on infection by bacteria as a cause of many diseases at a time when the study of viruses was in its infancy. And his friendship with Sir Almroth Wright lent further support to the bacteriological theory of the rheumatic diseases and to the probable value of vaccine treatment of which Wright was regarded as the founder. Willcox's name became so well known as a protagonist for the theory of focal infection that some came to believe that he was the founder of it. But this was not so. He merely followed up the work of previous investigators in this sphere, as he described in several of his addresses, notably the one on "Dental Sepsis—a Retrospect" (Proc. R. S. Med., June 1930). Willcox never abandoned the theory, remaining a firm believer in it for the rest of his career. It is therefore worth recalling the history of the theory at the time of his appointment as physician to In-patients in the wards of St. Mary's.

Until about 1900 the teeth were regarded as nothing more than organs of mastication. Though Benjamin Rush of Philadelphia had appreciated it in 1812, the idea that dental infection could undermine the general health of the body had not been generally accepted. In 1879 the eye surgeon Nettleship had recorded a case of choroiditis and keratitis caused by an infected tooth. Professor Schweinitz of Philadelphia, in an address to the 17th International Congress of Medicine in 1913, referred to examples of eye infections of similar cause (Goulden 1911, Lang 1913, Lawford 1913).

In 1900 William Hunter (1861–1937) in a paper entitled "Oral Sepsis" to the Odontological Society of Great Britain drew attention to the importance of dental infection in the causation of systemic diseases, his pioneer work being done at Charing Cross and the West London Hospitals. Later, Horder in 1914 read a paper at the Royal Society of Medicine on "Dental Sepsis from the point of view of the Physician", and A. P. Beddard (1867–1939) in 1918 in a paper at the Medical Society of London expressed a firm opinion that 90% of his cases of rheumatoid arthritis were associated with dental infection, involving either the gums or the dental roots.

Willcox's experiences firmly supported Beddard's views and were described in his first papers on this subject before the Derby Division of the B.M.A. in February 1921 (British Med. Journal June 4th) and the Bromley Medical Society in January 1922.

It had already been recognised that bacteria could infect joints when the blood stream was infected (bacteriaemia) by staphylococci, streptococci, gonococci, pneumonococci and the bacilli of typhoid, dysentery, undulant fever and tuberculosis, and it was known that allergic joint swellings might follow injections of animal sera. But in rheumatoid arthritis no bacteria had ever been recovered from the joints. Nevertheless Hunter, Billings in the United States, Beddard and Willcox, all believed that the joint disorder of rheumatoid arthritis was caused by toxins from a distant focus, most often in the teeth, less often from the sinuses or colon. In various addresses on the subject Willcox drew attention to several analogies to illustrate the basis of his belief in focal infection. There was the example of the local carbuncle or infected wound leading to septicaemia, a common happening before the days of antibiotics; malignant endocarditis, well known as a sequel to dental infection; rheumatic fever, which followed infection of the tonsils. What could have been more logical than to suppose that in rheumatoid arthritis, as in rheumatic fever, a streptococcal toxin could invade the tissues of the body from a chronic localised focus in teeth or throat?

The theory had therefore considerable backing in the profession by the time Willcox settled down to work at St. Mary's after the first World War. His early success in treatment by removing proved foci of infection encouraged him in the belief that his approach would lead to universal acceptance. But as the years passed, the decline in the popularity of the theory was due to the common experience that removal of infected teeth in cases of arthritis often achieved little benefit or else improvement was attributed by sceptical observers to other concomitant methods of treatment such as rest and various forms of physical treatment.

The cause of rheumatoid arthritis is still unknown. The theory of auto-immunity has not yet been proved, and it is interesting from time to time to hear beliefs expressed in the infective cause of the disease.

Willcox's work and teaching achieved one notable object which was often forgotten. He drew the attention of the dental profession to the important influence for harm which infected teeth can exert on the general health of the body. In this way there is no doubt he contributed to the advance in dental hygiene which made rapid strides between the two World Wars. Perhaps it was this success that led to the decline of dental infection as an entity in itself, and the decrease in its importance in causing rheumatic disorders as the years passed. Willcox's detailed interest in this subject can be studied in his published address to the Medical Society of London (Dec. 1922), the Section of Odontology of the Royal Society of Medicine (1923) on "Dental Sepsis as a factor in Disease of other Organs" and in lectures on behalf of the Dental Board given in 1923 at London, Manchester and Edinburgh on "The Diseases of the Periodontal tissues and their systemic effects". To illustrate the frequency of dental sepsis as the cause of rheumatoid arthritis and "fibrositis" at the Royal Society of Medicine he selected his last hundred consecutive cases, of which seventy-two had been found to show evidence of dental infection—a rather smaller proportion than Beddard's—while ten had infection of the nose and throat and thirteen were examples of intestinal infections.

Willcox was no supporter of the policy of wholesale dental extractions, but insisted on the most detailed clinical and radiological investigation of the teeth for evidence of root infection, which could so often be overlooked. His other main attack was at the bacterial source of infection in which the co-operation of the St. Mary's bacteriologists played a great part, of Almroth Wright, Fleming, Freeman and others, leading to the use and production of autogenous vaccines. But, though stimulated and encouraged by Wright's pioneer work, the use of vaccines in arthritis cases never caught on in popular appeal and by many was considered to exert an influence for good primarily by its psychotherapeutic effect coupled with the benefit gained from intensive physiotherapy.

The Rheumatic Diseases as a National Problem

From 1924 onwards it came to be realised that the rheumatic diseases, which included backache, sciatica and arthritis in its many forms, were causing a very high sickness rate in the community to the extent of affecting the efficiency of basic industries; that the provision of measures for intensive physiotherapy was woefully lacking in the community. The Ministry of Health report on this subject (1924) indicated that the total length of sickness-absence caused by rheumatic disease was for males one sixth, and for females one seventh, of the total sickness absence due to all diseases. Calculating on the figures for the sample population of 91,000 insured workers the total sick benefit paid for rheumatic diseases in 1922 was over £1·8 million, and 3·14 million weeks of work were lost on an average yearly estimate. Chronic rheumatoid arthritis cost the approved societies nearly half of the sum of £1·8 million. This sum of money may seem comparatively small now, but in present day values could be multiplied by nearly ten times. The rheumatic problem was therefore a major one involving both the public and the medical profession; it cannot be denied that the challenge was taken up by several leaders of the profession with the interest and enthusiasm required. In April 1925, an International League against Rheumatism was created by the Society of Medical Hydrology with Dr. R. Fortescue Fox as Chairman, his Dutch friend Dr. J. Van Breeman as secretary, and in November a meeting was held at the Royal Society of Medicine to consider "The Treatment of Rheumatism in Industry". At about this time the British Committee was formed as a branch of the international organisation, the original members being Dr. Fortescue Fox, Lord Dawson of Penn, Sir Thomas Horder, Sir Humphry Rolleston, and Willcox, with Dr. M. B. Ray as secretary. In those days it was all very well to plan rheumatic clinics for non fee-paying patients, but the financial provision was unobtainable from state funds and had to be met by money contributed by voluntary donation, legacies and so on. In order to raise funds public attention had constantly to be drawn to this desirable and necessary development in the treatment of the rheumatic diseases. Letters appeared in the *Times* on September 7th, 1925; and on March 16th, 1927, the British Committee submitted their plan for a new physical treatment centre in London, capable of treating up to 400 out-patients daily, a plan supported by the Ministry of Health and the British Red Cross Society. At a meeting of the latter body, presided over by Sir Arthur Stanley, at the R. A. Club on January 27th, 1928, an appeal for £40,000 was launched. Willcox was one of the main speakers. He drew attention to the national importance of the rheumatic diseases in industry to the Cardiff Medical Society in February 1927, to the 38th Congress of the Sanitary Institute at Hastings in July of the same year, to the Southampton Medical Society in 1930 and to the Royal Institute of Public Health in January 1932. The British Red Cross Society Clinic was opened by H.M. the Queen in 1931 after great efforts to raise funds. The same year the B.M.A. constituted a special committee of eighteen members with Rolleston as Chairman to report on "The Causation and Treatment of Arthritis and Allied Conditions". The terms of reference were to correlate the current knowledge of the subject, the methods and organisation of treatment, the spread of knowledge of the subject within the profession, the direction in which future research should be undertaken with most probable profit and the means whereby such research could be directed and correlated.

The report was published in 1933. It went a long way to resolve the difficult task of classification of the rheumatic diseases at that time. In this survey of the subject comment was made on the value of treatment in British Spas.

The appointment in 1934 by the Royal College of Physicians of its own special committee on Rheumatic Diseases marked a great step forward in the campaign. Its purpose was to provide a permanent body which would meet at regular monthly intervals, one of its main purposes being to co-ordinate and sponsor worthwhile research and to maintain a link with the International League. The Committee, with Sir H. Rolleston as Chairman, published annual reports from 1935 to 1938. But it had no source of money to finance its plans. But important and useful though it was, it was felt that this committee would be able to wield more power and influence if the laity were brought into its fold. As a result of the national importance of the problem confronting it the committee recommended to the Royal College of Physicians that the inauguration of an Empire Rheumatism Campaign, supported by medical and lay members, would be the most effective method of carrying forward the objects they had at heart. On January 30th 1936 the Committee of the Royal College with Lord Dawson in the chair approved the proposal that the existing committee of Chronic Rheumatic Diseases should act as the Scientific Advisory Committee to the major organisation. On February 7th the Empire Campaign was inaugurated and the Empire Rheumatism Council constituted with Sir Humphry Rolleston as President, Willcox Chairman and Dr. W. S. C. Copeman as Honorary Secretary, Sir Frank Fox being the organising secretary. Later, H.R.H. the Duke of Gloucester became

President, Willcox handed over the Chairmanship to Lord Horder and himself became Vice-Chairman of the Executive Committee. In his inaugural address on October 29th Lord Horder emphasised the need for organised and extensive research on the great national problem of rheumatic diseases and spoke of his hopes for moral and financial support from industrial leaders of the nation, trade unions, Friendly Societies and other bodies. Several travelling and research fellowships were set in motion and encouragement given to the improvement and development of special clinics.

It was under the Auspices of the Scientific Advisory Committee of the Council that the new journal "The Rheumatic Diseases" was first published to replace the Annual Reports of the R.C., Physician's Committee.

Willcox's work for the Empire Rheumatism Council as Vice Chairman and member of its several committees was an extensive and enthusiastic effort over a long period. Many committee meetings were held at Welbeck Street. He gave lectures and addresses to draw attention to the importance and nature of the campaign and was a constant source of encouragement to various members of the committees of which the Scientific Advisory Committee was probably the most important. Dr. Copeman, its original secretary and the first honorary secretary of the council at its inception, became Chairman of the Council after Lord Horder's death. His continuous and distinguished efforts for the campaign, both before and after its change of name in 1961, has extended over a longer period than that of any other person.

Willcox supported the Appeal held at Vintner's Hall on January 27th 1937 on behalf of the eighteenth century Bath Royal Hospital for Rheumatic Diseases, the first hospital in the world to be built solely for its purpose. The only way, he said, in which the problem in Bath could be adequately dealt with, was by the provision of an entirely new and much enlarged hospital with its necessary accommodation for nursing staff, administration and facilities for up-to-date requirements for investigation, treatment and research. Research should form part of the scheme and in close contact with the hospital as it was only in this way that new methods of treatment could be developed.

He took a keen interest in research projects submitted to, or sponsored by, the scientific committee in various fields, as his correspondence so clearly indicated. In submitting one of the annual reports he praised the efforts of his numerous colleagues and alluded to the generosity of some of the chief financial supporters outside the profession, namely Spedan Lewis, Gordon Selfridge, Alexander Maclean, Sir Joseph Burn of the Prudential Insurance Company, Sir Benjamin Cohen, Sir James Roberts, Colonel (later Lord) Gretton, and Sir Alexander Walker.

Willcox had so many commitments in his busy life and practice at home that he could not be regarded as an enthusiastic continental traveller. Nor did he take the necessary trouble or effort to master any foreign language. Nevertheless, his visits to the continental spas, though perhaps few and far between, were a constant recurring delight for he enjoyed meeting French rheumatologists, of whom Professor Lobbé, Dr. Benjamin and Dr. Forestier are well remembered, the latter being the initiator of the use of gold injection treatment of Rheumatoid Arthritis. Willcox was no linguist yet he made many friends among foreign doctors at his visits to various spas over the years; of these may be mentioned Pistany in 1926; Vittel (accompanied by Mildred, John and Philip for ten days) in 1929; Aix-les-Bains in 1921 and again in 1934 (accompanied by Philip) and to Vittel in 1939 for his last continental spa visit on the occasion of the opening of the new thermal springs there.

From time to time he visited British spas either on casual visits or on the occasions of rheumatic congresses, notably Harrogate, Droitwich in 1927, Bath in 1928, the re-opening of Bridge of Allen in 1930, a second visit there in 1932, and Llandrindod Wells in 1932. On each occasion he spoke on the importance of the rheumatic diseases to the community and to the medical profession.

References

Nettleship, T. 1879. Royal Lond. Ophth. Hospital Rpts. IX, part 2, P. 182.

Goulden, C. 1911 The Ophthalmoscope, IX, P. 177.

Lang, W. 1913 The Lancet, May 17th.

Lawford, J. B. 1913. Proc. R.S.M., May 13th, P. 121.

Hunter, W. 1900 Proc.Odontological Society of Gt. Britain.

Horder, T. 1914 Proc. R.S.M.

Beddard, A. P. Trans. Med. Society of London, 1919, XLII, P. 20.

Billings, F. 1921 Focal Infection. New York. Appleton & Co.

B.M.A. Committee on Arthritis, 1933 B.M.J. June 17th.

Willcox, W. H.

1. The Clinical, Pathological & Radiological Aspects of Infection of the Teeth and Gums, Med. Society of London, B.M.J. Jan. 13th, 1923. Med. Press, Dec. 1922, p. 515.

2. Dental sepsis as a factor in Disease of Other Organs, Proc. R.S.M. 1923 vol. XVI, P. 7.

3. Diseases of the Periodontal Tissues and their Systemic Effects. Brit. Dent. Journal, June 1st 1923, The Dental Surgeon, June 9th, 1923, P. 363.

4. The Toxic Factor in Disease, with special reference to Chronic Rheumatic conditions and Diabetes, Practitioner, May 1925.

5. Rheumatoid Arthritis. Bath. Meeting B.M.A., B.M.J., Oct. 3rd, 1925.

6. The Nature, Prevention and Treatment of Fibrositis (Discussion at Royal Society of Medicine). Cl. Journal, Nov. 11th 1925.

7. Nasal Sinusitis as a cause of Toxaemia. Practitioner, Sept. 1926.

8. The Aetiology and treatment of Chronic Rheumatic Conditions, Cardiff Med. Soc., 17th Feb. 1927., Practitioner, August 1927.

9. Chronic Rheumatism in relation to Industry. Journ. Royal Sanitary Institute 1927, vol. XXVIII, No. 2. August 27th P. 56.

10. The Treatment of Underlying Infections, Lancet, July 28th, 1928.

11. Dental Sepsis—a Retrospect, Proc. R.S.M. June 1930 vol. XXIII, P. 21.

12. The Aetiology of Chronic Rheumatic Disease, Practitioner, Nov. 1931.

13. The Aetiology of Chronic Rheumatism with special Reference to Infective causes (Royal Institute of Health Lecture), Journal of State Med. vol. XI, 4, 1932, Med. World, July 22nd 1932, P. 417.

14. The Prognosis of Chronic Rheumatic Conditions, Practitioner, Feb. 1935.

Chapter 22

Accidental Poisoning

Pharmaceutical Mistakes

Remedies to be taken by mouth are usually prescribed nowadays by doctors in the form of tablets or pills. Medicine in liquid form is far less often used than formerly was the case except for certain conditions like indigestion and for patients objecting to swallow tablets or pills. The latter are prepared in bulk by pharmaceutical firms so that the pharmacist working in a chemist's shop is rarely required nowadays to make tablets and pills himself. Errors by pharmacists in dispensing prescriptions have therefore become rarer, likewise the liability for claims against pharmacists for negligence are seldom made. In law the doctor has always been well favoured in this respect. If he prescribes inadvertently the wrong dose of a drug the pharmacist often acts as a protective screen by communicating with the doctor before dispensing the medicine. But the qualified pharmacist is entirely responsible for the accuracy of a prescription and is liable for negligence if he dispenses either a larger or smaller dose than prescribed. Under the terms of the Food and Drugs Act of 1875 inspectors employed by Medical Officers of Health may sample medicines sold in chemists' shops and order expert analysis of the ingredients to be carried out, a form of bureaucratic inquisition for which Willcox had an intense dislike. The terms of Section 7 of the Act read as follows:

> "No person shall sell any compound article of food or compounded drug which is not composed of ingredients in accordance with the demand of the purchaser, under a penalty not exceeding £20."

Willcox never condoned carelessness for he had at an early age acquired a reputation for scrupulous accuracy in chemical analyses. Nevertheless he would always be prepared to support with the weight of his authority the cause of any pharmacist in trouble, provided he was acting in good faith with honesty of purpose. If a pharmacist was convicted, Willcox regarded the event as a reflection on his own reputation because since 1908 he had been, as Privy Council Visitor to the Pharmaceutical Society of Great Britain, a referee and assessor of the standard of knowledge in Pharmacy necessary for candidates to pass their final examinations.

Preparations for National Health Insurance prescriptions would from time to time be checked by drug inspectors acting for Medical Officers of Health. Where there was evidence provided by a public analyst of a faulty prescription the police would be informed and prosecution might follow. Whether blameworthy or not, the pharmacist stood to suffer damages to his reputation which was far greater than financial loss. A qualified pharmacist therefore needed to be insured against litigation for negligence unless the firm for which he worked was adequately covered.

In 1923 Willcox was three times approached by the Chemists' Defence Association in support of chemists' shops against allegations of faulty prescriptions. When he appeared at Hampstead Police Court on May 31st, 1923, he was able to kill two birds with one stone in support of two chemists summoned under Section 7 of the Food and Drugs Acts. Both cases adequately exposed bureaucratic ignorance and stupidity. In both cases quinine sulphate had been prescribed in medicines in doses of 6 grains per dose of medicine, whereas the amounts on analysis were 5·3 and 5·25 grains respectively. Both summonses were immediately dismissed by the magistrate after receiving Willcox's evidence. He made several points which are not always appreciated by doctors. Without taking into account the permissible and inevitable errors in weighing and measuring the ingredients, one must allow for variation between the amount of drug present and the amount discoverable by analysis. It may be impossible to extract by analysis the entire quantity of an alkaloidal salt put into a medicine, some of which has combined with another ingredient, for example chloroform water or hydrobromic acid, as was probable in these two cases. Medicine bottles are not always accurate in capacity; a bottle of 8 ounce size may sometimes contain up to 12% more or less of liquid. Unless, therefore, the exact capacity of these two bottles had been ascertained, the findings of the analysts do not afford any evidence of incorrect dispensing. "I should not be satisfied", he concluded, "if I knew that my chemist deliberately put in 10% less quinine than I ordered but I know that it is not always possible to have the finished product scientifically exact. I should not be dissatisfied if, once in a while, he accidentally got a little bit out. I should fix the limit of excusable error at 10% either way. Chemists' scales cannot be made as accurate as analysts' balances."

The third summons in that year was against a chemist for selling a medicine containing an excess of potassium iodide to the extent of 4/5ths of a grain per dose. The summons at the same police court was at first adjourned on account of the illness of the inspector. The amusing aspect of this complication lay in the circumstance that the inspector obtained medicine for himself from the same chemist to whom the summons had been issued. The case was accordingly abandoned.

Belladonna Poisoning

Sometimes a mistake which to the uninitiated may seem trivial, may have disastrous effects both for the patient and for the pharmacist. In December 1923 a doctor prescribed a bottle of medicine for a well educated gentleman suffering from indigestion. He took the first dose before his lunch. His throat became dry, his vision blurred; after the second dose at night he became worse and was delirious. Perhaps his doctor frightened him by telling him he had belladonna poisoning. Had he avoided doing so litigation would most probably have been avoided. The patient sent his medicine for investigation to an analyst and informed the chemist accordingly. Unfortunately the amount of belladonna in the medicine was seven times as much as it should have been but the firm denied having dispensed inaccurately. After correspondence between the solicitors for both parties Willcox was consulted in January 1925 by the lawyers acting for the chemist against a claim for negligence resulting in belladonna poisoning. Unfortunately liquid extract of belladonna had been dispensed by mistake instead of tincture. The effect of the overdose lasted for three days. On the fourth an ophthalmic expert considered there was no residual damage to the eye but only slight inequality of the pupils. Nevertheless, the patient began an action for damages, refusing to accept an offer of £100 which had been paid into court. The claim appeared to be a mild form of blackmail.

Willcox found that the doctor's prescription had been correct but unfortunately by mistake a dose of belladonna equivalent to 107 minims of the tincture had been taken—seven times the maximum dose. He considered that the effects would be expected to have worn off after seven days and that there would be no permanent damage to the eye or to other organs. The liquid extract of belladonna has no official dose because it is not used for internal administration. It was a remunerative illness for the case was settled out of court for £200 inclusive of damages and costs.

Accidental Strychnine Poisoning

In May 1922 Willcox was consulted by the solicitors acting for the Chemists' Defence Association in a case of accidental strychnine poisoning, which resulted in a claim for damages against a chemist, in the King's Bench Division, tried before Mr. Justice Darling. In this case Willcox decided, after receiving all available evidence, that there was insufficient scientific support he could render by his appearance in court for the defence. The case illustrates the stupidity sometimes exhibited by patients who take quack remedies suggested by friends for the common cold, and the complicated litigation which may ensue. In this case, the remedy was a Scottish one consisting of a mixture of equal parts of sweet spirits of nitre and tincture of rhubarb in hot water—an ancient Scottish remedy before whisky was invented, as Darling wittily described it.

The claimant and his wife obtained six pennyworth of each ingredient at a chemist's shop and consumed the whole lot between them at bed time, but developed convulsions within half an hour. A nurse who happened to live in a flat below their own, being summoned, diagnosed strychnine convulsions and noted the bitter taste in the remaining drops in the bottle. Both this and the symptoms pointed to strychnine in her opinion, and that of the doctor. The county analyst found 1/10 grain (a poisonous dose) in the analysis of the vomit. Unfortunately, none of the medicine remained for analysis; the few remaining drops contained no strychnine. The bottles of ingredients obtained by the police from the chemist's shop likewise contained no strychnine. The main task of the court was to find out how the strychnine had got into the medicine. As Willcox had pointed out, the analyst was known to himself, as they had both been trained by Sir Thomas Stevenson together and were familiar with the comparatively easy detection of strychnine; consequently for legal purposes strychnine poisoning must be assumed to have been an accurate diagnosis. The only possible conclusion of Mr. Justice Darling was that strychnine had been accidentally put into the bottle in mistake for one of the other ingredients by the pharmacist. He gave judgment for the plaintiffs for £150 and costs.

A lady, aged 45, residing with her husband at Montague Square, obtained a box of pills from a local chemist in July 1926. The main ingredients were those commonly used in aperient pills but strychnine 1/120th grain per pill was also included. The label's instructions were to take not more than 4 pills at bedtime. On retiring to bed after taking four pills on July 31st she was seized with spasmodic painful contractions, severe constriction of the chest "as if held in a vice" and mental anguish. Medical aid was sought that night and the next morning. On August 2nd the second dose of four pills was taken. Her doctor diagnosed strychnine poisoning and ordered a new prescription to be made up specially without strychnine. On December 7th a writ was issued by her solicitor against the firm of chemists claiming damages for negligence. Even at this late date she claimed she was still ill. The solicitors acting for the chemists claimed that the patient was neurotic in the first place and that her residual symptoms were hysterical.

On analysis it was found that each pill contained 1/28th grain of strychnine instead of 1/120th grain. The taking of four pills therefore meant that each dose contained 1/7th grain which is more than four times the maximum pharmaceutical dose.

This time Willcox was approached by the solicitors for the plaintiff and agreed to act on condition, as was his invariable custom, that he consult with the patient together with her own doctor. A joint consultation and examination was held at Welbeck Street on January 5th, 1927. The patient said that her symptoms had cleared up only ten days previously, the third week in December. There was no doubt that her symptoms, described without any prompting, were indicative of strychnine poisoning, the physical effects having by then entirely cleared up though she had undoubtedly suffered a degree of mental shock customary after strychnine poisoning. Neither doctor considered she was a neurotic or hysterical personality. Willcox's view differed slightly from that of Dr. (later Sir Charles) Symonds who, acting for the other party, considered that the effect of the overdose would not have persisted for more than a few days. The chemist had already admitted negligence before Christmas and had paid £50 into court. Short of litigation in Court there only remained the question of a fair assessment of reasonable damage, argued at some length by the lawyers. A sum of £62, plus costs, was the solution of the dispute.

A similar but even more serious case of strychnine poisoning was brought to his notice in 1929 by the solicitors acting for a well-known firm of chemists in the West End of London, a firm often recommended by Willcox as having an untarnished reputation. In this case the damages paid were considerably greater. The reasons for this were that the firm was so well known and the lady concerned was the wife of a solicitor.

A doctor prescribed for the lady for the treatment of a menstrual abnormality, a medicine the main ingredients of which were liquid extract of ergot ($\frac{1}{2}$ dram) and liquid extract of nux vomica, 2 minims (drops) per dose. The Pharmacist unfortunately dispensed the quantities of drugs the wrong way round so that each dose contained $\frac{1}{2}$ dram of nux vomica, equivalent to 2/5ths grain of strychnine, equal to fifteen times the normal dose and almost as much as a fatal dose. She took only one dose on July 3rd which caused typical symptoms of strychnine poisoning lasting eight hours. Her doctor advised by telephone that she should take no further medicine but as her symptoms had greatly lessened he did not consider it necessary to travel from London to Worplesdon to see her at that time; her symptoms cleared up in 36 hours. When he attended her on July 5th he unsuccessfully tried his best to persuade her to avoid litigation. In November the managing director of the firm visited her, in company with the doctor who insisted that the effects of the overdose had terminated after thirty-six hours. The patient's solicitors at first claimed £1000 damages, clearly a grossly exaggerated estimate in view of the small cost of medical expenses amounting to no more than £20.

When consulted by the chemists on November 6th Willcox had to admit the seriousness of the mistake and suggested that substantial, though far less than the suggested sum, should be paid as damages. The dose of strychnine was fifteen times the normal dose, bordering on a fatal one, but as strychnine is fairly rapidly excreted the danger would not be long-lasting nor would the pain from muscle spasms persist. As she had been known to be neurotic beforehand the overdose could not be blamed for all her subsequent symptoms. The claim was settled for a sum of £500 and costs, half the amount originally claimed by the plaintiff.

An Incorrect Verdict

In carbon monoxide poisoning the differentiation between death due to accident or suicide is usually straightforward but, contrary to popular belief, it is not always easy to diagnose death due to carbon monoxide from death due to natural causes. When questioned Willcox could speak at length on this subject from his experience as analyst to the Home Office. But in later years as Medical Adviser, it was unusual for him to be consulted unless special medico-legal issues arose. The following are two cases of unusual interest—

Difficulty arose on August 8th, 1930 as a result of a verdict recorded at Deptford Coroner's Court on the death of Mrs. Alice Nunn at the age of 71, the verdict being that of death from misadventure. The facts, as the medically qualified assistant coroner stated, were that the old lady had turned on the gas to heat a kettle for making tea, subsequently collapsing on the scullery floor. The report of the inquest immediately attracted the concern of the South Metropolitan Gas Company. The company was anxious if possible to prevent the case being officially classified as accidental coal gas poisoning unless there was certain or adequate reliable evidence that death was so caused. No doubt there was inherent in the verdict an underlying reflection on the efficiency of the gas supply to the household involved, for the death would be entered on the Registrar-General's returns as accidental carbon monoxide poisoning.

The Joint Manager consulted Willcox on August 25th and sent him the Coroner's depositions. Before writing his report Willcox contacted the deceased woman's lady doctor who had attended her before she died.

Mr. and Mrs. Nunn were a poor and aged old couple. Both had been ill recently. Mr. Nunn had rested in his bedroom on the afternoon of August 6th and saw his wife for the last time at 3.0 p.m. when she went to his room to see if he was comfortable. She went downstairs. At 4.30 p.m. he went downstairs and found her lying unconscious on the scullery floor the door of which was open to the outside. The gas stove was turned on as if to heat a kettle. She was still alive and with help was put to bed. Her doctor saw her at 7.0 p.m. and she died at 7.30 p.m. Her breathing was stertorous and her colour blue. Her medical history was well recorded. She had had three stomach operations for gastric ulcer, the first two for haemorrhage in 1911. In 1924 she had been seen by Dr. James Collier, the famous neurologist, following a minor stroke and at that time was found to have a severely high blood pressure and an irregular heart.

Willcox provided abundant reasons to suppose that death was caused by a severe stroke. She was not in a closed space likely to contain a high percentage of carbon monoxide, her death was delayed by more than two hours after her removal from the source of the gas and her colour was not pink as is invariably the case in coal gas poisoning. He readily agreed that the inquest verdict had been incorrectly recorded and that the case would be wrongly classified in the Registrar-General's returns. The deputy coroner, and the coroner for whom he had acted, agreed that an erroneous verdict had been made but were unable to suggest any feasible methods of correcting the error except by application to the High Court for a fresh inquest. Sir Walter Schroder was consulted and gave the opinion that either this step should be taken or application be made to the Home Office for an exhumation. For the reason that the Gas Company were unwilling to cause additional embarrassment to the relatives they decided to take no further action.

Death in a Garage

The second case was that of a man living in relatively affluent circumstances in which at first sight it appeared to be a clear case of accidental death, but was it really so? The case resulted in dispute concerning the circumstantial evidence, and arbitration at law.

Major James Dunning, aged 59, was a banker with interests in the City, being a main shareholder in the firm of James Dunning and Company. An American by birth, he had served in the United States Army. He certainly lived in a style which nowadays would suggest a millionaire with his home at 25 Hans Place, Chelsea, and his weekend retreat at Legsheath Farm at Forest Row in Sussex. At his death on February 25th, 1931, he left £19,661 gross but he had many income tax burdens on his estate.

After his death Mrs. Dunning said that her husband occasionally stayed at the farm by himself and similarly sometimes she stayed there by herself with the domestic staff of a maid and a cook. He was not a communicative man about business matters, taking the line that their business affairs was his own concern. He had hinted to her that, owing to the financial depression in 1930 and 1931, which affected most of Europe and this country, they should try to economise. He had been in excellent health and was of a confident disposition. He held a Life Insurance policy for £10,000 with the Ocean, Accident and Guarantee Corporation and several smaller policies with different companies which added up to cover for about £770. Mrs. Dunning also held an insurance policy on the life of her husband for £10,000 with another company. This sum was duly paid to Mrs. Dunning as were those small sums amounting to £770 from the smaller policies. The accident policy under dispute was dated November 13th, 1923, and did not insure against death consequent on suicide "whether felonious or not".

Dunning was so fond of his 1913 model Rolls Royce car as to be almost obsessional about its efficiency and was mechanically minded enough to do minor repairs on it himself, although he employed a chauffeur. His chauffeur drove it to the Cricklewood Depot for certain repairs, including decarbonisation, on February 17th, 1931. On February 23rd he told his wife in the evening that he intended to do business at Birmingham the following day. He set out early in the morning from London by train.

In the afternoon the butler received a telegram instructing him to tell the chauffeur not to collect his car from the depot as he intended to collect it after a trial test. Later that day his wife received a further telegram from an hotel in Birmingham to say that he intended returning home the following day. Poor Mrs. Dunning never saw her husband alive again for at breakfast on February 25th she was informed that he had been found dead in his garage at the farm.

Evidence at the inquest revealed that he had arrived at the depot at 4.0 p.m. on February 24th, collected his car and driven himself to the farm at Forest Row, arriving at 6.30 p.m., telling the maid that he would spend the night at the farm, and was on his way to Hove but had had some trouble with his car. Ordering breakfast for 9.0 a.m. he took dinner followed by coffee. After a short sleep in his armchair he tackled a cross-word puzzle and told the maid that he was going to the garage to attend to his car. He was not depressed nor mentally abnormal. According to the maid and the cook he went to the garage at 10.35 p.m. When they retired to bed at 11.15 they heard the car engine running in the garage and smelt the fumes in their bedroom situated above the garage. The engine was thought to have run for some twenty minutes. The cook thought the engine stopped about 11.45 p.m.

The following morning at 7.30 the cowman arrived at the house, as was his custom, and was told by the maid that the Major had not slept in his bed. The hall light had been left on and the front door unbolted. The garage doors were locked on the inside. Later, he said it was the custom for anyone working in the garage during cold weather to lock the doors as otherwise they would not remain closed and the draught would be unpleasantly cold. Through the window he could see the Major lying dead on the floor and he forced an entrance by breaking the window. The dead man was lying on his back with his feet toward the near-side back wheel. Tools were scattered here and there, some on the table, others on the bench and floor. The car bonnet was open and an electric inspection lamp was still alight inside the engine. The dickey seat was open with a kit of tools open on it. The ignition was switched on but the engine had stopped running. A pipe was seen on the near side of the front driving seat. The chauffer considered that Dunning had been adjusting the clutch mechanism.

Post-mortem examination showed that death was due to carbon monoxide poisoning, the blood being found heavily saturated with gas. There was a severe bruise on the back of the head where it was resting. The verdict was death by misadventure from inhalation of carbon monoxide fumes from a motor engine.

On August 10th Mrs. Dunning's solicitors were informed that the Ocean, Accident and Guarantee Corporation was not prepared to admit liability. This was the only insurance company that took up this attitude.

Willcox was consulted on November 19th and asked to report, after assessment of all the evidence, including the inquest depositions and other documents. His conclusions were reached on December 8th. He entirely agreed with the inquest verdict. The circumstantial evidence, and particularly the bruise on the head, pointed strongly to accidental death. Carbon monoxide is present in a concentration of six per cent or more in the exhaust fumes of a car. A Rolls Royce 1913 model would be expected to emit at least two cubic feet of carbon monoxide per minute. Within thirty minutes about sixty cubic feet of gas would be emitted in this closed garage (all the windows were shut) of 2,902 cubic feet capacity, yielding a percentage of 2·01; an amount quite sufficient to cause death. Not only so, but the engine would be likely to stop running owing to insufficient oxygen in the contaminated atmosphere of the garage.

The lawyers acting for the Ocean Insurance Company and for Mrs. Dunning decided to proceed to arbitration. The case was heard at the Law Society before Mr. Stuart Bevan K.C., the sole arbitrator, on January 7th and 8th, 1931.

The Insurance Company did not doubt the cause of death but claimed that suspicious circumstantial evidence had been overlooked at the inquest and suppressed by Mr. James Dunning, son of deceased, who as a young business man himself, knew all about the state of his father's company of which he was a shareholder.

Major Dunning had been in difficulties with income tax for several years. It was a complicated matter as his personal finances were mixed up with the firm of Dunning & Company, but claims for income and super tax for the years 1920 to 1931, amounting in all to £66,896, had not been settled at the time of his death. His appeal against assessment had been protracted from November 1927 until as recently as February 16th, 1931, when the hearing had been postponed until March 9th. His financial position was therefore at any rate sufficient cause of suspicion of suicide.

A sufferer from insomnia, he had obtained from his doctor prescriptions for sleeping tablets on several occasions; the last prescription dated February 23rd for 10 Medinal tablets (grains 5) had been presented to the chemist by the chauffeur, who delivered them to his master. Though this had no bearing on the cause of death it could be interpreted as evidence of mental strain.

Then there was the locked door of the garage; but the evidence of the chauffeur and others was that the hinges were such that the doors would not remain ajar without swinging wide open and draughts could not otherwise be excluded. The doctor who arrived on the scene noticed a rug lying on the floor, no doubt put there to keep out the draught.

The movements of Dunning on February 24th and 25th were puzzling features of the case which were not brought out at the inquest. In the past it had not been unusual for the Major to stay at the farm with the knowledge of his wife but on this occasion she had been led to believe that he would return from Birmingham to London on February 25th whereas in fact he travelled by car from Birmingham, presumably through London, to Forest Row on February 24th. Why had he deceived his wife? Was it to get peace and quiet away from his family or was it part of a staged suicide plan, as the Insurance Company argued?

The housemaid at the farm recalled at the inquest that on his last evening after dinner he had explained to her "my car is not running right and I shall go out later to see it, so if you hear a noise there will be no need for alarm. If Mrs. Dunning rings up, don't say I am here as they will only think I am an old fool." But he was cheerful and in normal health doing a crossword puzzle.

In spite of suspicious circumstantial evidence and the theory of the insurance company that suicide had been carefully staged, the arbitration resulted in favour of Mrs. Dunning.

Between 1925 and 1928 Willcox from time to time reported on the health of employees of the London, Midland & Scottish Railway and the South Metropolitan Gas Board suspected to be suffering from occupational lead poisoning due to the use of lead paints. In five out of seventeen cases clinical evidence was supported by chemical analysis. In the remaining cases claims could not be considered justifiable nor were the analytical results positive. In at least two cases malingering was suspected.

A Rare Compensation Claim

Of greater interest was the tragic story of gradual poisoning in a rat-catcher by chemical substances used as rat poisons which was told at an inquest held at Watford on January 22nd, 1932. The illness of the deceased had been so insidious and unusual that the true cause of death escaped recognition until litigation commenced after the inquest. At this stage Willcox was consulted and assisted in fighting a successful legal contest in support of the National Union of Railwaymen to obtain a pension for the deceased's widow.

Jesse Sayell, aged 64 at the time of his death, had been employed as a professional rat-catcher by the L.M. & S. Railway Company for over 11 years. He was employed on the line between Euston and Birmingham.

His wife's evidence, supported by that of the doctor, was that he had complained of stomach trouble since 1925. Attacks of vomiting and diarrhoea occurred intermittently. Mr. Sayell was a conscientious man who refused to be away from work even on his doctor's advice. Knowing that Sayell had used arsenical rat poisons, Dr. Martin reasonably suspected chronic arsenical poisoning in 1925 and again in 1927. At the end of 1930 Sayell began to suffer from heart failure and had periods off work, six weeks from December to January, a month in April and May. The final illness commenced in August 1931 and terminated in death on January 19th, 1932, from heart failure.

The doctor, thinking this a clear case of chronic industrial poisoning, reported to the coroner and at the inquest gave his opinion that death was due to heart failure consequent on chronic arsenical poisoning. Indeed, at an earlier stage, in September he had consulted the National Union of Railwaymen, urging them to claim on behalf of his patient compensation under the Workmen's Compensation Act. Unfortunately the certifying surgeon under the Act refused to agree (in October) that the illness was caused by arsenical poisoning contracted by his employment, his reason being that at that time it was not a recognised industrial hazard among rat-catchers.

The jury's verdict was that death was due to heart failure due to high blood pressure which in its turn was due to arsenical poisoning contracted by the deceased during the course of his work. They added a rider "we suggest to the railway company that there should be better protection for men in this occupation".

The inquest findings, though just and fair as it finally became apparent, were to a great extent unsatisfactory. The coroner had omitted to arrange a post-mortem examination, no analysis for poisons had been carried out and he had entirely overlooked the fact that the question of a widow's compensation would later arise. Though it was true that Sayell had used arsenical rat poison no inquiry had been made concerning other chemical substances which had also been used for the same purpose over a period of many years. With regard to the jury's rider, the railway company had taken necessary steps to provide overalls and gloves to be used by Sayell at work. But what was lacking was the provision of necessary instruction of the workmen to take every preventive measure to avoid accidental poisoning in the handling of substances used at work.

Notwithstanding the inquest verdict and the medical opinion of the patient's doctor the railway company refused to admit the case as one of industrial poisoning under the rules of the compensation acts. It had been perhaps unfortunate that the certifying surgeon had seen the patient on October 12th at a time when he had partially recovered from his illness, having been away from work since August suffering from heart failure; at the time of consultation there were indeed no symptoms suggestive of arsenical poison. The error of the second doctor was understandable but was nevertheless support for the railway company in taking a firm line of resistance to the claim.

The National Union of Railwaymen took every necessary step in supporting the widow's claim. Fresh evidence was collected, but, more important still, scientific evidence and analysis of the rat poisons used over a period of eleven years provided evidence which turned the scales of justice in the right direction. There was no doubt that arsenical rat poison had upset Sayell so much that he refused to use it after September 1930. He subsequently used Rodine, which was shown by William Partridge, the well-known analyst, in his report of September 29th 1932, to contain no arsenic at all, but phosphorus to the extent of 1·91% (of total phosphorus). In fact, Rodine had been used by Sayell continuously throughout the whole period of eleven years. The arsenical raticide, Omezone, used before 1930 was shown to contain 1·95% of arsenious oxide.

The opinion of Willcox was therefore requested by Counsel for the N.U.R., Mr. W. Shakespeare, in November 1932. The discovery that the likely source of poisoning was phosphorus, and not arsenic, had an important bearing on the course of the legal dispute. Phosphorus was a rare poison used mainly in suicide cases and by accident. It was quoted by Willcox in the Lumleian Lectures in 1931 as an example of a powerful liver poison. It was at one time used in the manufacture of matches and was occasionally the source of poisoning in the industry. At the time of writing phosphorus poisoning no longer occurs or is so rare as to be merely an episode in the history of toxicology. No longer are phosphorus rat poisons used. Willcox reported on January 6th, 1933, that the case was clearly one of phosphorus poisoning suffered over a long period. The history of recurrent ulceration of the mouth, heart involvement and bouts of jaundice indicated that phosphorus, rather than arsenic, was to blame. Arsenic had not been used for a period of almost two years before death. The small percentage of arsenic taken previously would have been excreted a long time ago and could not have played any part in causing death. Phosphorus had been taken into the system both by inhalation of fumes given off from Rodine and probably also by hand and mouth contamination.

The case of *Sayell* v. *L.M.S. railways* was fought before His Honour Judge Hill-Kelly, at the Bloomsbury County Court on April 6th, 1933. By then Dr. F. B. Martin, the patient's doctor, had been persuaded to agree with Willcox that Sayell's illness was consistent with poisoning by phosphorus, and not by arsenic. In his evidence he admitted that his patient had been jaundiced on several occasions but all the symptoms had been consistent with phosphorus poisoning. The verdict for the plaintiff was based on the medical evidence of Martin supported by Willcox's expert and decisive opinion. In spite of his diagnosis of the wrong poison as the cause of the fatal illness Martin had deserved his successful struggle on behalf of his patient and the widow, achieving victory in the end. In making an excusable mistake he had accepted the patient's opinion that arsenic was the cause of his illness. The patient knew nothing about the danger of phosphorus in the rat poison.

Chapter 23

Food Poisoning and the Law

In the years between the wars medico-legal work in connection with food poisoning and food "adulteration" was repeatedly presented to Willcox in the form of requests for opinions on the medical evidence; in these cases this was of paramount importance in deciding whether the evidence was such as to lead to litigation in court or otherwise. The Food and Drugs Acts of 1887, subsequently modified from time to time, were designed to control the purity and safety of food supplied to the public in a state fit for consumption. A shop or hotel or restaurant is liable for claims for damages if a customer is rendered ill as a result of breach of contract. The Acts were liable to be abused by unscrupulous litigants making unjustifiable claims on large firms resulting from illness supposedly caused by food purchased or meals eaten at restaurants, cafes and hotels. The question of "post hoc propter hoc" rested almost entirely on medical evidence, and there was not necessarily agreement between the doctors acting for both parties in a dispute. Between 1920 and 1940 Willcox gave opinions on about thirty-two such cases; many disputes were settled out of court by mutual agreement between the lawyers on both sides. Some claims were abandoned after expert opinion at an early stage whereas others were disputed in court.

Willcox's influence and experience both as toxicologist and physician played a major part in combating the tendency, which became almost a fashion, for unjustifiable and unscrupulous claims for damages. In some cases well-known firms or restaurants would be far too ready to pay damages rather than face open litigation in Court, not only in order to save the reputation of the business being questioned in public and reported in the Press, but to avoid the heavy cost of litigation which would far exceed the necessary damages hoped for by the plaintiff. Nevertheless, this practice amounted to a form of blackmail, being an admission that the claim of the plaintiff was justifiable, which very often was quite untrue. Such a case was that of a twenty-four-year-old lady, a student of music, who developed diarrhoea and sickness twelve hours after eating half a tin of herrings in tomato sauce in 1926. She continued at work though mildly ill for three weeks, after which she was kept in bed by her doctor. She was diagnosed by a well-known expert in tropical diseases as a case of bacillary dysentery, the bacteria being found in the excreta. The canning firm requested Willcox's opinion as to the attitude they should take up. Willcox emphatically repudiated liability, considering that as dysentery bacilli (not food-poisoning bacteria) had been found in the excreta there was no evidence that her illness had been acquired from the tinned fish; and no bacteria had been found in the fish after full investigation. Notwithstanding his report, the firm's representative wrote in reply "Though it is clear from your report that our goods are not responsible, we have to bear in mind that considerable publicity might be given if the matter reached a hearing in the High Court. Even if a verdict were given in our favour, it is not certain that the Press would put it in such a way as to help us with our public, which unfortunately is usually suspicious of all canned goods. To pay an unjustifiable claim under these circumstances is a kind of blackmail which it displeases us to give in to, but we have spent a large amount of money in creating goodwill and have to think very seriously about risking it." In fact the firm's insurance company did pay her medical expenses to the tune of several hundred pounds, though the patient had fully recovered from her illness by the time Willcox saw her in November 1926.

The same year a fifty-year-old sanitary engineer opened a bottle of milk, poured off the cream, and drank some milk containing pieces of glass which he spat out, wrapped in paper, and presented to the dairy the next day. A small bleeding abrasion to his mouth was his only disability, the rest of the milk having been consumed. Five weeks later he consulted his doctor for indigestion, never having suffered from this before. His claim was settled by his lawyer and the legal adviser to the dairy for compensation of £20 to the customer. Similarly, in 1927, dirt found on the inside of a bottle of milk proved to be of similar value to a lady who claimed that she had had gastro-enteritis lasting for a week.

A man who owned an outfitters' business in the East end of London purchased a packet of biscuits at a local grocer's shop in August 1927, not realising the important consequences which might ensue. He found insects (weevils) burrowing in some of the biscuits, felt nervous and nauseated, with abdominal discomfort, though his doctor found no physical disorder, merely psychological distress. But the symptoms became worse, though he was able to continue working. He was seen by Willcox in consultation with his own doctor, and the medical adviser to the well-known biscuit manufacturer. They agreed that his illness was not caused by the insects, but probably by indigestion due to his septic and deficient teeth causing ordinary indigestion. For the sake of its reputation the firm decided to fight their cause. The case was fixed for hearing in the King's Bench Division in December 1930. Willcox appeared at Court, but the case was settled by mutual agreement of the parties at the last moment, the plaintiff withdrawing the charge on condition that the costs were shared by both sides.

Surprisingly, one of the feeblest claims was that of a disgruntled doctor, a medical officer of health, who developed gastro-enteritis after eating a mince pie at teatime following a round of golf on Christmas Eve 1920. He was ill over Christmas, his complaint to the lawyer being his inability to enjoy the seasonal festivities. His failure to justify his claim was due to the simple mistake of failing to call his own doctor to certify the severity of his illness in support of his theory that the mince pie was to blame. Willcox, who always regarded mince pies as indigestible, again diagnosed ordinary indigestion, in a man with a previous history of it, who had been upset while in an exhausted condition by an indigestible article of food.

When he ceased to be a Home Office analyst Willcox was seldom consulted concerning food "adulteration" though a few examples are worthy of mention. Food Inspectors were the cause of enquiries brought to his attention in 1922 and 1923 for expert advice. A well known cocoa and chocolate manufacturer sought his advice concerning the presence of arsenic in a brand of soluble cocoa. A small proportion of potassium carbonate was added to the cocoa to render it more soluble; the arsenic was present in this substance and not in the cocoa before its addition to the mixture. The arsenical content was one eighth grain per pound of soluble cocoa. It was a case of simple arithmetic. Yet Travers Humphreys had been engaged as Counsel for the firm following a summons charging the firm with "aiding and abetting the grocer concerned by selling to him cocoa containing arsenic". One pound of cocoa being calculated to supply a hundred cups of drink, ten cups (five pints) would contain no more than one eightieth of a grain of arsenic, a smaller amount than a medicinal dose, quite harmless to the public as even a cocoa addict would be satisfied with less than ten cups in a day.

The adulteration of tinned peas became a matter of public interest in 1923. Tinned peas often contained small amounts of copper sulphate which preserved the peas but, more important, their green colour during storage. The Bedfordshire County Council obtained a conviction against a firm selling tinned peas containing 2·7 grains per pound of peas. The defendants gave notice of Appeal. The Medical Officer of Health succeeded in enlisting Willcox's expert support of the Council at the Appeal Court, but the case was abandoned in view of the expert evidence the firm expected to encounter. An exactly parallel case was brought by the Kensington Borough Council in 1923 when a conviction was obtained for selling peas containing copper sulphate in a strength of 1·5 grains per pound. The Appeal was abandoned in this case as a result of Willcox's opinion.

Many years later, in 1934, a consulting chemist appealed to Willcox for influential support in aid of an importer of tinned tomato purée found by analysts to contain copper to the extent of less than ¼ grain per pound (35 parts per million). The sale of the purée had already been stopped by the Bermondsey Medical Officer of Health in view of the analyst's findings. Both Willcox and the analyst thought this step unnecessary for several reasons; that copper was officially permissible in peas up to 70 parts per million; that Marmite contained 80 parts per million; and the medicinal dose of copper sulphate was one half to two grains. The Medical Officer of Health withdrew his ban of the sale.

Curried Prawns at Pagani's

The case of the Wimpole Street dentist who sued Pagani's restaurant in 1923 was the only case in which Willcox supported a plaintiff in an action in court for alleged food poisoning. Though Willcox did not appear as a witness his report was probably a decisive factor in winning the action.

The dentist lunched at Pagani's on March 13th on curried prawns and rice, followed by coffee. While working in the afternoon he became so ill that his doctor was summoned at 5 p.m. and Dr. Gow of St. Bartholomew's Hospital was also called. Collapsed and cold, with vomiting and diarrhoea, the patient was admitted to a Nursing Home where he recovered in three days. He then convalesced for three weeks before resuming work. The only article under suspicion was curried prawns; Willcox considered this as the certain cause. The claim was contested but the dentist was awarded damages of £100, a fraction of a claim which the judge considered was exaggerated.

Willcox and Spilsbury opposed

A forty-six-year-old spinster who worked as a Court Hairdresser's assistant in Dover Street, London, had supper at 7 p.m. on June 2nd, 1926, at Appenrodt's Restaurant, her meal consisting of liver sandwiches and Russian salad, as she had often eaten on other occasions. She had had tea and bread and butter for breakfast but by the time litigation arose she was unable to recall what she had eaten at Vasco's Restaurant for lunch on the same day. She became ill overnight, feeling "hot and irritable", with a rash on her shoulders. Though she claimed she felt ill the next day she went to work. In the evening, failing to contact her doctor, she was given a peppermint mixture by a chemist. On the second night diarrhoea, vomiting and pain followed. She was seen by Dr. Smith and attended by him almost daily until June 17th, being certified as suffering from food poisoning. Dr. Robinson took over her subsequent care. Symptoms recurred on June 19th when she vomited repeatedly. Dr. F. Moseley saw her in consultation on June 22nd. She was then in a tearful and hysterical state, feeling "terrible" and thinking "she would go mad". She had an urticarial (nettle) rash, abdominal pain, sickness but no diarrhoea, her temperature being 102 °F. She had apparent suicidal feelings and an accurate account of her symptoms could not be given; she was in fear of losing her job. She recovered within three weeks and convalesced with relatives in Sheppey. She did not return to work.

The lady had already been seen by three doctors. As if this was not enough, Dr. Stephen Lewis, a psychiatrist, saw her in consultation with Dr. Robinson and Dr. Moseley on November 5th. Dr. Lewis's advice to Appenrodt's solicitors was to repudiate liability. It was impossible to prove that symptoms had been due to a particular meal, nor could the patient recall what she had eaten for lunch on June 2nd. She had been subjected to various mental strains; several relatives had recently died and she had quarrelled with a landlady about her accommodation. Litigation became more likely as a result of disagreement between Dr. Robinson and Dr. Lewis, the former considering that her mental strain was the result of her illness and not its cause, and that she had primarily suffered from food poisoning. But the doctors agreed that she had recovered sufficiently to return to work and would benefit by doing so. But she was still in a highly neurotic state, complaining of bizarre symptoms, hiccough, flatulence and difficulty in focusing.

The firm firmly repudiated liability on the grounds that the liver and pork in the sausages came from a respectable dealer; that twenty pounds was used daily at the restaurant and the salad was prepared daily by a lady with thirty years' experience of this particular work. There had been only one other case of alleged food poisoning in the history of the restaurant, in which herring salad was incriminated. The firm had been defended by Mr. M. Shearman K.C. fourteen years previously and the case dismissed with costs.

Willcox was consulted by Appenrodt's Solicitors on May 16th. His report in favour of the defence was based on many aspects of the case. No other cases of poisoning from the same source had occurred; there was no evidence of unhygienic preparation of the food in question, no details of the food taken by the plaintiff within three days of the illness had been submitted; no pathogenic bacteria had been cultured from the excreta; there was no proof that symptoms were due to the food as alleged; nor could the recurrent symptoms of June 21st possibly have been caused by food taken on June 2nd. All her symptoms could have been due to nervous strain and indigestion or other natural cause. Indeed, many of her symptoms were quite inconsistent with food poisoning alone. According to his invariable custom Willcox consulted with defence Counsel before the case came to Court. This time his consultation with Mr. Malcolm Hilberry K.C. lasted for two hours, an indication of the care and trouble they both took in a cause they both felt was correct and just.

The case was heard before Mr. Justice Horridge in the King's Bench Division on October 24th, Mr. Samuels appearing for the prosecution. The case surprisingly lasted three days. Apart from Willcox and Dr. Smith, all other medical witnesses were in support of the plaintiff; Dr. Perkins, physician to Waterloo Hospital, Dr. Robinson and Sir Bernard Spilsbury. Willcox stood firmly by the opinion expressed in his report. Though his evidence was shorter in duration than that of Spilsbury it was instrumental in achieving a notable victory for the defence. The case was dismissed with costs. Hilberry's letter speaks for itself:

2 King's Bench Walk,
Temple, E.C.4.

October 27th, 1927.

My dear Sir William,
Unsatisfactory as I know your treatment was at the hands of the Bench in the Appenrodt case, you must surely feel that the jury by its verdict has made it apparent that it preferred your evidence, and if I may venture to say so, the perfect fairness with which it was given, to that of the plaintiff. I hope this result will obliterate any unpleasantness in your memory about the case. I want to thank you very much for all your help and patience.

Yours very sincerely,

Malcolm Hilberry.

Food Poisoning at a Famous Hotel

On March 28th 1930, Willcox was approached by the Management of one of the most important hotel groups in London to help solve a mysterious outbreak of food poisoning which had already affected numerous guests at the hotel and at several public dinners held during February and March 1930. During this period over a thousand meals had been served without any serious consequences. The outbreak was a source of the greatest anxiety and fears that further cases would occur with consequent enormous financial litigation costs. Though litigation was fortunately averted, nevertheless the outbreak proved costly by reason of the extensive investigations carried out to detect its cause. The painstaking investigation directed by Willcox, and the labours of the bacteriologists consulted, provide an object lesson in public health measures necessary to stamp out disease on a large scale. For this reason alone it deserves description.

The history of the outbreak is summarised as follows:

February 27th Fly Fishers' Club Dinner. 140 guests. Seven complaints.

March 1st After lunch, a member of the staff and a friend affected. Tin Box Manufacturers' Association Dinner. 147 guests. 60 guests ill, including the Club Secretary. One guest claimed damages calculated at £53 for replacement of wife's evening gown and his dinner jacket soiled by vomit, and costs of cleaning carpets and other clothes. This claim was promptly settled by the management.

March 23rd A Director and his wife, and Sir Cyril Atkinson K.C. affected after dinner.

March 24th The Assistant Manager and his wife affected.

March 26th Mr. Comyns Berkeley, the gynaecologist, and his wife affected at night, following dinner.
The Royal Caledonian School Dinner. 170 guests. Six affected.

March 28th Oxley Golf Club Dinner. 170 guests. Six affected, including the Captain's wife.

In all affected cases gastro-enteritis commenced several hours after the meal, often in the middle of the night. Fortunately there were no fatal cases.

Early in March the analyst to the City of Westminster carried out analyses of foods eaten at the hotel for lead, tin, copper, arsenic and mercury and other poisons with negative results.

After studying all the evidence, including details of the menus, Willcox called a meeting on March 31st, attended by the Manager of the Hotel group, the Hotel Manager and their medical adviser. The only probable source of the infection was ice cream, as this was the only item appearing in all the menus at the various meals. Willcox suspected a "carrier" of infection existed among the kitchen staff.

He enlisted the services of Dr. John Freeman, the St. Mary's Hospital bacteriologist and colleague of Wright and Fleming, to investigate the cream and ice cream, the excreta from affected patients and the kitchen staff. The investigations took nearly three weeks to complete. Three unaffected "carriers" of infection were discovered among the kitchen staff, working entirely in the ice cream section of the kitchens. The ice cream production was stopped, the carriers suspended from duty, one being admitted to St. Mary's Hospital for observation and treatment. Willcox made a thorough inspection of the kitchens on April 1st and found that all the foods supplied to the hotel were of the highest quality. Storage was carried out with the greatest care. He considered that ice cream was certainly the cause of infection. It was made in a special room adjoining the kitchens. There was probable contamination during the handling of the ingredients, the beating of the egg yolk, and the mixing of sugar, milk and cream. Though the mixture was heated, it was not raised to boiling point, and bacterial contamination by handling of the eggs would escape destruction by heat.

At the end of April the Principal of the Royal Institute of Public Health, Sir William Smith, investigated the source of cream supplied by the Faringdon Dairies and found no source of infection at its source. Finally, on May 12th, Willcox made a further inspection of the kitchens to ensure that no measures had been overlooked to prevent further recurrence of food contamination.

A poisonous sandwich ?

Every doctor is familiar with the patient who quickly jumps to conclusions about the cause of his illness, however erroneous or false they be. It is human nature to search for something or someone to blame. Food is often blamed, particularly so when symptoms of gastro-enteritis follow a meal. In the case of a restaurant considerable risk is taken by the Management in respect of claims for compensation of the victim for medical expenses or financial loss through inability to work. The risk which managements carry is almost always carried by insurance companies; compensation is usually by settlement between both parties without recourse to litigation in court.

The case of *Harris* v. *Barnett & Co.*, which was heard in the King's Bench Division in 1936, was an example in which a claim brought out medical evidence of a conflicting nature. The court had to decide whether or not Mr. Harris's illness was attributable to food poisoning contracted from eating two beef sandwiches at The White City on February 20th, 1936.

A 53-year-old Jewish gentleman, a firm's representative, had his usual cup of tea for breakfast on February 20th. He purchased four sandwiches of salted beef and three gherkins, wrapped up at Barnett's shop, and later commenced eating them at the British Industries Fair. On eating the second sandwich he noticed a peculiar flavour and ate no more. After returning home he began to suffer from a dry throat, vomiting and diarrhoea, for which he was seen by his doctor on the third day, and later by a London surgeon, Mr. Dickson Wright, for suspected intestinal obstruction, but his x-ray did not support this diagnosis. On February 26th he developed phlebitis in his left leg and vomiting persisted. Two days later the right leg was affected. A physician, Dr. Bruce Williamson, was called and admitted the patient to hospital; he remained there from March 10th to 28th.

As so often happens, one complication was followed by another. He developed urinary obstruction, due to his prostate gland, and spent further periods in hospital, from April 21st to June 15th, and again for two weeks in July, for surgical reasons. His last admission on September 10th was followed by the main operation for removal of the prostate gland. He left hospital on October 8th and had fully recovered by November 10th.

Many doctors had seen the case by the time Willcox saw the patient in consultation with his own doctor and the medical adviser to the defendants' insurance company, on November 3rd. Willcox considered that he probably did suffer from food poisoning, in spite of negative laboratory evidence. Phlebitis, he thought, was a complication of this, but his subsequent bladder disorder was due to an entirely different cause. There were no grounds for a claim for any illness after April 12th. He urged a compromise financial settlement by the lawyers. But this was not to be. The patient was also seen by Mr. John Everidge, one of the leading urinary surgeons in London, who considered the entire illness had been caused by disease of the prostate and uraemic poisoning from this cause. At a joint consultation with Willcox, Everidge converted him to his own view of the case. Together they formulated on behalf of defence Counsel the questions to be put to the plaintiff in cross-examination. A week before the case was heard, Willcox visited the Barnett establishment, and was unable to fault the methods by which the beef was salted, and the sandwiches prepared.

The case was heard before Mr. Justice-Greaves Lord on December 10th, and lasted four days. Mr. Roland Oliver K.C. appeared for the defence, and Mr. Levy for Harris. Willcox consulted Oliver before the case commenced, but gave his evidence on the last day. It was a contest between two rival medical teams holding their respective opinions. For the plaintiff, Bruce Williamson and Dickson Wright, supported by the patient's own doctor, considered that the early part of his illness was caused by food poisoning. For the Defendants, Everidge and Willcox, supported by Mr. R. Coyte, another genito-urinary surgeon, claimed that the whole illness was due to poisoning resulting from uraemia, including the diarrhoea and vomiting which followed the consumption of the beef sandwich. They considered that phlebitis was a complication of the prostatic disorder.

Judgment with costs was awarded to the plaintiff on December 18th. Willcox and Everidge accepted half their normal fees at the request of the defendants' Solicitors, as a cost of their defeat.

Paratyphoid at Sea

Illness contracted on board ship while on a pleasure cruise can be a most irritating and expensive experience, apart from the discomfort of the illness. The sufferer may be so aggrieved at missing his holiday that it is only too easy to blame the management as the alleged cause of the illness.

The Empress of Australia sailed from Southampton on August 1st, 1936 on a Mediterranean cruise lasting three weeks. A thirty-eight-year-old man felt faint and sick on the second day of the voyage after his dinner. The following day he complained to the ship's doctor that he felt sick and had abdominal discomfort, which led to a diagnosis of sea sickness. But his temperature remaining up till August 11th, the doctor called into consultation two doctors on board, the first on August 7th when spots were seen on the abdomen. Correctly suspected of typhoid infection, he was isolated in the ship's hospital. The third doctor agreed, but the patient refused to remain there, and returned to his cabin, complaining that he had been poisoned by food eaten on the ship. On August 10th he had much improved, but complained that his buttocks had been burned by a disinfectant on the ship's commode. Fortunately the burns were mild in degree, but the patient was abusive when his illness had almost terminated.

The plaintiff claimed that his illness was caused by eating stuffed duck on August 2nd at dinner. He alleged that the stuffing had an unpleasant taste and he ate about three quarters of it. Other claims concerned the burns from the disinfectant and criticism of the treatment rendered by the ship's doctor.

Willcox was consulted and issued his report on January 18th to the solicitors acting for the Canadian Pacific Steamship Company. He expressed the emphatic opinion that the illness was either typhoid or paratyphoid (most likely the latter), contracted before the patient had embarked. The nature of the rash strongly suggested this diagnosis in spite of a negative agglutination test for typhoid and related fevers, carried out at Athens on August 10th.

Though the second doctor called into consultation on board supported the plaintiff's cause, the medical evidence was strongly in favour of the defendants. The fact that there had been no other cases of food poisoning on board was an important point.

The case was fixed to be heard in the King's Bench Division by Mr. Justice Greaves-Lord on January 20th, 1937. Willcox arrived ten minutes late, to learn that the case had been settled out of court before the hearing. The defendants agreed to compensate a small proportion of the medical expenses resulting from his illness.

During the years between 1923 and 1927 Willcox dealt with six claims for alleged food poisoning against restaurants; these were settled by the lawyers acting for the respective parties without recourse to litigation in Court. In one case, a person who had previously suffered from colitis unjustifiably blamed a restaurant's meal for symptoms which followed, and was persuaded to drop her claim. Tinned peas eaten at a Windsor restaurant in 1930 certainly caused severe illness in four members of a family who lunched there. Likewise, poisonous mushrooms accounted for a serious illness in a man who supped at the Criterion in 1932. Lobster salad affected two doctors who attended a social evening at the French hospital in 1933. In one of these cases gastro-enteritis was followed by phlebitis and pulmonary embolism, from which she fortunately recovered. All these claims were settled privately as a result of Willcox's reports.

In 1935 a gentleman lunched at a London club on oysters, a pork chop and milk pudding. In the early hours of the next morning he had headache and abdominal pain, but he went to work and had no diarrhoea or vomiting. But diarrhoea started on the third day. He would not have consulted his solicitor, had not a specialist in consultation diagnosed (incorrectly, as it later transpired) food poisoning. A week later he developed a rectal abscess which required an operation. His troubles did not end there, for a stone in the kidney was diagnosed four months later, his kidney being removed in 1936. The patient's claim was abandoned as a result of Willcox's opinion that his illness could in no way have been caused by food poisoning, and the stone was quite unrelated.

Claims which at first sight appear ridiculous were sometimes the source of concern to lawyers who required medical advice. Willcox was approached by solicitors acting for the Criterion Restaurant in 1937 in the case of a lady who had supper with friends on June 12th at the restaurant. Plates with rolls were placed before each guest. The waiter's attention was called to a roll broken by the lady, revealing a number of ants which ran over the plate and table. A portion of the roll was eaten followed by cold meat and salad. For three weeks thereafter she complained of nausea, poor appetite and occasional vomiting, but not diarrhoea. A surgeon being consulted, appendicitis was diagnosed and at operation a diseased appendix was removed but no ants were found. Willcox reported that her illness was entirely due to appendicitis which commenced by chance soon after the meal was eaten. The claim was duly abandoned.

Chapter 24

The Battle of the Barbiturates

The story of the use of drugs to produce sleep, termed hypnotics, started just about a hundred years ago. At the beginning of this century few drugs were available for this purpose, but from that time onwards there commenced an astonishing increase in the production of drugs on a commercial basis designed for the sole purpose of inducing sleep in people, not necessarily suffering from physical illness, but more often for those enduring mental strain, depression or minor frustrations of life. The theory, then becoming fashionable, that insomnia was a disease to be feared, and that sleep was one of the cardinal ingredients of existence, probably contributed to the alarming increase of the use of hypnotic drugs from 1900 onwards.

Willcox qualified as a doctor at the time of this notable advance in medical practice. In his early days as a practising physician, and as analyst to the Home Office, he soon encountered cases of suicide due to hypnotic drugs. Some of these unhappy stories were described in his writings and addresses on the subject of drug toxicity; the dangers and pitfalls associated with the increasing number of derivatives of barbituric acid were repeatedly brought to his notice during the whole period of his career as a physician until his retirement in 1935 and thereafter. It can be said that he was almost alone prophetic in foretelling of the dangers inherent in the indiscriminate use of these drugs many years before the truth of his beliefs came to be widely recognised in the profession.

"The Battle of the Barbiturates", as it later came to be called, was a professional controversy which took place in the medical press and was, perhaps unfortunately, yet unintentionally, reported in the lay press a long time before the days of broadcasting, in the days when newspapers were the main sources of public information about medical affairs.

Willcox's awareness of the potential dangers of Veronal, the first of the barbiturate drugs, first came to the surface of his mind in 1909, three years after he commenced practice in Queen Anne Street. It was in that year that fatalities from these drugs increased. In several of these cases he carried out analyses of port-mortem specimens. Later came the First World War, when he was temporarily away from practice for four years.

A full account of the Battle of the Barbiturates has never previously been written. It has been the source of much misunderstanding and confusion even among experts in drugs and among psychiatrists interested in a subject that has already become an important chapter in medical history. Even Dr. M. M. Glatt in his careful and painstaking survey referred to again later, on the subject of the Abuse of Barbiturates in the United Kingdom (1962), overlooked the early part of the controversy. The battle was unwittingly commenced by Willcox at a meeting at the

Royal Society of Medicine (Therapeutics Section) in 1927. It was fought in two parts, so that it can be said that there were in fact two separate battles; the last one in 1934 commenced on the same ground. In each case it was fought between Willcox with "behind-the-scenes" supporters against two prominent psychiatrists who openly challenged his views. No account of Willcox's life would be adequate if it failed to describe the battle in detail, in view of its importance in the history of Medicine and Therapeutics. In the history of any military campaign, it is necessary to describe the antecedent history of the opposing forces. Likewise in this medical controversy the history of its development must first be adequately discussed. It is convenient to do this in several phases.

The History of Hypnotic Drugs—1906–1918

Before the introduction of chloroform to anaesthesia in 1847, the drugs used to induce sleep were opium and its preparations, including the camphorated tincture (paregoric); belladonna and its related substances stramonium and henbane; and Indian hemp.

Chloral hydrate was introduced in 1869, the year before Willcox's birth. It has sustained its reputation for over a century, being still used as a safe hypnotic for adults and children. Then came sulphonal in 1886 followed by its derivatives trional and tetranol; they gradually fell into disfavour owing to their potential toxic effects on the red blood cells.

The drug Barbitone, better known later as Veronal, was first synthesized in Germany in 1898. By 1905 its properties and effects could be studied in the German and French journals; one of the earliest fatalities was described by Kress (1905) in a girl psychiatric patient aged 23, who secretly took the drug in excessive doses as great as two grams, though not with suicidal intent.

Willcox carefully studied the current methods of analysis for barbitone in urine, body fluids and in organs after death, work which was then quite unknown in Britain. Between 1905 and 1907 there were twelve fatal cases of veronal poisoning in Berlin alone, and many others in France and the U.S.A. The Frenchman Mongeri (1905) had studied the toxic effects, attributing these to impurities, while noting the hypnotic value of the drug. He went so far as to issue a warning that special care should be taken with its use in patients with defective kidney function.

In 1906 Veronal came into common use and superseded the sulphonal group of drugs as hypnotics. In the same year Dial (diallyl barbituric acid) and Luminal (phenobarbitone) were launched on the market. The latter is still the basic drug for epilepsy. They could all be freely obtained without medical prescription.

Several fatalities were reported in the press during the years before the First World War, and in some of them Willcox actually carried out the analyses for poison. Suspicion of foul play, which followed the death of Hugh Trevanion in 1912, led to the exhumation by Spilsbury and Willcox. It was estimated that a dose of at least 150 grains of veronal had been taken, ten times the proper dose, either with suicidal intent or by repeated overdoses taken in a state of mental confusion. The jury's rider was to the effect that it should be made illegal to supply this hypnotic without the prescription of a doctor, and that veronal should be scheduled accordingly. The case was referred to in a B.M.J. Editorial (March 15th, 1913) which drew attention to the dangerous properties of these drugs, the numerous fatalities, and the risk of drug habits.

Trevanion died at Hove. By a curious coincidence a retired doctor living nearby at Brighton died of veronal poisoning in March 1913, as the inquest verdict recorded—clearly a suicide case. From that time onward Willcox made repeated attempts to achieve the restriction of the barbiturates to medical prescription.

The manufacturers of veronal laid stress on the danger of exceeding the maximum dose of fifteen grains, but through Willcox's efforts the official dose in the B.P.C. was reduced to ten grains in 1911. Willcox's views were publicly expressed for the first time in a paper on Veronal Poisoning, read at the Seventeenth International Congress of Medicine in August 1913. The paper was mainly on the subject of the pathology and chemical aspects of veronal poisoning, but several far-reaching and significant observations attracted attention. Among the toxic features he mentioned headache, delirium, ataxic gait, allergic rashes, and broncho-pneumonia. It was quite likely for a case of poisoning to be mistakenly diagnosed as broncho-pneumonia, certified after death as such, and to escape detection unrecorded in the official statistics. Chronic poisoning could be mistaken for various nervous diseases and be overlooked. Tolerance would sometimes lead to increasing doses, as he had found in his own experience and had been recorded in the foreign literature. Admitting that veronal was a powerful yet useful hypnotic when carefully prescribed, he warned the medical profession and the public of the dangers of taking the drug without the knowledge and prescription of a doctor (1913). That year was significant in that the barbiturate drugs were placed in Part 2 of the poisons schedule under the Poisons and Pharmacy Act of 1908, which meant that these drugs could only be sold by a qualified pharmacist, though without medical prescriptions.

The B.M.A. met in July of that year, strangely enough at Brighton, only a mile or so from the scenes of the two tragedies mentioned above. In his address on "The Use and Abuse of Hypnotics" the whole subject of insomnia was surveyed. There had grown up the absurd theory that insomnia could be instantly relieved by the taking of drugs and the exaggerated notion that sleep was of vital importance in maintenance of mental, as distinct from physical, health. His views on the subject are worth recalling:

"In every case of supposed insomnia it will be well first to make sure that absence of sleep really exists. Not infrequently a patient imagines that he has had a sleepless night, whereas he may in fact have slept or dozed for several hours. When insomnia really exists it must be remembered that this condition is only a symptom, and its cause must be carefully investigated. The immediate recourse to hypnotic drugs is to be deprecated, since frequently harmful results follow. Not only is there danger of the development of a drug habit, but commonly the patient develops a sad lack of self-reliance, thinking that he cannot exist without artificial aids to sleep. It must also be remembered that sleep induced by drugs is not the same as natural sleep, nor has it the same beneficial value." After classifying the causes of insomnia, he continued "the first measure should be directed towards treatment or removal of the cause, then attention to modification in the daily habits of the patient, and the ventilation and temperature of the bedroom . . .

"Before resorting to treatment with drugs, the physician should always consider if true necessity exists for their use and continuance; bearing in mind the danger of drug habits, toxic symptoms, cumulative effects due to poor excretion in kidney failure or to slow absorption, the question of idiosyncrasy or allergy, and, perhaps most important, the danger of fatal poisoning generally caused by the patient increasing the dose unknown to his doctor, so that ultimately a dangerous dose is taken."

"It would be most desirable", he concluded, "if hypnotic drugs were only supplied on the prescription of a medical man. In the case of drugs with a powerful hypnotic action (including the barbiturates) it would be desirable if medical practitioners wrote on the prescription 'not to be repeated'." (B.M.J., 1913).

Those views may seem today merely expressions of common sense, but by 1913 the number of fatalities had risen year by year. There was nothing to prevent the public purchasing barbiturates from anyone who chose to sell them without medical prescription, as the B.M.J. Editor complained (1913). But the seeds of the recurrent controversy were sown by Sir Maurice Craig, the distinguished psychiatrist, who followed Willcox's address by a very different kind of approach. He stressed the great importance of gaining the patients' confidence to sleep, and the danger of not giving hypnotics early enough, and of allowing them to have bad nights. He regarded insomnia as a cause of mental disturbance rather than a symptom of it; this was the main difference in the views of these two experts. Nevertheless, Craig did believe in the close observation of the effect of hypnotic drugs by the doctor, and condemned the habit by which patients prescribed for themselves. The meeting was not otherwise controversial, but a doctor from Hartlepool condemned barbiturates in stronger terms than Willcox. Willcox took part in discussions at the Society for the Study of Inebriety on October 13th and at the Harveian Society on November 26th 1914, on the subject of Drug Addiction. The first of these followed an authoritative address on Drug Addiction in Mental Disorder by Dr. Robert Armstrong-Jones, the grandfather of Princess Margaret's husband, Lord Snowdon. In these brief addresses Willcox referred to the drug habit as a potential cause of suicide and accidental death from veronal and other barbiturates. (British J. of Inebriety 1914–1915 and B.M.J., 1914).

By the end of 1926 there had been no less than 268 fatalities of which 88 had been suicidal deaths (table I). The problem had therefore become of national importance, but other dangers appeared on the horizon in the form of the menace of German aggression. The dangers of barbiturates were put aside when the horrors and suffering of war were endured from 1914–1918. But public attention was directed to the barbiturates again early in 1918 when the death occurred of General Sir Beauchamp Duff. A sufferer from insomnia, Duff had been criticised by the Mesopotamian Commission for the part he played in the malhandling of the campaign in Iraq while serving as Commander in Chief in India. He was another victim of an accidental overdose of veronal.

Table I

Fatal poisoning from Drugs of Barbituric Acid Group. England and Wales, Accidental and Suicidal. Registrar-General's Return.

Date	Suicidal	Accidental	Total
1905	0	0	0
1906	0	1	1
1907	0	1	1
1908	2	2	4
1909	2	11	13
1910	3	12	15
1911	2	17	19
1912	4	12	16
*1913	11	19	30
1914	12	18	30
1915	7	18	25
1916	5	5	10
1917	8	8	16
†1918	3	9	12
1919	2	5	7
1920	3	6	9
1921	5	3	8
1922	3	3	6
1923	3	5	8
1924	2	6	8
1925	10	15	25
1926	1	4	5
TOTAL	88	180	268

* 1913. Drugs placed under Part II of poisons Schedule.
† 1918. Drugs placed under Part I of Poisons Schedule.

The Second Phase—1923 to 1927

In his Norman Kerr lecture to the Inebriety Society in 1923, Willcox referred to the danger of addiction in the case of barbiturates then in current use, Veronal, Medinal, Proponal, Dial and Luminal, to use the trade names. He spoke of the dangers of prolonged use, the moral degeneracy, and the symptoms which could mimic those of natural disease of the nervous system, and sometimes lead to addiction and suicide.

It was in 1924 that at Willcox's suggestion Sir Frederick Mott launched Dr. F. A. Pickworth on experimental research on the effect of barbiturates on animals, which was conducted in his laboratory at Birmingham.

The same year Willcox experienced another fatality in his own consulting practice. Mrs. Chotzner, aged 41, was the wife of a judge of the Indian High Court who was found unconscious in her bedroom and died the following day. Webster, who did the analyses, estimated that she had taken no less than 200 grains of veronal. An open verdict was recorded. In his evidence at the inquest at Hammersmith, Willcox related her condition as he found her when called into consultation shortly before death. "The danger of the veronal group of drugs was not realised as it should be by the public, or, I am afraid, by the medical profession, yet it was not included in the category of dangerous drugs. The veronal group of drugs was in a class which should be made subject to the restrictions of the Dangerous Drugs Acts. The number of deaths was far greater than the Registrar-General's returns showed." Barbiturate poisoning had become common in America and on the Continent. It was the subject of discussion at the Societé Medicale des Hospitaux de Paris early in 1925. On February 24th Willcox attended a conference at the Home Office arranged by Sir Malcolm Delevigne to advise Sir John Anderson (later Lord Waverley), the Permanent Under-secretary of State, of the importance of barbiturate poisoning in the community with a view to further legislation. Five other medical men were present; the B.M.A. representative Dr. J. W. Bone was unwilling to have these drugs placed under D.D.A. regulations, since this would involve the dispensing doctors in much extra clerical work. No agreement on alteration of the regulations for the drugs was arrived at, but there was initiated an enquiry by regional medical officers as to the extent of the use and abuse of barbiturates in general practices throughout the country. The results of the enquiry held in 1925 were not decisive:

1. General Practitioners who gave definite replies to questions: *291.*
2. General Practitioners who abstained from using them: *96.*
3. Veronal and Luminal were by far the most frequently used drugs in the group.
4. Veronal was generally useful as a hypnotic, but there were 17 addicts altogether; in four cases dangerous symptoms arose and in six cases accidental poisoning.
5. More than half the doctors interviewed considered that the drugs should be brought under the D.D.A. restrictions. Between a half and a third were opposed to this policy, the remainder expressing no opinion. After learning the findings of this research Willcox wrote to Delevigne:

"13th February, 1926.

Dear Sir Malcolm,

It was very kind of you to send me the copy of the Memorandum of the Ministry of Health on the use of Veronal and other drugs of the Barbitone group. I had delayed replying to you because I had hoped to be able to bring the Pharmacists and the Medical Professional into line on the matter. I have spoken to representatives of the British Medical Association and to the President of the Pharmaceutical Society, but the two professions do not see eye to eye on the matter.

As you know, I feel very strongly indeed as regards the danger to the public from the use of Veronal and other drugs of this series. I have had, under my notice, a very large number of cases of suicide and accidental death due entirely to the development of the Veronal habit. Moreover, the continued use of these drugs produces mental degeneration of serious character. I think that the restriction of the use of Veronal and the Barbitone group of drugs is one of the most urgent needs at the present day. I should not speak so feelingly on the matter had I not absolute personal knowledge of the great dangers to the public from these drugs. Many of the deaths from Veronal and its allies are not recognised and are attributed to other causes. Also the addiction habit to these drugs is relatively common. I think that Veronal and the other drugs of the Barbitone group should be added to the Dangerous Drugs Act but in a modified way, that is, the drugs should only be given by prescription and the same rules as regards prescribing, namely retention of prescription, etc., should apply as in the case of Morphia and Cocaine. I do not think, however, that it is necessary for registers to be kept.

The Pharmacists would agree to this procedure, and would welcome it, but they think that in return medical men should not dispense these drugs except in cases of urgency, and that the drug should only be obtained from a Pharmacist under medical prescription. I must say that I am in sympathy with the attitude taken by the Pharmacists. The dispensing doctors are very jealous of their privileges and they are unwilling to agree to this. As you know, the B.M.A. representatives are very obstinate and very difficult to deal with.

Personally I think the time has come when the Government should take some action in the matter. I do not think the public should be allowed to suffer because of slight differences of opinion in the commercial aspects of this question between the Pharmacists and the dispensing doctors. I shall be pleased to do anything I can in the matter.

I am,

Yours sincerely,"

In a second letter to Sir Malcolm, Willcox wrote on May 6th that he fully understood the technical difficulties of placing barbiturates in the framework of the D.D.A. as constituted at that time, owing to the many troublesome rules inherent in the regulations which should not be applied to barbiturates; he thought the difficulties would be overcome by making special regulations under the Pharmacy Act of 1868 and felt sure that there would be general approval for making barbiturates obtainable only on medical prescription as they had been under the Defence of the Realm regulations during the war. These views were expressed in a lecture to the joint meeting of the South West London Medical Society with the S.W.L. Chemists Association on May 5th, 1926 (Pharmaceutical Journal May 8th, 15th and 22nd, 1926).

It was unfortunate that Sir Frederick Mott died a month before the publication by Dr. Pickworth of his research at Birmingham on the Pathological Effects of Hypnotic Drugs on the Central Nervous System of Animals. The work was carried out with the sulphonal and barbituric acid group of drugs acting on cats and monkeys for periods varying from seven days to three weeks. It was shown that there occurred degenerative and inflammatory changes in the brain and spinal cord and an accumulation of a mucinoid substance in the white matter and in the neurones. Many of these changes were irreversible and destructive. It was thought that similar changes must occur in chronic poisoning in man. (B. J. Exp. Pathology 1926.)

The First Battle—1927

Had Mott survived a year longer in reasonable health he would have perhaps been able to provide powerful support for the value of this research in relation to barbiturate poisoning in man at the meeting at the Royal Society of Medicine in 1927 which saw the commencement of the first battle of the barbiturate drugs, for Mott was the leading authority on the pathology of mental diseases and a pioneer of research in that branch of pathology.

The Annual Meeting of the Section of Therapeutics and Pharmacology of the Royal Society of Medicine was attended by many distinguished physicians and drug experts on May 10th, when papers were read by Dr. Helen Young, a West End General Practitioner, Willcox and Dr. F. A. Pickworth on The Clinical and Pathological effects of Hypnotic Drugs of the barbituric acid and sulphonal groups (Proc. R.S.M. 1927).

Dr. Young discussed the history of the two groups of drugs and not only gave an extensive survey of barbiturate toxicity but described her own personal experiences of two recent cases. She referred to the Registrar-General's returns for 1905–1925 (Table I) for England and Wales and the frequent admission rate of cases of poisoning to hospitals in U.S.A. and Germany.

Willcox described how he had been shown sections of brain tissue from experimental animals by Mott himself; they both considered that the changes found would run parallel with those found after death from barbiturate poisoning if the proper technique was employed at post-mortem. The importance of the research lay in the irreversible nature of many of the microscopic changes in the brain, heart, lungs and kidneys which, both Mott and himself agreed, would account for the mental changes and depression which were so common and often resulted in suicide. He therefore warned the profession of the dangers of the drugs given over long periods without a break. He did not deprecate the use of phenobarbitone in epilepsy when used with due care to avoid cumulative overdosage, nor barbiturates given in insomnia on an intermittent scale, on two or three nights a week. The margin between a full dose and a toxic dose was so narrow that the scales might be easily tipped against a patient in severe illness. His colleague John Webster, the analyst, had recorded sixteen cases of acute poisoning from 1916–1925. In his own consulting practice Willcox had seen twelve cases between 1912 and 1927 of acute poisoning, and five of chronic poisoning causing neurological disorders resembling cases of encephalitis. Quite apart from the official statistics, he considered that many fatal cases of poisoning were certified after death under the heading of broncho-pneumonia and had escaped recognition by coroners throughout the country. He warned the profession to be aware of the widely circulated advertising of new drugs with fancy names which were coming on the market frequently. Barbiturates, he firmly considered, should only be administered by medical prescription for short periods not exceeding one week at a time, the prescription to be retained by the pharmacist.

Pickworth then read his paper on the experimental effect of the drugs on cats and monkeys referred to above, leaving his audience to draw their own conclusions about its significance. A full discussion followed the three papers, and general agreement was expressed on the views put forward.

Sir Maurice Craig (1866–1935), the distinguished physician in Psychiatry at Guy's and other hospitals, had become a strong believer in the preventive aspects of mental disorders and the need for popular enlightenment on the subject. He was not at the meeting, but read his account of it in his copy of the B.M.J. of May 14th, responding by a letter to the editor (May 28th) expressing his own somewhat divergent views. Insomnia, he claimed, was not merely a symptom but a common cause of mental disturbance. He had used Medinal at first intermittently, but later, finding that plan ineffective, had resorted to the plan of giving a minimum effective dose consistently and nightly for long periods, often for several years. "I have spent fifteen years in mental hospitals among the wreckage of humanity and the next twenty years trying to correct the conditions leading to mental disorders. Defective sleep is high on the list. . . . To call barbiturates dangerous is unjustifiable and addiction is practically non-existent and where it is found in a patient other drugs of addiction have usually been taken."

The difference in outlook between two leaders in their own specialities attracted great interest in the profession, but could easily be understood. Willcox saw the problem from the point of view of the general practitioner, the coroner and the public; Craig, from his own experience alone. Yet Willcox readily conceded Craig his right and skill in the handling of these drugs. In his reply (B.M.J. June 4th) he referred to the meeting at the Royal Society of Medicine, continuing:

"It is unfortunate that Sir Maurice Craig did not attend the meeting and take part in the discussion for I feel that the most suitable place for a critical discussion of this subject would have been the meeting at which the papers were read. It is, I fear, trespassing somewhat unduly on your generosity and your valuable space by correspondence which would more appropriately have formed part of the Society's discussion. My paper has not yet been published in the Transactions of the Royal Society of Medicine so that the criticism of Sir Maurice Craig is somewhat premature. Since the introduction of the Barbituric Acid Compounds from 1906 to 1925 inclusive, no less than 257 deaths from poisoning by these drugs have been recorded by the Registrar General's statistics for England and Wales. (Corrected figure including 1926 was 268.) These figures by no means express the actual number of fatal cases, for the Registrar General's returns contain in addition a group of deaths due to Narcotic Poisoning, 'kind not stated', some of which were doubtless due to Barbituric Acid compounds. In addition, as pointed out in my paper, the Veronal compounds in large doses commonly cause coma and broncho-pneumonia, and some deaths from Veronal poisoning are undoubtedly certified as pneumonia.

"I personally saw a number of the fatal cases of poisoning and in a large proportion of these one found that the patient possessed a medical prescription and had been taking the drug over a long period. There was often clear evidence of addiction to the drug. As a result of this addiction together with the consequent mental depression a large and fatal overdose had been taken. Very many of the deaths were in persons of education and in the prime of life. When fatal poisoning occurs the Physician who has given the prescription is not usually called in to deal with the grave emergency and in all probability never hears of the fatal consequences. Are the frequent deaths from poisoning by Veronal, Medinal and their allies to be lightly brushed aside as of no consequence? My clinical experience of a large number of these tragic cases compels me to raise my voice against the practice of prescribing these drugs over long periods and of leading patients to believe that they are harmless.

"To quote a few cases:

"On February 21st, 1921 a patient (Mrs. J.) who had taken forty 5 grain Medinal powders was seen by me. This patient had been taking a daily dose of 5 grs. of Medinal over a long period on the prescription of an eminent physician. This culminated in her taking forty powders at once with fatal result.

"On April 29th, 1921, I saw a patient (Miss B.) who had for one year been taking 10 grs. of Veronal every night on medical prescription. This caused mental depression leading her to take 10 ounces of pure Lysol with fatal result.

"On November 25th, 1924 I saw a patient (Mrs. C.) suffering from Veronal poisoning and consequent pneumonia which terminated fatally. A very large dose had been taken and a similar history of the taking of Veronal on medical prescription over a long period was obtained.

"On February 22nd, 1927 I saw a patient (Mr. S.) suffering from Veronal poisoning and consequent pneumonia. This patient had been in the habit of taking Veronal on medical prescription nightly over a long period. He then took a large and fatal overdose.

"I have notes of many other similar cases. I do not question that it is safe for so expert a physician as Sir Maurice Craig to prescribe Veronal or Medinal over long periods to patients under his continued personal observation, but to give a patient a prescription for prolonged use when not under continued skilled medical observation is, I unhesitatingly say, a dangerous practice.

"Addiction to the Barbituric Acid compounds undoubtedly occurs and is a real danger. I have personally seen many cases of marked addiction. The literature on the subject has been carefully collected by Dr. Helen Young, all the references of which are at the disposal of Sir Maurice Craig. The evidence from this is overwhelming.

"In 1912 a fatal case of Veronal poisoning (H.E.T.) in a young man was investigated by the Director of Public Prosecutions in conjunction with the Coroner. I have before me the deposition of the distressed mother which states 'I knew he took Veronal for years, I implored him to give it up but he said he could not . . . he took it first for pneumonia and never could give it up . . . He had been taking Veronal for six years. . . he told me he should never be able to give it up . . . he seemed to lose all self control when he wanted it . . . apart from that he was mentally all right'. What stronger evidence of Veronal addiction could one have than that?

"Veronal addiction is only discovered when the drug is withheld. If Sir Maurice Craig advocates the taking of Veronal and Medinal daily over long periods I can readily understand how he does not discover when his patients have in fact developed addiction. Sir Maurice Craig expresses the opinion that addiction to Barbituric Acid compounds is 'practically non-existent' and then goes on to quote two classes of persons who might become addicts, the chief one being the degenerate type. Such a statement is a direct contradiction to my clinical experience. Even a perfectly normal person if exposed to the continued action of Veronal and its allies in moderate doses over long periods runs a grave risk of becoming an addict to the drug.

"The late Sir Frederick Mott was deeply interested in the pathological effects of the Barbituric Acid group of drugs and in conjunction with Dr. Pickworth and Mr. D. L. Woodhouse, M.Sc., carried out during the last two years of his life a research into this subject. This work was published in the British Journal of Experimental Pathology in 1926. The pathological evidence from this research shows conclusively that organic changes are caused in the central nervous system by the continued taking of such drugs, and that when the drugs are discontinued these changes gradually clear up. Clinical evidence supports this research. I have on many occasions seen definite objective nervous symptoms such as ataxic gait, diplopia, anarthria, paralysis, etc., result from the continued daily administration of a Veronal compound in a therapeutic dose.

"On November 27th, 1926 I saw a patient (A) suffering from ataxic gait, diplopia and defective articulation. This patient had been taking a full dose of Allonal daily for 6 weeks.

"On December 25th, 1926 I saw a patient (X) suffering from ataxy, drowsiness, diplopia and thick speech. In this case Veronal was found in the urine and cerebro-spinal fluid.

"In both of these cases the symptoms completely cleared up on discontinuance of the drug. Sir James Purves Stewart saw these two cases in consultation with me, and I have his permission for stating his entire agreement with the diagnosis of poisoning by Barbituric acid compounds.

"The occurrence of definite objective nervous symptoms following the continued use of these drugs in therapeutic doses is a strong reason for the exercise of caution in their use. I am compelled to express my conviction that to advocate the daily use of the Barbituric Acid compounds over a long period unless the patient is under continued skilled medical supervision is misleading to the medical profession, dangerous to the public, and above all highly dangerous to the patient."

W. E. Dixon, Professor Pharmacology of Cambridge University, who had been present at the meeting, wrote to Willcox on May 31st: "I read what Craig had to say, and think you will have no difficulty in demolishing him. I can see that there is likely to be a long correspondence on the subject, but this is really a compliment to you. It is only uninteresting stuff that is neglected", and again, on June 8th, "So far you have made a complete answer to Craig." Willcox wrote back to Dixon: "It seems impossible to convince Maurice Craig since he shuts his eyes to all evidence of the toxicity of barbiturate compounds."

In the B.M.J. issue of June 18th were published letters from four other doctors, two in support of Willcox, one against, and the fourth was neutral. But a fifth, the psychiatrist R. D. Gillespie, entered the battle with a letter along with Craig's second letter. These two letters were far too long to reproduce here. Both evaded the issue of addiction, which anyhow was not the main topic of dispute, but directed their attack to the experimental research of Pickworth and Woodhouse. It was true that the cats had been given enormous doses compared with the customary dosage in man; and cats could not be regarded as suitable subjects in comparative trials of toxicity. They had certainly made a point here, but they made little headway in other directions. Having admitted having had no experience of addiction, Craig was content to ignore those cases seen by others, and to look the other way. He certainly attached great importance to the necessity and value of sleep. "It is incumbent on the medical profession to treat defective sleep far more seriously than has been the custom in the past . . . knowing how crippling and at times how devastating insomnia may be, one is compelled to examine every avenue to prevent its results." Craig had already admitted the dangers of the sulphonal group and abandoned their use in his practice in spite of the fact that the Registrar-General's returns had shown a fatality rate about four times higher for barbiturates in the years 1906–1925. He concluded by refusing to face up to the national problem of barbiturate toxicity. "I still await any proof that these drugs, given in therapeutic doses, even over a long period, are harmful or cause any ill effects other than the simple rash at times produced in those who have an idiosyncrasy to them."

Willcox in his last letter (B.M.J. June 25th, 1927) made his views quite clear:

> "I must apologise for further trespassing on your valuable space but feel that a reply is needed to the letter of Sir Maurice Craig in your last issue. It contains the astonishing statement that as regards the toxicity of Sulphonal and Trional he is fully in agreement, but apparently the toxicity of the Barbitone group of drugs is disputed. There is overwhelming evidence that on human beings the Barbitone group of drugs is, weight for weight, much more toxic than the Sulphonal groups. The Registrar General's returns for England and Wales show for the 20 years 1906–1925 inclusive a total number of deaths from the Barbitone group of drugs of 257 deaths, while the total number of deaths from poisons of the Sulphonal group is only 53 for the same period.
>
> "The British Pharmacopoeia Committee of the General Medical Council after careful deliberation gave in the last edition of their work a maximum dosage of 10 grs. for Barbitone and 30 grains for Sulphonal, figures which to my mind give an approximate idea of the relatively higher toxicity of Veronal as compared with Sulphonal. All authorities are agreed as to the still greater toxicity of other Barbitone compounds such as Luminal, Dial,

Allonal, etc. I have on several occasions seen coma result from 50 grs. of Veronal, which may be regarded as an average fatal dose.

"In 1913 I read at the International Congress of Medicine in London what I believe was the first paper published in this country on 'Veronal Poisoning' and since that time I have given the subject my closest attention and have had a very extensive clinical as well as toxicological experience of the use of the Barbitone group of drugs. I have not the slightest doubt that the Barbitone Group of drugs possess potent toxic properties on man, and I beg of the medical profession to exercise great care and caution in the prescription of these drugs. Sir Maurice Craig asks 'Where are the addicts and what are they doing?' My answer to this is that many of them are dead and buried as the result of fatal Veronal poisoning, and suicide from other causes. It is something more than a coincidence that in a large proportion of the Veronal fatalities there has been to my personal knowledge definite evidence of previous addiction to the drug.

"I have met with a number of persons suffering from Veronal addiction in my own practice, and many of my medical friends with whom I have discussed the subject have had a similar experience. The subjects of addiction to this group of drugs are often brain workers and people of high intellectual grade. In addition I have very strong grounds for believing that Veronal addiction, like other forms of drug addiction, is relatively common amongst the pleasure-seeking class of the night club type. I have on several occasions seen dangerous nervous symptoms such as ataxy, anarthria, diplopia, etc. result from the daily use of the drug in therapeutic doses. Some of these cases were quoted in my paper and others have observed many similar cases. I am fully aware that persons suffering from active mental disease can often tolerate large doses of hypnotic drugs over relatively long periods, and that it may be necessary and advisable in such cases to use the Barbitone group of drugs daily over long periods, provided that the patient is under close medical observation. This may explain the wide discrepancy between the experience of Sir Maurice Craig and myself.

"I stated in my recent paper (which unfortunately Sir Maurice Craig has not read) that the Barbituric Acid compounds are rapidly acting and fairly certain hypnotics. It is for this reason that they are so commonly used. A single therapeutic dose is usually followed by a satisfactory period of natural sleep, and no marked after effects follow when the therapeutic action has passed away, which should be after six to twelve hours. The attitude that these drugs may be given in therapeutic doses daily over long periods to persons who are not suffering from active mental disease is in my judgment and experience most dangerous and misleading teaching."

While this correspondence was going on *The Lancet* was advertising Medinal (made by a German firm) as a drug which could safely be used for long periods. When this was pointed out to Willcox he retorted "No doubt the public will learn in time, painfully by experience, but it is difficult to see what can be done while people like Craig continuously advocate the continued use of these drugs."

In his presidential address to the Medico-Legal Society on October 27th, 1927, Willcox alluded to the tendency in this country to use new and much advertised drugs of foreign manufacture supposedly free from toxic effects and the power of addiction. Enormous quantities were at that time being imported from abroad with little or no restriction, while Willcox complained of the hampering restrictions to exportation of drugs from Britain. This part of his address was prominently reported in *The Times* and other papers (Transactions of the Medico-Legal Society 1929).

Two letters in *The Lancet* of November 19th from leading manufacturing chemists drew a further letter from Willcox (Lancet December 3rd, 1927) on the subject of Dial toxicity, quoting three cases in his personal experience, who fortunately recovered.

"I have no desire to belittle the deservedly recognised therapeutic value of the barbituric acid derivatives.

"I am strongly of opinion that the firms responsible for the introduction and sale of these drugs should take the medical profession fully into their confidence and give a frank statement of the dangers of overdosage, the early signs of toxic effects, and the care and caution necessary in the use of the drugs.

"The esteem in which these firms are held by the medical profession would be thereby enhanced, and a feeling of confidence in the use of their drugs ensured.

"I am quite sure that by so doing there would be no danger of the sale of their remedies suffering in consequence."

Deaths from barbiturate poisoning did not escape the attention of the daily press at that time. The death from suicidal poisoning by allonal, a newly released barbiturate, of Mrs. Selwyn, a 38-year-old nurse in December 1927, was fully reported in the *Daily Mail* and *News of the World*, including Willcox's expressed views in their accounts of the inquest at the Marylebone coroners' court. Though Willcox attended neither the patient nor the inquest, his views were added to the account of the case, without his sanction. The evidence of the chemist who supplied the drug may be quoted as illustrating the state of the law in relation to barbiturate drugs prevailing at that time. The Coroner: "In dispensing the prescription, did you require the signature of a doctor?"—"No, we have only to enter it in the poison book." "Did you not think it unwise to dispense such a quantity of that drug?"—"I recalled our having done so before." "Would you prepare a similar prescription if called on to do so?"—"I might get the confirmation of a doctor, but the law does not compel me to do so."

The account of the inquest in the *Daily Mail* caused the manufacturers such embarrassment that their representatives threatened legal action against the paper, but this was avoided by a published apologia in the issue of December 27th, following an interview between the news editor and the representatives of Hoffman-La Roche, the manufacturers. There were clearly no grounds for litigation, for there had been no criticism expressed at the inquest of the dispensing of the drug or its method of sale. The firm must have dealt with the *News of the World* in the same way. Their headline was far more libellous and embarrassing to Willcox, who had never contacted the lay press at any stage.

"NURSE'S SUICIDE. KILLED BY NEW GERMAN DRUG."
"TOOK NINETY-NINE TABLETS OF DANGEROUS REMEDY."

"Allonal, a new German Drug, which had been the subject of strong comment by Sir William Willcox, the poison expert, in a recent issue of the British Medical Association magazine, was alleged to have been the cause of death of a nurse . . . The doctor agreed with Sir William Willcox that it was a dangerous remedy to supply."

Hoffman-La Roche of Basel was one of the largest suppliers of narcotics and hypnotics in Europe. A vast advertising campaign on the continent had launched Allonal and Sominfaine, a drug designed for use in twilight sleep which soon caused a number of fatalities in France. While a campaign was being prepared to launch these drugs in Britain an employee of the firm selected as a future manager of the British Company had read Willcox's address to the Medico-Legal Society. Agreeing with his views, he unfortunately became the first martyr to his cause. At the meeting as one of the firm's representatives with the *Daily Mail* news editor, he supported the paper in their stand in support of Willcox's views. He later received notification from the management that owing to ill reports concerning his conduct they were obliged to terminate his appointment. Not even allowed an interview with a director, he had to content himself by writing a letter of protest and challenge, but he had lost a good job.

In March 1932 Willcox was approached by the solicitors acting for the publishers of the novel "No Friendly Drop" by Henry Wade, an ex Grenadier Guards Officer. The novel featured the unexpected death of Lord Grayle following an overdose of "Didial" and hyoscine, both prescribed by his doctor. Didial was a combination of di-allyl barbituric acid of morphine with the barbiturate dial. Willcox carefully read the novel. Compared with the usual novels describing cases of poisoning, he considered the medical and analytical aspects surprisingly accurate though he did suggest some alterations concerning the probable dosages taken likely to lead to a fatal outcome and the quantities likely to be found after death by the analyst. Willcox took a reasonable view, that as a definite overdosage had been taken, along with an additional excessive dose of hyoscine, it was no reflection on the integrity or efficiency of the firm that publication of the novel should be continued, but the firm succeeded in their legal efforts to suppress further publication of the novel.

The Second Battle, 1933

Early in March 1933 Willcox received an unusual request in the form of a private letter from Mr. Inglebie Oddie, the Paddington Coroner, to attend the adjourned inquest on the death of Mrs. Beech "either to sit by me as *amicus curiae* or to give evidence as to the dosage and effects of nembutal." Willcox agreed to attend as an ordinary witness in accordance with the legal right of any coroner, but declined the offer to sit with him in court for fear of arousing resentment among his colleagues, seeing that he was in active practice himself. The wisdom of this explanation was soon abundantly made clear, when he received the depositions of the first day of the inquest, for the patient had been under the care of none other than Dr. R. D. Gillespie who had taken Craig's side in the dispute in 1927.

It was a tragic and complicated case. Mrs. Beech, aged thirty-four, was the former divorce wife of the heir to an earldom, who had been under the influence of various drugs; paraldehyde, sal volatile, medinal and nembutal (both barbiturates). She had died on February 13th at 3.30 p.m. having on medical instructions taken $7\frac{1}{2}$ grains of medinal at 7 a.m. She fell asleep at 8.30 p.m. and never woke up. The day before death she had received the same dose in the morning, 60 grains of bromide and 6 drams of paraldehyde during the day, and 6 grains of nembutal in the evening. The post-mortem conducted by Spilsbury showed no other cause of death than poisoning would reveal, and Roche Lynch's analysis revealed barbiturates and bromides in the liver and kidneys, and paraldehyde in the stomach.

Roche Lynch considered death to have been caused by the combination of drugs but went so far in his evidence as to say that the giving of $7\frac{1}{2}$ grains of medinal on the last day resulted in a fatal termination.

At the resumed inquest on March 9th, there was considerable divergence of opinion on the cause of death. Mrs. Beech had apparently already become an addict to paraldehyde, accustomed to taking large doses for several months. In support of Gillespie's treatment his solicitor called C. H. Atkinson (the patient's doctor), E. Mapother, superintendent of the Maudsley Hospital, and a strong team of Guy's Hospital physicians, Sir Maurice Craig, J. A. Ryle, and A. Douthwaite, all of whom testified as to the doses of drugs being reasonable practice in this case.

Spilsbury and Willcox agreed with Roche Lynch that death was due to the combination of drugs. Willcox said that he knew of the four recent fatal cases at a hospital in London following the use of nembutal as an anaesthetic in relatively young subjects. In three, doses were $7\frac{1}{2}$ grains, and in one 6.7 grains (in each case about half was given by intravenous injection). These patients were acutely ill and probably highly sensitive to drugs. One of the great dangers of the drugs was, he considered, the small margin between a therapeutic and a dangerous dose. The Coroner, who sat without a jury, concluded that death was due to the combination of drugs, but found no evidence of negligence. Excluding suicide in his verdict, he recorded "that death was due to misadventure by narcotic drugs."

Ingleby Oddie held another barbiturate inquest, only a few days later, concerning the death of Miss Anny Ahlers, a well-known German actress and star of The Dubarry, who fell out of an open French window after taking four tablets of quadronox, a new preparation which contained 80% of veronal. In this case the dose was not greatly in excess of a normal dose, but it was taken after drinking nearly a whole bottle of champagne. The jury's verdict was recorded by a majority of seven to two, as suicide while of unsound mind.

The Poisons Board, established under the Pharmacy and Poisons Act of 1933, was established in November 1933 to submit to the Home Secretary for his approval a list of substances to be treated as poisons, later to be termed the poisons list or schedule. It was a powerful team with Sir Gerald Bellhouse representing the Secretary of State as chairman,

Willcox the Royal College of Physicians, Roche Lynch the Institute of Chemistry, and others representing the Minister of Health, the G.M.C., the B.M.A., the Royal College of Physicians of Edinburgh; there were five representatives of the Pharmaceutical Society of Great Britain. Their report was not completed until 1935, but at last Willcox achieved the hope he had held for so many years, namely the legal restriction of the barbiturates to medical prescription when they were placed in Schedule 4 along with sulphonal and its derivatives. But this step was preceded by a further "battle" contested in the medical press in 1934. The incidence of fatal poisoning in 1933 showed a marked rise to 50 compared with 30 in 1932, no doubt contributed to by the new drug nembutal, widely advertised for the use of anaesthetists and surgeons.

The opening paper at the Royal Society of Medicine combined meeting of the Sections of Therapeutics and Psychiatry on December 12th, 1933 was a survey of most of the hypnotics then in use, the subject being "The uses and dangers of Hypnotic Drugs other than Alkaloids." About half Willcox's address was in the form of warning about the barbiturates of which there were at that time twenty-one on the market, mostly developed since his first warning at a comparable meeting in 1913. This time his warning was directed to anaesthetists and surgeons as well as to doctors in ordinary practice. The more complex derivatives of barbitone were, he thought, more toxic. There was the question of allergy and addiction. Though withdrawal symptoms were less severe than those of morphine and heroin addiction, yet he had been impressed by the large numbers of patients in his own experience in whom a craving arose after repeated daily administration. There had been, as everyone knew who read the daily papers, numerous suicidal and accidental deaths, several of which he quoted including the death of a medical man from suicide. Barbiturates were more toxic when taken with alcohol, and when combined with pain-relieving drugs like phenacetin and amidopyrin. Willcox confessed that he had ceased to prescribe barbiturates in his own hospital and personal practice. (B.M.J. March 10th, 1934.) (Proc. R.S.M. Vol. 27, 1933–34.)

Papers were read by F. L. Golla, Professor J. A. Gunn of Oxford, and by P. R. McCowan on hypnotics in general; the last spoke against a too liberal use of hypnotics, claiming that addiction was usually limited to psychopaths.

Sir James Purves-Stewart spoke briefly in support of Willcox's views, quoting three cases of accidental poisoning personally encountered. Then Gillespie and Craig launched their counter-attack, resembling in many ways that of 1927.

Though Helen Young had done extensive research of the world literature, going back to the original sources in presenting her paper in 1927, R. D. Gillespie went to great length to indicate the inaccuracy of some of her findings, claiming an error of 56%. How accurate he himself was is a matter beyond the scope of this history, but it must be noted that he made no mention of cases that were never recorded in medical literature and uncertified cases of poisoning which, as Willcox had so often pointed out, had escaped recognition in the past. He pooh-poohed the thirteen suicidal deaths from barbiturates in 1931, but had come unarmed to the meeting with the figures for the following years of nineteen suicides and eleven accidental self-poisonings. The case of Mrs. Beech received no comment from Gillespie at this meeting.

Sir Maurice Craig said that for years he had failed to understand how two practising physicians like Willcox and himself had come to hold such opposite views. A few unfortunate cases could hardly be regarded as scientific evidence in support of the dangerous effects. When properly given the barbiturates were the most valuable of all sedatives, and he had never seen a barbiturate addict not addicted to some other drug as well. He much regretted their restriction on the poisons schedule (Proc. R.S.M., 1933–34).

Evidently feeling unsatisfied with his counter-attack, Craig commenced further correspondence in the medical press. This time he spared the patience and courtesy of the Editor of the B.M.J. and explored the pages of the *Lancet's* issue of February 3rd. Defending the use of the drugs he confined himself, he explained, in his practice to the few drugs he had learnt to use. Willcox's evidence was to him bewildering, particularly his inferences from the experiments of Pickworth on cats, which he had expressed at the 1927 meeting (Willcox did not mention the experiments at the 1934 meeting). Charging Willcox with drawing conclusions from incorrect figures which Helen Young had produced from the literature before 1927, he explained that 13 suicides out of a total of 5,147 for 1931 were negligible, though he omitted the figure for 1932.

The crux of the problem was his contention that insomnia was a cause of mental confusion and suicide and that restriction in their use would, in fact, penalise those patients accepting medical advice, and be circumvented. He had never himself yet seen a veronal addict.

Willcox's answer appeared in the edition of February 17th, (1934); admitting that the animal experiments were open to criticism, he made it clear that since 1927 he had no longer used that evidence as a basis for his warnings, but had confined himself to the incontrovertible and well-known clinical evidence. During 1933 he had seen and treated eighteen patients, most of them people of education, culture, and distinction, in their walks of life. He referred again to Hugh Trevanion and Anny Ahlers—some cases were suicides, and others cases of overdosage of drugs taken in a state of mental automatism. Barbiturate poisoning was becoming of such international importance that steps were about to be taken in the United States to control it and he had quoted his own five cases in 1927. All he pleaded for was the safety of the public by modifications of the Pharmacy Acts to achieve careful medical supervision of patients, medical prescription and the co-operation of pharmacists. *He did not see danger in barbiturates used intermittently, to avoid cumulative effects.*

In the same issue Craig had a further word to say, that suicide being caused by insomnia, patients were being distracted by the fear of these drugs. He again denied the existence of barbiturate addiction. And in a later issue of *The Lancet* he expressed doubts that restriction would restrict suicide rate, because patients would turn to other methods and in greater numbers. (*Lancet*, March 31st, 1934.)

The subject was referred to again at the Inebriety Society on January 9th, 1934, when Sir Humphry Rolleston occupied the presidential chair. After discussing the hard drugs of addiction, Willcox turned to other drugs of addiction and spoke of barbiturates in these terms:

"What I shall tell you is very controversial, but I stand by my statements. I know what I am telling you is true, and it is not the result of reading, but from tragedies which have come under my own notice, from many cases I have seen and treated personally. There can be no doubt that the very large number (he went on to quote twenty-one on the market) of barbituric acid derivatives occupy the foremost place amongst the drugs of addiction. The actual danger to the public in this country at the present time from addiction to these drugs is greater than that from any other group of drugs, even including the dangerous drugs, which are controlled by special Acts and regulations . . . The continued daily use of these drugs in therapeutic doses may cause impairment of speech, ataxic gait, paralysis of the eye muscles, and other motor nerve affections. Mental disturbances, such as hallucinations of vision, may also occur. The need for care in their use cannot be too strongly emphasised. The risk of suicide, accidental or purposeful, from overdosage, is a very real one. I have seen a large number of cases of suicide and attempts of suicide, in people taking these drugs over long periods. They take an overdose, sometimes with the desire to kill themselves, but often because their minds are so confused that they take the overdose not caring what may happen or hoping for the worst. It is essential that the public should not have access to these drugs except by medical prescription, the prescription being retained by the pharmacist and not repeated except on medical orders. The members of the medical profession should exercise due care in the prescription of these drugs." (British Journal of Inebriety, April 1934. *The Times* and *Daily Mail*, January 10th, 1934.)

Six days later Mrs. Hamilton-Russell, fifty-seven-year-old sister-in-law of a peer, died at her home in Hampshire as a result of accidental overdosage of dial. Her death illustrated what Willcox had just described and was in accord with the coroner's verdict in this particular case, as described in *The Times*, the *Daily Mail* and *News of the World*: "death from an overdose of Dial, self-administered with intent to induce sleep. There was no suggestion of suicide, as her letters went to prove that she was happy and making plans for the future. The explanation was that on this very rough night she was unable to sleep and took more than one dose of dial."

This case is typical of many others recorded in the press of that time, but in the same edition of the *Daily Mail* of January 18th there appeared an article by the Medical Correspondent on "Drugs as a doctor sees them". It prominently displayed the views of Willcox, Craig and Gillespie under the heading "doctors agree to differ". The writer certainly gave a fair and honestly attempted assessment. "To the question, should full use of the barbiturates be made, I would unhesitatingly answer, Yes. Their advantages are well suited to the requirements of modern life, but it must be realised by everyone, doctors, chemists, nurses and patients, that the drugs in question are powerful weapons and are not without their dangers."

When Dr. W. H. Houghton committed suicide by gassing himself a few days later, he left a long letter addressed to the coroner, explaining that he was a morphine addict treated with luminal. His letter concluded "Since that time I can honestly say that I have never known a happy day. Of all the drugs that, and its fellows in the barbituric acid group, are the ones to be studiously avoided. Please make that quite clear for the benefit of posterity." But this was not a fair judgment as it was made by a morphine addict who was already incurable by any known method of treatment.

Though the reader will be tempted to agree with the assessment of the *Daily Mail* Medical Correspondent of 1934 with regard to barbiturates as hypnotics, it must be remembered that at that time there were available no modern methods of treatment which today are available to save the majority of patients from suicidal or accidental overdosage; no respirators or antibiotics, and no drugs to raise the blood pressure or hasten excretion of the poison. The mortality rate was much higher before the Second World War. Yet the total cases have increased to such a vast degree that correspondingly the death rate from barbiturate poisoning has also startlingly increased (Table II).

Table II

Fatal Poisoning from Drugs of Barbituric Acid Group.
England and Wales, Accidental and Suicidal, 1927–1960.
(Registrar-General's Returns)

Year	Suicidal	Accidental	Total
1927	10	10	20
1928	11	16	27
1929	14	7	21
1930	8	25	33
1931	12	11	23
1932	19	11	30
1933	25	25	50
1934	29	15	44
*1935	39	30	69
1936	32	20	52
1937	25	19	44
1938	39	14	53
1939	43	13	56
1940	52	30	82
†1941	45	38	83
1945	55	40	95
1946	78	54	132
1950	278	127	405
1955	427	192	619
1960	645	293	938

*1935. Drugs placed under Part IV of Poisons Schedule.
1935. The Death of Sir Maurice Craig.
†1941. The Death of Sir William Willcox.

Treatment of cases of barbiturate intoxication in 1934 consisted in eliminating the drug by stomach washing, by nursing, and the correction of the fluid balance mechanism. Willcox, with Purves Stewart, himself contributed an advance in the treatment. In 1923 they made the observation that barbitone was excreted into the spinal fluid in high concentration, and that tapping the fluid at intervals by lumbar and cistern puncture, had a remarkably beneficial effect leading to recovery. Later six more cases were reported in *The Lancet* (Jan. 6th, 1934, March 10th, 1934). In speaking of this work to the Society of Public Analysts in an address in 1938, Roche Lynch claimed that the treatment had led to a reduction in mortality (Analyst, April 1928) but the treatment was, of course, later superseded.

The Aftermath

Willcox achieved his object in May 1935 when the report of the Poisons Board was submitted to Parliament, whereby barbiturates were placed on Schedule 4 of the Pharmacy and Poisons Act of 1933. It had been a long struggle of twenty-two years, costing Willcox the effort of many addresses and much correspondence. The reader may well ask whether two heated battles in print had been necessary. A large body of medical opinion was on his side, as can be seen from his files of correspondence; and Willcox was not the sort of man to throw away letters of criticism. The lay press, particularly the *Daily Mail*, had taken a keen interest and without being solicited, supported the cause of barbiturate control which became effective in 1935 when their purchase was limited to medical prescription. Yet, despite his prophetic utterances from 1913 onwards, there were few supporters prepared to support him openly in print or in public addresses, and a few thought him an obsessional crank, but let the statistics speak for themselves. (Tables II & III).

Table III

Deaths from Barbituric Acid Derivatives in Relation to Deaths from all Sources of Poisoning, 1960–1966, England and Wales.

Year	Barbiturates			All poisons
	Male	Female	Total	
1960	372	566	938	5086
1962	616	860	1476	5921
1964	803	1195	1998	6069
1966	824	1231	2055	5572

The Hospital Treatment of Acute Poisoning, H.M.S.O. 1968.

Sir Maurice Craig died in January 1935—before the legal control of barbiturates became effective. A man of charming personality, he had fought the battles with fairness and honesty of purpose throughout. No insult or discourtesy being exchanged by either side, the battles had been fought with the courtesy characteristic of the generation in which both men were born. Craig took the point of view of a practising psychiatrist; Willcox that of the general public and the medical profession as a whole, as he thought.

The new regulations certainly appeared to have stemmed the tide of barbiturate deaths until the onset of the Second World War, but from Willcox's death in 1941 onwards the figures gradually rose, possibly accentuated by war conditions. The mortality rose by leaps and bounds after the war was over, and has not yet been controlled in spite of the use of new drugs for suicidal subjects and the more effective treatment of poisoning at the present time (Table III). By 1962 deaths from barbiturate poisoning were eleven times as great as those of 1940 and eighteen weekly deaths were occurring in that year.

An editorial heading in the *Practitioner* in August 1953 on "The Barbiturate Menace" pointed out that the death rates of 1950 and 1951 were a striking confirmation of the dangers lying ahead. In the same issue T. N. Morgan stated "They are much too dangerous to be used as a substitute for the careful search for the cause of a patient's insomnia which used to be the hallmark of the family doctor. A nation dependent on barbiturates is as unreliable a structure as the biblical house built on sand." (The Use & Abuse of Sedatives.) This was Willcox's view all over again, expressed in other words. But how can an overworked doctor in N.H.S. conditions be expected to explore in every case the causes of insomnia, knowing that a quicker method of treatment is the prescription of an hypnotic drug?

M. M. Glatt, the distinguished psychiatrist and writer of an authoritative survey of this subject (Bulletin on Narcotics April-June 1962), which should be studied by those interested in this important subject, speaking in 1964 of Willcox said "He was, as far as I know, the first person to stress the addictive potentialities of barbiturates (1913) at a time nobody else thought of it, and in fact many people pooh-poohed the idea. Nowadays, of course, everyone realises that the barbiturates are drugs of addiction."

The reader is left to guess what should be done about the appalling figures of deaths of 1966. No official committee has the answer, but each one is facing the fact that barbiturate deaths amounted in that year to over 2,000, nearly half those resulting from all poisons.

References

British Medical Journal, 1913, March 15th p. 566 Editorial
Craig, Sir Maurice. B.M.J., 1913, Sept 13th, p. 661.
              B.M.J., 1927, May 28th, p. 983.
              B.M.J., 1927, June 18th, p. 1126.
              Proc. R. S. Medicine, 1933–34, 27, p. 517.
              Lancet, 1934, Feb 3rd, p. 260.
              Lancet, 1934, Feb 17th, p. 372.
              Lancet, 1934, March 31st, p. 708.
Gillespie, R. D. B.M.J., 1927, June 18th, p. 1125.
              Proc. R.S. Medicine, 1933–34, 27, p. 504.
              Lancet, 1934, Feb. 17th, p. 337.
              Lancet, 1934, March 3rd, p. 482.

Glatt, M.M.   Bulletin of Narcotics, April–June 1962, Vol. XIV, 2.

Kress, T.   Therap. Monats, September 1905.

Mongeri, L.   Semaine Med. May 24th, 1905.

Morgan, T. H.   Practitioner, August 1953, p. 197.

Mott, Sir F., Pickworth, F. A. and Woodhouse, F. L., B.J. Exp. Path., 1926, vol. VII, p. 325.

Practitioner, 1953, August, p. 230. Editorial.

Roche Lynch, G.   Analyst, 1929, April, 63, p. 240.

Willcox, Sir W. H.   Lancet, 1913, Oct. 25th, p. 1178.

B.M.J., 1913, Sept. 13th, p. 661.

B.M.J., 1914, Dec. 12th, p. 1026.

B.J. Inebriety, 1914–15, Jan. 15th, 3, p. 125.

B.J. Inebriety, Jan. 1924.

Pharmaceutical Journal, May 8th, 15th and 22nd, 1926.

—, Pickworth, F. A. and Young, H. Proc. R.S.M. 1927, vol. XX, p. 1479 et seq.

— — B.M.J., 1927, May 14th, p. 877.

B.M.J., 1927, June 4th, p. 1031.

B.M.J., 1927, June 25th, p. 1163.

Trans. Medico-Legal Society, 1927, vol. XXII, p. 1.

Lancet, 1927, Dec. 3rd, p. 1210.

Proc. R.S. Medicine, 1933–34, 27, p. 489.

B.M.J., 1934, March 10th, p. 415.

Lancet, 1934, Feb. 17th, p. 370.

B.J. Inebriety, 1934, April, vol. XXXI, p. 131.

—, Sir J. Purves Stewart, Lancet, 1934, p. 6, Jan. 6th

— — Lancet, 1934, p. 500, March 10th.

Chapter 25

Drug Addiction and Alcoholism

"They were drinking a drug to quiet all
pain and strife, and bring forgetfulness of
every ill . . ."   Homer.

The World Health Organisation recently defined drug addiction as a
"state of chronic or periodic intoxication detrimental to the individual
and society, produced by the repeated consumption of a drug, be it natural
or synthetic. Its characteristics include an overpowering desire or need
to continue it, and to obtain it by any means, and the tendency to increase
the dose to maintain psychic and physical well-being." Drug addiction
is not the same thing as drug dependence. A person dependent on alcohol,
tobacco, tea or coffee requires the stimulant to maintain contentment,
but an addict is one who cannot enjoy reasonable physical or mental
health without it. But there is even more harm in addiction than moral
degeneration to the individual, to whom the Church and religious
organisations in general have devoted much attention and sympathy.
Addiction to drugs is highly infectious, and at times vicious in its effects
on society, especially the young, so that both mental and physical corrup-
tion in society reaches such a degree that affected victims become virtually
parasitic on the State, often incurable by medical means, likely to affect
others, and liable to early death from other disorders. It was not until
after the second World War that drug addiction became a national
menace in Britain. Until then, though a matter of concern, it was in
comparison far less common than now. It has been estimated that there
are now at least one thousand addicts in London alone (*Lancet*, April 20th,
1968, p. 853), and that the average yearly incidence of fresh addicts
amounts to four hundred in Britain. In 1966 three hundred and twenty-
nine addicts known to the Home Office were under twenty years of age.
It is, of course, true that amphetamines (dexedrine and allied drugs)
contribute to this high incidence, but at least 40% of these figures are
addicts to the "hard" drugs—morphine, heroin and cocaine.

Though addiction was never a major problem in this country in the
first half of this century, the high incidence in America and the Middle
and Far East was always a threat to world society. It has been estimated
that the incidence in America is at least one in three thousand of the
population. The threat of spread to Britain has increased owing to the
expansion of international travel, especially by air, in recent years; no
doubt immigration brings a quota of cases of addiction.

As mentioned elsewhere, Willcox was gifted with an uncanny ability
to see clouds on the horizon in the shape of threats of a medical kind

to a highly developed society. Though drug addiction was never of common occurrence within this country during his lifetime, his work from 1910 to 1938 contributed a constant effort to the cause of its prevention. This is well seen in a study of the history of legislation in which he played a prominent part for a longer period than any other medical man, and in his addresses and writings. In his personal practice of his early years he encountered addicts among his patients and heard of many others through his Home Office connection. Some recovered when taken in hand early, but most cases ended tragically, often by suicide.

Speaking to the Harveian Society and to the Society for the Study of Inebriety in 1914, he said that most cases were examples of mental instability with a strong family history or a history of personality disorder. In some cases drugs were taken out of curiosity to discover their effects at times of stress and strain. Merely temporary relief followed the taking of cocaine or morphine or the barbiturates; their repetition would lead to a drug habit, often with the aid of the doctor's prescription, but the habit often persisted unknown to the original prescriber, the patient getting further supplies from another doctor.

In addition to the "hard" drugs, the barbiturates, chloral, sulphonal and its derivatives, hyoscine and paraldehyde were also recognised at that time as drugs of dependence, and sometimes of addiction. Until 1908 they were obtainable without restriction, but the Poisons and Pharmacy Acts of that year, by placing these drugs in part 2 of the schedule, at any rate restricted their sale to qualified pharmacists.

The International Opium Convention signed at the Hague in January 1912 contained important safeguards for control of the import and export of all forms of opium and cocaine. The adoption of these safeguards was delayed by the outbreak of hostilities in 1914 but Willcox gave evidence to the special committee of the House of Commons appointed to draft the regulations to carry out the terms of the convention; his evidence included the borderline pharmacopeial preparations of opium and cocaine.

At that time there were very few addicts in Britain. The majority acquired the habit on medical prescriptions but another class of "underworld" addict existed. This class included those engaged in pleasure seeking and the search for new excitements in association with addicts to the hard drugs. They lived in London and the larger cities, but they were relatively few compared with the present-day incidence.

The position in the United States was far worse. The attitude of the campaign in the press following the narcotic laws after the Opium Convention of 1912 was deplorable. The unfortunate addicts to morphine and cocaine were publicly branded as dope fiends; there was general self-congratulation that addiction had at last been overcome. But the plight of the unfortunate addicts had been overlooked, their health was jeopardised, the victims of a campaign stigmatising them as criminals rather than as patients mentally ill. The underground traffic in hard drugs expanded enormously; by 1919 it was believed to be as extensive as the legitimate traffic. Even as early as 1910, the opium consumption exceeded any other country in Europe and 75% was illegitimately obtained. Dope pedlars obtained supplies by smuggling from Canada, Mexico and elsewhere. In 1918 it was estimated that there were at least one million addicts in America, judged by reliable statistics.

In 1916 a wartime Defence of the Realm regulation enabled the government in this Country to stamp out cocaine addiction among troops by restricting its use except by medical prescription. The same regulation applied to other hypnotic drugs such as cannabis, the barbiturates, codeine and sulphonal. In 1919 the Peace Treaty at Versailles ratified the recommendations of the Opium Conventions, one of the main ones being to confine to medical and other suitable purposes the use of drugs of addiction.

The next step was the Dangerous Drugs Act of 1920 followed by minor amendments in 1921, 1922 and 1923. By it the Secretary of State was empowered to make regulations for the manufacture, sale, importation and distribution of drugs of addiction. The draft regulations imposed the prohibition of morphine and cocaine for any other than medical purposes. Learning that the requirements for dentists and veterinary surgeons had been overlooked, Willcox formulated several alterations to the draft regulations of this committee, whereby their requirements were ensured. On his advice, special measures provided for the use of addiction drugs in research laboratories, the regulations for records and certification were simplified, and the pharmacist's regulations clarified.

But the Act achieved in 1921 less than had the temporary Defence of the Realm Act in 1916, for drugs such as the barbiturates, cannabis and sulphonal were not included among those only obtainable on medical prescription, as they had been during the war. Though Willcox did not regard the D.D.A. as perfect, the Act was drawn up with the greatest care by the Home Office in co-operation with representatives of the professions of medicine, dentistry, veterinary surgery and pharmacy. It represented an organisation as efficient as was possible to control addiction and the trade in drugs.

The subject was discussed at the Society for the Study of Inebriety in January 1923 but Willcox's views were clearly given in his comprehensive survey of the subject in his Norman Kerr memorial lecture to the Society on October 9th. He painted the picture of the chronic addict as the deplorable victim of a disease rather than as a criminal, a person to be pitied in his desperate state of drug withdrawal. Turning to the value of the D.D.A. he explained that they were necessary to prevent spread of addiction on a dangerous scale, but that he had been disappointed that he had failed to achieve his personal hope, considered so necessary, of compulsory rules for the restraint of addicts to ensure treatment on medical grounds. The legal standpoint at that time was quite firmly held that compulsory restraint was unenforceable, however desirable on medical grounds, owing to lack of adequate provision of institutional treatment by the State. He considered, therefore, that the most effective step to carry out the spirit of the regulations was the loyal co-operation of the professions with the Home Office (British Journal of Inebriety, January 1924).

Drug Addiction as a world problem was the subject of several books by doctors, writers interested in the problem, and criminologists. It was the subject of the International Opium Conferences held at Geneva from November 1924 to February 1925. One of the main problems was to control the world production of opium effectively. The production immeasurably exceeded, by about ten times, the requirements for medical and scientific purposes of the whole world. Likewise cocaine was over-produced. The conference concerned itself especially with the control, sale and trade of hard drugs and Indian Hemp (Cannabis). In countries such as India, China and Persia Opium was an important source of revenue and until that time its export was encouraged by these governments. Encouraged by the underground drug traffickers in America, addiction was common enough there, but among Chinese communities in the Far East it was far more prevalent. In some districts it was a greater cause of ill health than malaria, and an important factor causing death from infection, dysentery and parasitic diseases. As a consequence of the victim's expenditure of money for drugs, impoverishment led to malnutrition, vitamin deficiency, and inadequate personal hygiene. Dr. J. P. Williams, writing of his experiences in India, Ceylon, Burma and Malaya to the *Lancet* in 1922, pointed out that in certain districts about 10% of the adult male population would be opium smokers, obtaining supplies openly from traffickers. He had found that about half the inmates of a Chinese hospital were smokers in a district where opium could easily be obtained from unlicensed premises.

The Ministry of Health, headed by Neville Chamberlain, was fully aware of the dangers of the spread of addiction. Willcox was appointed a member of a special Cocaine Substitutes Committee in 1923 to investigate the value for therapeutic purposes, and the risk of addiction, of suggested possible substitutes for cocaine for local anaesthesia. The enquiries which followed demonstrated that addiction from cocaine used for local anaes-thesia was so rare as to be negligible. Research in dogs carried out by W. E. Dixon at Cambridge pointed the same way.

Cocaine Addiction was the special subject for discussion at the Inebriety Society in October 1929, the main speaker being W. E. Dixon, Professor of Pharmacology at Cambridge. During the war cocaine addiction was prevalent in certain cafés in Paris and Berlin, thanks to illegal underworld traffickers, and in America there had been a great increase after the war. Rapid tolerance was acquired by devotees using snuff, resulting in moral and physical degeneration, though withdrawal symptoms are less severe and dangerous than those of morphine and heroin. The addict to the latter drugs would often turn to cocaine as a substitute when supplies ran short, so that cocaine addiction would often be a late stage of the history of an addict.

The Ministry of Health turned its attention to Morphine and Heroin Addiction in September 1924, when a departmental committee was appoin-ted with Sir Humphry Rolleston as Chairman and eight members, including Willcox. Sir Humphry, who was President of the Royal College of Physicians at that time, was, along with his brother Dr. J. D. Rolleston, a staunch supporter of the Inebriety Society against the evils of intem-perance. A scholarly and erudite physician in the Osler tradition, he impressed all those whom he met with his grace and charm. He was a well-loved figure among undergraduates at Cambridge where he was Regius Professor of Physic. J. D. Rolleston, an authority on Infectious diseases, was familiar to St. Mary's students taking courses in his subject at the Western Fever Hospital at Fulham in the 1930's.

The terms of reference of the Rolleston Committee were to advise as to the circumstances in which the supply of morphine and heroin (including preparations of these drugs) to persons suffering from addiction to these drugs may be regarded as medically advisable, and as to the precautions that medical practitioners should adopt to avoid abuse in their prescription, and to suggest any administrative measures that seemed expedient for securing observance of such precautions.

The terms of reference were later (February 1925) extended to include preparations containing morphine and heroin of a lower percentage than that specified in the Dangerous Drugs Acts in order to decide is they should be brought into the future amended Acts and Regulations.

This important Committee met on twenty-three occasions at seventeen of which oral evidence was obtained from thirty-four witnesses, representing the B.M.A., the Pharmaceutical Society, the Society of Apothecaries and the Retail Pharmacists' Association. The final report was published in January 1926, defining an addict as "a person who, not requiring the continued use of a drug for the relief of symptoms of organic disease, has acquired as a result of repeated administration an overpowering desire for its continuance, and in whom withdrawal leads to definite symptoms of mental or physical distress or disorder."

It was concluded that in Britain addiction was rare and had become more so, thanks to the effectiveness of the Dangerous Drugs Acts whereby it was rendered more difficult to acquire supplies. Nevertheless, it was a threat to urban centres, and occurred among those who handled the drugs for professional or business reasons, especially those liable to mental strain, overwork and insomnia. Addiction was to be regarded as a manifestation of a morbid state rather than merely as a form of vicious indulgence in so far as it most often ensued after previous treatment for medical conditions, usually after injudicious prescribing. Estimates of complete cures following treatment varied from claims between 15 and 70%, the best results being obtained by doctors working in hospitals and nursing homes. It was advised that in treatment of cases, every doctor should obtain the second opinion of a colleague, both in his own interest and that of his patient.

The evidence of Sir Archibald Bodkin was of special interest and importance when the committee devised the legal procedure to be adopted to control injudicious prescribing and illicit possession of drugs. He had carefully studied the history of the twenty-five addicts known to the Home Office since the end of the war. They were made up as follows:

Doctor Addicts	10
Injudicious prescribing to patients	6
Other Addicts under medical care	4
Forged Prescriptions	3
Patients attending several doctors	2

A new step in administrative procedure was devised whereby the Home Secretary, on the advice of a medical tribunal, was empowered to withdraw a doctor's authority to possess and supply drugs of addiction without the necessity of resorting to a conviction of the doctor in a Court of Law, as had been the custom in the past. The tribunal would be constituted to consider whether or not there were reasonable medical grounds for the doctor to carry on administration of the drugs, either to his patient or to himself, if an addict. The tribunals would advise the Home Secretary, if necessary, that the doctor's right to be in possession, to administer, and to supply the drugs, should be withdrawn. Each tribunal, for England and Scotland, would consist of representatives of the General Medical Council, the Royal College of Physicians, the B.M.A, and a legal assessor.

The Committee fully discussed the relative merits of different forms of treatment from a professional aspect and advised that no alterations should be made to the existing regulations in the Dangerous Drugs Acts concerning preparations of morphine and heroin containing low percentages of these drugs.

Their report attracted the attention of the Drug Addiction Committee of the American Bureau of Social Hygiene. The secretary, Dr. C. E. Terry, a well-known expert on this subject, congratulated Sir Humphry and his committee in these terms: "Let me take this opportunity of congratulating you and your committee on this very valuable document. In a subject so fraught with controversy, as is the case in the United States, it is refreshing to read so broad-minded and sound an exposition of the facts involved in opium addiction. I wish your report might be placed in the hands of every American physician."

Addressing the Inebriety Society again in April 1926 on the Prevention and Arrest of Drug Addiction, Willcox traced the history of state legislation in this field and advocated the firm handling of patients by doctors. He spoke of the danger of resorting to drugs for trivial reasons, quoting the man who was frequently asked to give public speeches; unfortunately he resorted to morphine supplied by a doctor, to increase his eloquence, but had been an addict for ten years. At a time when broadcasting was in its infancy he urged the extension of education against addiction by every possible means, in schools, universities and other institutions. Yet it is this aspect of prevention that has been most sadly neglected in recent years in spite of the enormous opportunities available to television and broadcasting authorities. Willcox would consider this a national disgrace at the present time.

A month later he delivered a notable address to a combined meeting of the South West London Medical Society and Chemists' Association on "The Dangerous Drugs Acts and their application by the Physician and Pharmacist", published in the Pharmaceutical Journal (May 8th, 15th and 22nd, 1926). His knowledge of the intricacies of the legal and professional responsibility of the Pharmacist was of course linked with his position as Visitor for the Privy Council to the examinations of the Pharmaceutical society. The institution of the D.D.A. he explained, did not arise as a result of the occurrence of drug addiction in Britain, which was extremely low, but was the consequence of international action at a time when the British Empire was at its zenith and had a controlling interest on so many countries overseas. Addiction had to be regarded from an imperial standpoint, like an infectious disease liable to be imported into any country in the world.

Nine years were to elapse before Willcox next gave an address to the Inebriety Society on this subject; this was in January 1934 on the Medico-legal Aspects, when Sir Humphry was President. The incidence had become rarer, he claimed, as a result of the success of the D.D. Acts and the Rolleston Committee, but it was still not possible legally to compel addicts or alcoholics to be treated in an institution except under the provisions of the Mental Treatment Act of 1930 or the Mental Deficiency Acts. But the danger of spread from Europe and Egypt was always present.

The Director of the Central Narcotics Intelligence Bureau, T. W. Russell Pasha, who was also Commandant of the Cairo City Police, reported in 1932 that the main source of illicit supply of the hard drugs had tended to shift to Bulgaria, though Egypt was still much involved in smuggling. The main source of supply of Indian Hemp (Hashish or Cannabis) was Syria, whence it was smuggled to Europe via Egypt. Hashish addiction usually led to addiction to opium or heroin addiction in the individual; Willcox considered hashish addiction in Britain as extremely rare in his time but he firmly believed that its source of supply should be permanently stopped.

Willcox was appointed to his last official committee on drug addiction in 1937 by the Royal College of Physicians during the presidency of Lord Dawson of Penn, who himself became a member under the chairmanship of Dr. Bernard Hart, the psychiatrist. The other nine members were all psychiatrists. The report was helpful up to a point, but one of the chief recommendations met the stumbling block of the legal profession. Again, the most interesting evidence came from the Home Office, supplied by Major W. H. Coles. The majority of addicts known to the Home Office had been voluntarily reported by their medical attendants, though there probably remained an obscure quota of unreported doctor-addicts.

In 1937 the annual return for Great Britain was 616, and in 1938 630 cases were known to exist; women slightly exceeded men in number, but of the 145 doctor-addicts only 10 were women. In most cases drugs were legitimately used and there were extremely few cases of suspected *malpraxis*. Illicit traffic in drugs was almost unknown to the Home Office at that time. The startling disparity in the incidence of addiction in U.S.A. compared with Britain was explained by the difference in the natural characteristics of the two peoples. Many of the races from which the population in the U.S.A. were drawn were addicted to the opiates.

The reason for the unfavourable attitude of the Home Office towards compulsory notification of addicts was the existence of many doctor-addicts and the interference with the doctor-patient relationship which would be likely to arise. But the system of voluntary notification was, however, working well. Compulsory detention in an institution would require a complete change in the law, as it was no offence to be an addict.

The Home Secretary had so far never exercised his right to appoint a medical tribunal to control prescribing; a power invested in his office as a result of the work of the Rolleston Committee in 1926.

The Committee unanimously agreed that compulsory treatment in an approved institution was desirable, but felt that the extent of addiction in Britain was so small, and the curative effect of treatment so uncertain, that it would not be possible to pass through Parliament legislation of a far-reaching character involving a totally new principle, namely the interference with the freedom of the individual for sufferers from addiction who were neither criminal nor insane.

Alcoholism

The release of public inhibitions after the Armistice in 1918 was accompanied by an increase in alcohol consumption and a rise of incidence of chronic alcoholism in the gay twenties. Willcox's interest in this subject dated from his early years as a physician and his association with the Law in cases in which heavy drinkers were charged for various offences. Serious attention was directed towards the prevention of inebriety both by doctors and public-spirited individuals in society who appreciated the dangers. In order to assess Willcox's efforts in this direction, comment must be made on the history of the prevention of inebriety.

The Habitual Drunkards Act of 1879 was the first Act of Parliament to deal with the problem, but it was not until 1898 that a further Act was passed which compelled persons convicted for offences three times in a year to be sent to a state-run reformatory, and in the case of certified inebriates for a period of three years. Donald Dalrymple, who had sponsored this Act through Parliament, founded the first home for Inebriates, the Cedars at Rickmansworth, which was licensed under the Act for the reception of sixteen male patients in 1883. Development of further similar institutions followed, some of them run privately, but accommodation for non fee-paying patients was at first quite inadequate and only the fringe of the vast problem could be tackled. Only the very severest cases could be compulsorily treated, unless patients were certifiable under the Lunacy and Mental Deficiency Acts.

Normal Kerr was the first secretary of the Cedars, and founded the Society for the Study of Inebriety in 1884. At first thought to be doomed to failure, it achieved astonishing success and encouraged the development and expansion of other institutions of a similar nature, such as the National Temperance League. Willcox supported both Societies by his influence and attendances at meetings throughout the rest of his career.

He had not been a member very long before he was elected President of the Society for the Study of Inebriety in 1924. The Society, at first concerned with alcoholism, later came to embrace the problem of drug addiction, the subject of Willcox's first address (the Normal Kerr Lecture) in 1923.

The honour came as a surprise because, unlike most of the members, he had never claimed to be an abstainer from alcohol, and in fact appreciated the value of whisky and wine in the success of his personal life, later being regarded as a connoiseur of wines. In his presidential address on July 8th, he modestly announced his sense of unworthiness at following such a distinguished line of presidents as Claye Shaw, and Hyslop (psychiatrists), Sir William Collins, Sir Alfred Pearse Gould, and C. J. Bond of Leicester (surgeons). He said that the yearly expenditure by the nation of £307 millions exceeded the interest on the National Debt and was three times the expenditure on milk. He advocated an extension of the Act to allow non-criminal inebriates to be compulsorily placed under supervision; many such sick people were often unfit for ordinary society but if they could not be certified as insane or had committed no offences they remained free to ruin not only themselves but their families and dependants. He pressed for unremitting investigation of the causes of inebriety and for further education about the dangers of alcoholism and drug addiction.

The National Temperance League was mainly a lay organisation, founded in 1856, with the same objects in view. It was supported by the Church of England and the Salvation Army, and was concerned with the importance of educating the public through schools and colleges. The Temperance League breakfasts had already become a regular feature of annual B.M.A. meetings. At the Bradford meeting of 1924 Sir Thomas Barlow, the President of the League, was unable to be present and Willcox took his place at short notice. Willcox spoke again at the Bath meeting in 1925 and at the 74th Anniversary meeting in 1930.

At the Inebriety Society he followed Sir James Purves Stewart in a discussion on Acute Drunkenness in January 1925. At a time when there were no statutory tests of intoxication based on analysis of the blood, urine or breath, he emphasised that great care was necessary before the diagnosis of Drunkenness was made, in order to exclude physical disease, quoting examples of people known to have taken sleeping tablets (usually barbiturates) or who were probably concussed yet wrongly suspected of being drunk. In one case in his experience the early symptoms of General Paralysis of the Insane had been confused with intoxication by alcohol in a police court case. During his presidency he reinstituted the annual luncheons, a custom of the society which had lapsed for forty years. When he presided, many interesting and distinguished supporters of the society attended including Sir Humphry Rolleston, President of the Royal College of Physicians, Lord Riddell, and Sir Thomas Barlow, the grand old man of medicine, who had been President of the Royal College many years earlier. At these functions no alcoholic beverages were taken, but they were interesting social functions to which members brought guests of their choice.

The B.M.A. Committee on Drunkenness

Towards the end of 1925 the Metropolitan Police Surgeons in London were so often criticised by the public for their opinions on cases of persons, charged with being "drunk in charge of a car", that their association appealed to the B.M.A. for guidance by an authoritative body representative of all grades of professional opinion.

The Council of the B.M.A. appointed a formidable Committee of eighteen members with Sir William Macpherson, a retired army medical services doctor, as Chairman. B.M.A. representatives were Sir Robert Bolam (Chairman of Council), Dr. (later Sir Henry) Brackenbury (Chairman of Representative Body), Dr. Bishop Harman (Treasurer), Mr. R. G. Hogarth (President). There were five police surgeons, two metropolitan magistrates, four practising doctors, Sir Farquhar Buzzard and Willcox (physicians). The references were " to consider and report on the present tests for drunkenness with recommendations as to their improvement".

The publicity in the press attached to persons convicted in Magistrates' courts on charges of drunkenness while in charge of cars was a special source of concern. Decisions of magistrates were based on all the evidence, both legal and medical. When an appeal was made the conflicting evidence of medical witnesses summoned by counsel on both sides often led to press publicity harmful to the profession of medicine. The Committee defined drunkenness, as applied to a person, as meaning "that he was so much under the influence of alcohol as to have lost control of his faculties to such an extent as to render him unable to execute safely the operation on which he was engaged at the material time."

They decided that there was no single test of drunkenness, but their definition should be supported by all the evidence of the circumstances at the material time, coupled with the medical examination and findings in the patient itemised by the committee in the report. Analysis of the alcohol content of the blood, urine and spinal fluid were not considered practicable owing to the conditions limiting their application. These conditions were fully discussed at the meetings where it was pointed out that insufficient research had yet been done with regard to alcohol excretion in the urine in disease of the kidneys, that paraldehyde gave similar chemical reactions to alcohol, and that alcohol would anyhow be present in the urine of persons who had consumed medicine containing alcohol.

The deliberations of the Committee lasted for over a year. Willcox attended every meeting. Meanwhile, research had been progressing at Sheffield where H. W. Southgate, Lecturer in Pharmacology, in co-operation with G. Carter, Lecturer in Forensic Medicine and police surgeon, were researching to find a more accurate method of diagnosis in police court cases. Working in the laboratory of Professor Edward Mellanby with a grant from the Temperance Research Committee (not a state grant) they estimated the blood and urine alcohol content from persons under arrest at the police station. Their work was reliable and of great technical merit. They concluded that the blood alcohol level was the best estimate of intoxication, but as this was not an investigation which could legally be made compulsory, the alcohol concentration in the urine was a sound practical alternative as it ran parallel with the blood level. (B.M.J. March 13th, 1926).

The committee had carefully considered this report before the final report was issued (B.M.J. supplement of February 19th, 1927). So little mention of his work appeared in the report that Southgate cavilled at it in a letter to *The Lancet* of April 9th for paying too much attention to the smell of the breath in cases of alleged drunkenness, while the alcohol content of the urine had not been accepted as an acceptable legal test, in spite of the scientific value of his research carried out during the last four years.

Macpherson was so embarrassed by the letter that he consulted Willcox for advice as to how to reply. This was not the first time in his life that Willcox had been called upon to smooth troubled waters. His diplomatic and courteous reply earned him the thanks of the chairman, who wrote on April 17th:

"My Dear Willcox,
Many thanks for the copy of the reply to Southgate's letter. It is admirable, and I know no one who could have put the case of our committee so clearly and convincingly as you have done. The only superfluous matter in it is your kindly allusion to myself.

Yours very sincerely,

W. J. Macpherson."

The full text of Willcox's letter to *The Lancet* was as follows:

"Dear Sir,   April 13th, 1927.
The British Medical Association Committee under the able and wise guidance of its Chairman, Major General Sir William Macpherson, gave the fullest attention to all possible methods for determining whether 'a person concerned was so much under the influence of alcohol as to have lost control of his faculties to such an extent as to render him unable to execute safely the occupation in which he was engaged at the material time.' The evidence put before the Committee proved conclusively (1) that in different individuals the quantity of alcohol required to impair the function of the higher nerve centres was subject to great variations, e.g. in a person unaccustomed to alcoholic consumption a very slight amount might cause serious impairment while in the case of the person inured to the effects of alcohol relatively large amounts might be ingested without appreciable impairment of control of the faculties; (2) that in the performance of complex occupational acts such as the driving of a motor car an experienced driver might be little affected by relatively large amounts of alcohol since his long experience of driving has caused his control of the car to become almost automatic. On the other hand, a driver of less experience who has to think of each of the special actions required for the complete control of his car before their execution would be seriously affected by a relatively small amount in his driving efficiency, whereas as regards other occupations to which he had long been accustomed his faculty control might be perfect. It was considerations such as these which caused the Committee to refrain from placing definite limits on the percentage of alcohol in the blood, cerebro-spinal fluid or urine which would serve as absolute indications of drunkenness.

"The Committee attached the highest importance to the valuable work of Dr. Southgate on the excretion of alcohol in the urine and its presence in the blood, and each member of the Committee was provided with a copy of the paper. I myself presided at the Meeting of the Medico-Legal

Society at which Dr. Southgate and Dr. Godfrey Carter read their paper 'On the Excretion of Alcohol in the Urine as a Guide to Alcoholic Intoxication' and at that meeting I described this work as a most important and valuable contribution to the Science of Toxicology. In the present state of our knowledge, however, it is impossible to give exact figures of the percentage of alcohol in blood or urine, which would in any individual mean that the borderland of sobriety had been passed, and the authors of the paper refrained from giving such an exact figure. Apart from this difficulty there were definite legal objections to the application of the test by the prosecuting authority, for example the taking of a sample of blood from an accused person who was unwilling might be technically regarded as a legal assault. There is no objection to the application of the test provided that the accused person is willing, and it is to be hoped that this test will be used with increased frequency and so lead to an extension of our knowledge in the diagnosis of drunkenness. I can imagine no better defence for an accused person than the evidence that the blood and urine at the time of arrest were free from alcohol.

"The diagnosis of drunkenness is attended with great difficulty and the Committee stated that no single test by itself would, as a rule, justify a decision one way or the other. Dr. Southgate is under a misapprehension when he suggests that the Committee regarded the smell of alcohol as a test for drunkenness. A careful perusal of the Report will show that all that was claimed for the olfactory test was that 'the smell of alcoholic liquor in the breath or in vomited matter (if any) is a sign of the consumption of alcohol' and conversely that the absence of any smell of alcoholic liquor in the breath of a person at the time of arrest renders it improbable that he had recently consumed alcohol. The decision as to drunkenness would not rest on this test at all, but on the other tests enumerated in the report.

I am,

Yours faithfully,

William Willcox."

As a result of the findings of the B.M.A. Committee the Road Traffic Act of 1930 was passed. It established that the driver of a motor vehicle who is under the influence of alcohol to such an extent as to be incapable of having proper control of the vehicle he is driving shall be liable to conviction.

Willcox opened a discussion on the Toxicity of Methylated Spirits and Impure forms of Alcohol at the Society for the Study of Inebriety in July 1929.

The dangers of methylated spirit had been recognised in 1904 as being so serious that, among 275 cases in U.S.A. 122 died and 153 became blind, the blindness being associated with its wood-naphtha content. In 1926 it was said that 2,000 deaths were caused by this form of alcohol. Fortunately, the incidence in England had always been low, mainly on account of the denaturing process and the presence of a small percentage of pyridine and petroleum rendering the drink impotable or likely to cause vomiting. But numerous cases in Scotland had led to steps being taken to prevent the evil of intoxication there, while a special alcohol committee, set up by the Home Office in 1926, investigated the subject. Several outbreaks had occurred on the Continent—in Rumania, and in the Ruhr district of Germany in 1929 where ten deaths and several cases of blindness were the subject of litigation. The incidence in England had been so low that Willcox himself had encountered only two cases in his practice, in 1922 and 1929. This discussion was widely reported in the press, particularly the daily papers in Scotland and Northern England.

When lead tetra-ethyl was introduced and manufactured in America several deaths among workers in the industry occurred from inhalation of the fumes causing acute lead poisoning. The substance was added to petrol in minute proportion (1 in 1300 parts) to increase efficiency and to prevent "knocking" in motor engines. It was such an unqualified success that the mixture began in 1927 to be used as the ordinary ethyl petrol in current use. But its use in Britain and the Continent caused so much alarm in press reports of accidental poisoning in America that a special Departmental Committee was set up in April 1928, of which Willcox and Professor W. E. Dixon of Cambridge were members. Such an enormous amount of research of a technical nature was considered and so many persons gave evidence before the Committee that the final report could not be provided before two years had elapsed. Willcox's preserved documents and correspondence weighed no less than twenty pounds. The report recommended the new petrol as safe to consumers and to manufacturers and handlers alike, provided strict precautions were taken in the handling and selling of motor fuel and tetra ethyl in particular.

Alcohol, Fume Poisoning and the Motorist

Willcox never learnt to drive a car himself, even when on holiday with his family. He enjoyed the luxury provided by his chauffeur Walter Mallett who served him faithfully for many years, devoting the same care to his car as if it was his own child. Yet he soon realised the increasing importance of the medical aspects of motoring. He was invited in February 1934 by the Temperance Council of the Christian Churches to submit guidance and warning to the Minister of Transport concerning the dangers of driving a motor car after drinking alcohol in any form. A deputation to the Minister had already been sent in 1931 and Willcox's report was merely a repetition of their warning. Pointing out that 7,305 deaths and 180,000 cases of injuries had been caused by road traffic accidents in 1930, he pressed the Minister to give the widest publicity to the dangers of alcohol in every possible way, but in particular in leaflets to be issued with driving licences. The subject of driving and alcohol was again referred to in his last important address on alcoholism at the 20th International Congress on Alcoholism on August 2nd, 1934. Referring to the absorption of alcohol after drinking a pint of beer or three ounces of spirit, a period of nearly twelve hours is required, he considered, before its complete utilisation and excretion. This was a most important matter from the point of view for drivers of motor cars and airpilots. Abstention was absolutely necessary for perfect safety. "If you want 100% efficiency, do not take any alcohol." His plan to deal with Drug Addiction at the

290

same time as Alcoholism was greeted with pleasure and approval by Sir Thomas Barlow, then in his 90th year. He wrote by hand the next day:

10 Wimpole Street, W.1.

"Dear Willcox,

I thought your address yesterday afternoon was one of the best I have ever heard on the temperance question. It was so concise and terse, but it evidently went home, proved by the close attention of the audience. I cannot doubt that your plan of considering alcohol along with drug addiction is a sound method and I consider your observations on the result of control are very important, giving rise to many reflections. I cannot forbear to thank you for the fine stand you have made in the Inebriety Society for some time past. It has made a solid contribution to the whole subject. I consider the line you have taken has done a great deal to secure the honest consideration of the medical profession. It had been on my mind to say this for some time, but your address gives me the opportunity. Believe me,

Yours sincerely, Thos. Barlow."

The close similarity of the early symptoms of carbon monoxide poisoning to those of drunkenness had often led to the false diagnosis of drunkenness by the police in motoring offences. In an article in the *Practitioner* (1937) Willcox reported two cases in which Professor J. S. Haldane and himself had respectively given successful evidence in support of the defence.

A car containing the driver and two gamekeepers stuck in a flooded road. The exhaust pipe was under water, the car closed, the windows being shut owing to the cold weather. The engine was left running while the driver left the car to seek help. He was arrested by the police as drunk on account of his ataxic gait, vomiting and peculiar behaviour. When the police returned to the car its two occupants were found dead. Post-mortem examination showed all the signs of carbon monoxide poisoning, the blood being saturated with it.

A medical man driving a closed car was found by the police to be suffering from loss of memory, headache and giddiness. He was charged with being drunk while in charge of a car. Examination of the car by an expert mechanic showed a defect in the exhaust pipe leading to the entrance of the fumes into the car. In this case examination of the blood indicated carbon monoxide poisoning.

References

"The Pathology and Treatment of Morphine Addiction". British J. of Inebriety, April 1923.

The 10th Norman Kerr Lecture on "Drug Addiction". British J. of Inebriety, January 1924.

"The Prevention and Arrest of Drug Addiction". British J. of Inebriety, July 1926.

"The Medico-Legal Aspects of Alcohol and Drug Addiction". British J. of Inebriety, April 1934.

"The Toxic Effects of Methylated Spirit and Impure Forms of Alcohol". British J. of Inebriety, October 1929.

"Fume Poisoning and Motoring". The Practitioner, September 1937, vol. CXXXIX, p. 225.

Chapter 26

The Jubilee Year and After—1935–1936

Between 1930 and 1935 Willcox was said to have had one of the largest consulting practices in London though he never had a Harley Street address. He was certainly one of the busiest physicians, so widespread were his interests and activities. A frequent attender at Medical Society meetings, he had already been President of at least four learned societies, the Harveian (1922), the West London Medico-Chirurgical (1923–24), the Society for the Study of Inebriety (1924–1927) and the Medico-Legal (1928–1929), missing no meetings during the periods of office. His recreations were riding and hunting and shooting in the appropriate seasons. For the whole period between the two world wars he was a member of the Cottesmore Hunt and would attend the Saturday meets in Leicestershire. In December and January he would often find time for an extra day in the week. Only once did he sustain an accident. When he was on his way to the opening meet of the Cottesmore at Greetham in November 1929 his horse slipped on the verge of the road, fell, and rolled on his leg, which was broken. But within two weeks he was back at work in plaster. An amusing story was heard at St. Mary's some weeks later. A student taking his final clinical examination saw a man in the examination hall with his leg in plaster. He offered him five shillings for information about the diagnosis of his injuries. The man was Willcox, one of the examiners. The story is perfectly true.

At this period he kept two horses in London and rarely missed his early morning ride in Rotten Row, accompanied by John or Philip. Gerald was already in practice having qualified at St. Thomas's Hospital. Nancy had married in 1929 and lived in London.

Willcox was a man with the unusual ability to work for over twelve hours a day and make do with no more than six hours of sleep at night. He had never suffered from insomnia or taken any hypnotic drug in his life. Though he seldom retired to bed before 1 or 2 a.m. he was called in the morning at 7.30, mounted his horse at Marble Arch at 8 a.m. and returned home for breakfast at 9 a.m. He would see his first patient at 9.30 at Welbeck Street. The afternoons were occupied with visits to St. Mary's, the London Fever Hospital or St. Luke's Hostel for the Clergy, a private nursing home for the Clergy and their dependants which he served as an honorary physician for many years. His ward rounds at St. Mary's took place on two afternoons weekly, and were attended by his house physician, the medical registrar, clerks (students) and sometimes by physicians from abroad visiting the hospital.

His bedside teaching was essentially practical and designed more for the education of good practitioners than to the problem of passing examinations which he expected his students to do without any difficulty. From time to time he liked to discuss selected patients to illustrate the features and problems of some special subject he had in mind.

When he dined at home the meal would be followed by a rapid perusal of the daily papers or medical journals. Then came the time for a short period of sleep in his study followed by his literary activities—correspondence, preparation of articles, lectures and addresses. The more important of these would be carefully written by hand ready for his secretary to type on the following day. On simple subjects or for informal talks at society meetings a few notes with headings were sufficient.

Those colleagues who knew him best soon became aware that he was most approachable for consultations at a late hour of night. Bernard Spilsbury was one of them. Himself a very busy man, from time to time he consulted Willcox about matters of medical jurisprudence, drugs or poisons in connection with some particular problem in hand.

Whenever his work would allow during the hunting season he would catch the Friday evening train at Kings Cross, accompanied on different occasions by either Gerald, John or Philip. He could quickly relax and sleep for short periods when travelling by train or car. They arrived at the Crown Hotel at Oakham in time for dinner.

He never played golf, and the only ball game he played was cricket in village matches from time to time when on holiday in the New Forest in the 1920s. He never learnt to drive a car. His diaries of 1915 record a course of driving lessons but these were interrupted by his call to military service at the time of the trial of G. J. Smith. Gerald has described his attempt to teach his father to drive, while on holiday in the New Forest, as a complete failure: "He seemed hopeless at anything mechanical. I used to try to teach him to drive the old car but one day he got stuck on a hill and started to roll backwards. He told me to take over, and would never try again. He never seemed able to master the controls." Yet this inability never really affected his course of life. In Walter Mallet he had a chauffeur who served him faithfully for many years. He rarely asked Mallet to work on Sundays but either relied on members of his family to conduct him to consultations or took taxis.

On January 16th, 1935, he gave an address at the Royal Northern Hospital where he had served on the honorary staff for a few years before the War—to the North London Medical Society on "Certain Disorders of the Liver"—one of his favourite topics. Two days later was his 65th birthday, the day of retirement from the active staff of St. Mary's. During his fifteen years as Physician to in-patients great changes had taken place in the hospital and medical school. The establishment of professional chairs in Medicine and Surgery in 1920 had lightened the burden of teaching duties formerly shared by all the consultant staff. In 1933 the New Medical School had been opened by King George V and Queen Mary. It transformed the facilities for pre-clinical studies and provided new quarters for the Institute of Pathology presided over by Sir Almroth Wright (later known as the Wright-Fleming Institute).

The ceremony marking the retirement of consultants from the St. Mary's staff was customarily a special final round, at times embarrassing and even tearful. Willcox was in his modest way overcome by a crowd of over a hundred people gathered in Princes Ward on the afternoon of his birthday—students, the medical staff and old St. Mary's men. The ward was so packed that it was difficult for latecomers to squeeze in. From the first patient, an asthmatic, to the last two who were diabetics, each received words of encouragement and farewell. The treatment of each was discussed; "the cream of medical teaching, rich with a lifetime of study, observation and thought", the hospital gazette observed.

In his valedictory address, Dr. Maurice Long, his last house physician and now Senior Medical Adviser to the General Post Office, referring to the close of a chapter in his hospital's history, said that many of those present did not realise how his chief had carried the brunt of medical teaching on his shoulders for many years and at the same time had helped many old St. Mary's men to attain the highest qualifications or positions; facts which had been commented on by an American authority who conducted an investigation on medical education in Britain before the Great War; and further, that a noted French physician was once heard to say that he had never seen arthritis in such variety as in St. Mary's Hospital and that it should have been called "Willcox's Disease."

Willcox was too emotional for anything but the briefest speech of thanks to all for their attendance, to Dr. Long for his oratory and most of all, to the nursing staff for their help for so many years. If he had been in the mood he would have modestly repeated what he once said of his student clerks: "my clerks are like Nelson. They put their telescopes to their blind eye and fail to see my imperfections."

"What everybody thinks", wrote Dr. Charles Wilson, the Dean (later Lord Moran) afterwards "was shown by the turnout. I have never seen anything like it—everybody in the place . . . a most fitting end to all you have done for the place. You will be much missed."

But it was not a complete severance from the hospital, for within two years the private (Lindo) Wing was opened and he was able to have charge of occasional patients there from time to time. Relieved of one burden of responsibility, as an elder statesman of his profession, he still had enough work to occupy his time and energy for a few more years. Except for his hunting accident in 1929 he had never in his life been prevented from working through ill health. But he planned a long holiday—a voyage to Australia to attend the 103rd Annual B.M.A. Meeting at Melbourne. Meanwhile, there were the Jubilee celebrations, the procession on May 6th which he watched from the Athenaeum. A week later he delivered the Annual Oration to the Medical Society of London on the progress of Pharmacology during the last twenty-five years. It was a survey of new drugs and their dangers, the detoxication function of the liver, legislation in connection with the Dangerous Drugs Acts, the Therapeutic Substances Act of 1925 and the work of the Poisons Board of which he had been a member since its foundation in 1934.

Willcox was still Honorary Medical Adviser to the Home Office, a title which he retained until his death, but the increasing volume of pathology for the Home Office was carried out by Spilsbury, Roche Lynch and others. It came to be officially recognised that Medico-Legal work by these experts had hitherto been for many years carried out on the cheap. All these experts had been inadequately rewarded for their past services. This factor coupled with the increasing amount of work and its greater complexity arising from advances in scientific techniques, had promoted the idea of creating a more elaborate forensic service than had previously existed. During the Jubilee year, as a result of joint consultations between the Home Office and Police the Metropolitan Police Forensic Science Laboratory was started at Hendon.

At the end of June he enjoyed his last military honour when he presided at the 6th Annual Dinner of the Mesopotamia and Persian Forces which was a reunion attended by 135 people, old friends and colleagues of the Mesopotamia campaign, R.A.M.C. doctors and other officers who had served there in various capacities, including his old chiefs Generals Treherne and Blenkinsop, the successive Directors of Medical Services. He paid special tribute to the quality and endurance of the Indian troops who had comprised three-fourths of the troops there and to the R.A.M.C. doctors, most of whom had been civilian doctors in peacetime at home. It was appropriate that the health of those present should have been proposed by a distinguished Indian army officer, Major-General Nawab Sir Umar Khan.

The B.M.A. Tour

The visit to Australia was the longest holiday that Willcox had ever enjoyed. No less than 157 doctors and wives embarked on the voyage on July 26th. Mildred was already afflicted by troublesome arthritis and probably wisely considered she would be unable to cope with all the necessary activities associated with a strenuous tour. Willcox himself had always been a poor sailor. For the first two days after leaving Liverpool on the "Duchess of Richmond" he ate barely anything. His diary of the tour was the fullest record of his activities he ever made and in some respects was more interesting than the official record of the tour. So great was the hospitality received at various places that the tour had a kind of triumphal quality about it. At almost every place he met old students of St. Mary's, nurses, patients or doctors he had known in the past, even some who had served in Mesopotamia.

They reached Montreal and Quebec on August 2nd. Travelling across Canada the party visited Toronto, the Niagara Falls and Great Lakes, Winnipeg, Calgary, Banff and Vancouver.

After sailing from San Francisco on the Aorangi on August 15th they visited Honolulu and Fiji, arriving at Auckland on September 1st, Sydney on September 6th and Melbourne on September 9th.

His stay in Melbourne was no period of mental relaxation, for he gave three important addresses before large gatherings. Before setting out on the tour, when it became known that he would be coming to Melbourne, he had been invited by the Australian Dental Association to open a discussion on Dental Sepsis in relation to Systemic Infection. This took place on the day after arrival before a large gathering of doctors and dentists. The main speaker was Mr. E. W. (later Sir Wilfred) Fish.

The next day he was one of seven medical men who received the Honorary M.D. degree at a Convocation at the University—the others being Lord Horder, Sir Henry Gauvain, J. S. Fairbairn, Sir Henry Ferguson of Dunedin, Sir Ewen Maclean of Cardiff, and Dr. E. K. le Fleming. Fish received the Honorary degree of D.D.S.

The address on "The use and Abuse of Hypnotic Drugs" was widely acclaimed and reported in great detail. After recalling his address given at Brighton in 1913 on the same subject he spoke of drug addiction and the use of Avertin in anaesthesia, stressing the importance of care in the dosage used, especially in the presence of liver and kidney disease; the same applied to barbiturates as hypnotics, in which the danger of drug accumulation in the body and habit formation were special dangers. The enhancement of the effects of barbiturates following the intake of alcohol was alluded to as a new concept which had not hitherto been appreciated in any country in the world.

Willcox and Sydney Smith, Regius Professor of Forensic Medicine at Edinburgh, were the guests of honour at a Medico-Legal Society luncheon on September 11th. Robert Menzies, Attorney-General, who had travelled out on the Aorangi with the B.M.A. party after attending the Jubilee Celebrations in London and had become acquainted with Willcox on the voyage, gave an address of welcome to the B.M.A. in which he took the opportunity to do some good natured leg-pulling of Willcox which was responded to in an equally effective spirit. "England had a false reputation of being the home of strong silent men" commented Menzies. "On the voyage on the Aorangi I asked Sir William to give a lecture on 'Eminent Poisoners I have dined with', but Willcox had proved a wash-out by refusing. It was to be hoped that the presence of so many representing the greatest profession—the Law—would stimulate him to do something better". In the course of his reply Willcox pointed out that "at meetings of the parent organisation at home they always found it difficult to get the lawyers to speak, but on the ship it was quite different as the Attorney-General spoke the whole time, taking on his listeners in relays, exhausting each one in turn. The English Society enabled the doctors and lawyers to know each other better. This was difficult to achieve, for the doctors tried to view a subject from the point of view of justice and truth."

By a curious coincidence, on the same day that the B.M.A. party arrived in Melbourne there opened a trial there which was of quite unique interest; its details had been brought to Willcox's notice by two judges he had met in Sydney. A few months earlier a man had caught a shark while fishing in the sea. The shark was presented to an aquarium and soon after arrival had vomited a human arm with tattoo marks corresponding to those of a man named Smith who had mysteriously disappeared. A man, in whose company Smith had been seen, was charged with murder but was finally acquitted.

The homeward voyage included visits to Brisbane, Port Darwin, Batavia, and Singapore, where Willcox stayed for a few days with the Governor, Sir Shenton Thomas, and Lady Thomas. In a brief address to the Rotary Club he congratulated the Public Health authorities on the purity of the water and milk supplies which he had found time to investigate. The final voyage home embraced visits to Ceylon, Bombay, Aden, Suez, Port Said, Cairo and Malta, and was completed on November 2nd.

In 1935 Willcox was elected Master of the Worshipful Society of Apothecaries of London, that unique institution which combines the functions of a City Livery Company and a medical and pharmaceutical licensing body, whose medical registrable qualification under the Medical Act of 1886 was one of the oldest.

He held office for the customary period of one year. During this period of office the Court of Assistants submitted evidence to the Select Committee of the House of Lords appointed to consider the proposed Osteopaths Bill. The Bill was proposed as an attempt to legalise a form of treatment by granting a qualification after a period of study considerably shorter than the established curriculum preceding the medical qualification of a doctor. While the Court, in agreement with the B.M.A. and other professional bodies, considered osteopathy to be a reasonable postgraduate study, it considered the curriculum proposed in the Bill was inadequate to provide the necessary training before a person could practise Medicine for the good of the public, or to empower the holder to sign death certificates or make an adequate diagnosis of an illness. Such powers should, it considered, only be entrusted to practitioners undergoing a minimal period of training of six years' duration.

The Chelsea Physic Garden, formerly known as the "Apothecaries' Garden" had originally been associated with the Society since 1673 when a plot of land by the river at Chelsea was leased from Lord Cheyne at an annual rent of £5; the garden was developed to grow medicinal herbs used in their trade and as a centre of botanical research. Soon after Sir Hans Sloane became landlord of the garden he presented it to the Society in 1722 and it has remained in the Society's possession to the present day. At about the end of his term of office as Master, Willcox gave the annual (illustrated) Chadwick Public Lecture on the subject of "Plant Pharmacology and Medical Practice" in the open air at a memorable garden party on the fine, sunny afternoon of June 11th, 1936.

The Chadwick Lectures, he explained, were initiated in 1913 in memory of Sir Edwin Chadwick (1800–1890) "The Father of English Sanitation", who was not only the most notable pioneer of public health of his time but also the promoter of the first Public Health Acts leading to the origin of the Ministry of Health. He had founded the London Fever Hospital, the first of its kind in the country, for the care and isolation of infectious diseases of which typhoid, typhus, diphtheria and smallpox were the most serious menaces of that time. At his death Chadwick bequeathed £28,000 to be used as a trustee fund for the promotion of knowledge and research in public health and allied subjects.

In his discourse on the use of drugs obtained from plants, Willcox explained that the first research in England was carried out on drugs obtained from herbs grown in the garden by the early apothecaries of the 17th century. Though he considered that active principles obtained from plants rarely caused liver damage there were other dangers associated with their use, particularly from overdosage in the case of morphine and hyoscine in patients suffering from kidney and liver disease, whose power of excretion and detoxication was impaired. He appealed to the profession "to take greater care of dosage control". The address was afterwards described by the Chairman of the Trustees, Sir William Collins, as one of the most highly appreciated Chadwick lectures ever given and an eloquent vote of thanks was made by that venerable bearded doyen of British psychiatry, Sir James Crichton-Browne at the age of ninety-six.

A few weeks later Willcox was elected President of the Medical Society of London, the oldest medical society in the British Isles with its headquarters in Chandos Street. The subject of the Presidential Address, "Clinical Immunity", was more suitable for an audience of practising physicians and surgeons than a talk on drugs and poisons. Here again, there was a blend of medical history with a careful exposition of the development of treatment in medical and surgical practice since the early researches of Jenner (1796), Pasteur (1870), Lister and Almroth Wright and others, leading up to the successful prevention of smallpox, cholera, anthrax, typhoid fever and tetanus by the use of vaccines, antisera and antitoxins.

Amidopyrin Toxicity

After attaining the age of sixty-five Willcox experienced very little decline in his practice. Part of this had always been unremunerated service to professional colleagues and the clergy. More technical and financially remunerative but equally interesting was his practice in consulting toxicology carried out at the request of trades and commercial firms producing proprietary preparations. In this field his experience was then probably unrivalled. Ever since 1910 he had from time to time been consulted to advise on the chemical composition or the methods of manufacture of such articles as carbolic tooth powders (1910), golden syrup (1912, 1920, 1922), shampoos (1913), Caley's and Fuller's chocolates (1913), Steadman's Powders (1920, 1922, 1938), iron pills for anaemia (1928), Kaylene (1931), Mycalex (1931), Dr. Cassel's aperient tablets (1932), the antiseptic Izal (1933), Beecham's pills (1934), Sanatogen (1934), and the hydrocarbon insecticides (1938). In several instances he had visited the factories to observe at first hand the methods of production in order to provide a sound opinion.

When he returned from Australia the drug toxicity of Amidopyrin (also known as pyramidon) was in the forefront of the news in the medical press. It was not a new drug. Related chemically to aspirin it had been regarded for thirty years or so as an equally harmless reliever of rheumatic pains and headaches. Enormous amounts had been used in Europe either as the pure drug or as a constituent of proprietary remedies of which Yeast-Vite achieved the greatest publicity. It was advertised as a tonic and pain reliever, "the most powerful pick-me-up known to Medical Science". Each tablet contained vitamin B in the form of yeast, amidopyrin (about 12%), aspirin and several other harmless ingredients.

Despite its popularity amidopyrin had achieved the reputation, founded on reports of rare cases of fatal and tragic toxicity published between 1930 and 1935, of causing the rare condition termed Agranulocytosis, in which the bone marrow of the patient became damaged to such a degree that the granulocyte white blood cells ceased to be produced, leading to the condition in which the patient lacked the cells in the blood whose function it is to protect the body from bacterial infection. Yet amidopyrin was only one cause of this rare condition. The first recorded case due to this drug occurred in Germany in 1922 and was quietly forgotten. In retrospect it was suggested in 1935 that many similar cases had earlier been overlooked or mistaken for cases of diphtheria or other throat infections.

When the Poisons Board was founded in 1933, with Willcox and Roche Lynch among its members, to control regulations of the sale and distribution of drugs and poisons, amidopyrin was placed in Part I of the schedule. In September 1934 Willcox had been consulted by the solicitors acting for the Yeast-Vite company with the request to influence the Board to rescind the original decision and withdraw amidopyrin from the poisons schedule. Willcox had submitted to the Board that the case against this drug was still unproven and that, if it were kept in the list, the Board should be consistent and insert aspirin also. He pointed out that he had used the drug for twenty years without encountering any harmful effect, as had his senior colleague Luff before him; and that the well-known preparation Yeast-Vite contained less than one sixth of the pharmacopeial dose in each tablet. Nevertheless, Willcox failed to influence his colleagues on the Board and the drug was retained in the poisons list. The Yeast-Vite Company reacted, no doubt wisely, to protect their own interests and the public, by altering the constituents of their tablets by omitting amidopyrin from the new preparation to be issued by their factory after June 1935. But there were, of course, already many thousands of packets of the old formula in the hands of the consumer and the retail trade.

It was on behalf of the Yeast-Vite Company that Willcox gave evidence at two inquests in November 1935 and again in 1937, in which attention was focused publicly on the toxic properties of amidopyrin in Yeast-Vite tablets of the old formula. In both cases the Company naturally wished to preserve its reputation and deservedly so, since every possible step had already been taken to avoid any accusation that their tablets could be harmful to the public. If the verdicts at these two inquests had been different from what they turned out to be, the Company would have been liable for damages amounting to thousands of pounds. Willcox played a major role in protecting the Company from unmerited and unfair criticism.

The death of Mrs. Julier at the age of fifty-five on November 15th, 1935, in Bethnal Green Hospital was clearly due to septicaemia arising from pyorrhoea. A week earlier she had developed an abscess in the parotid gland which necessitated a small operation for drainage, but the remorse-less course of the illness to a fatal issue was not unexpected in the days before antibiotics had been thought of. Staphylococci were cultured from the blood. The death was reported to the coroner as due to amidopyrin toxicity and he had no alternative but to hold an inquest. Willcox attended the post-mortem at Stepney Mortuary carried out by Dr. Temple Grey. Clear signs of septicaemia were apparent. There was no ulceration of the mouth or throat as would be expected in death from agranulocytosis.

Willcox held a consultation at Welbeck Street with the manager and solicitor acting for the firm. The exact ingredients of the various formulae of Yeast-Vite were discussed in the greatest detail.

The inquest was resumed by Dr. R. L. Guthrie at Shoreditch on December 3rd. The advantage of having as coroner a medically qualified lawyer was well demonstrated here in a case in which the outcome depended almost entirely on medical evidence. Its interest lay in the slight difference of opinion held by Temple Grey and Willcox on the one hand, and by Dr. J. H. Ryffel, the Guy's Hospital and Junior Home Office Analyst, on the other. But it was this difference of opinion which had a very important bearing on the verdict.

The weakness of Ryffel's case lay in his evidence that he had found traces of a substance resembling amidopyrin in the liver, but he could not be certain that it was amidopyrin. And though no witnesses were forthcoming to testify how many tablets deceased had actually taken, and when they were taken, he went on to give his opinion that the drug had contributed to the cause of death by lowering the resistance to bacterial invasion. He said that he had had experience of one fatal case, though over a hundred had been recorded.

The hospital doctor who had reported the case altered his opinion during cross-examination and admitted that he thought death had been caused either by septicaemia or by amidopyrin alone, but he could not speak with certainty.

Willcox said that though the first case of agranulocytosis due to amido-pyrin had been recorded in 1922 it was only in the last four years that the danger of the drug had become generally recognised. He had prescribed the drug for many years without any unfortunate consequence.

"Do you still prescribe the drug?" he was asked by counsel for the Yeast-Vite Company.—"Yes, but these reports make one cautious. The position is this, that certain persons are very sensitive to certain drugs. What 999 people might take with safety the 1,000th person might be seriously affected by. That applies not only to Amidopyrin but to many other drugs as well. One does not want to take the risk of one in a thousand in treating patients. This is a hypothetical figure, of course". He went on to say that one tablet of Yeast-Vite contained 5/8ths of a grain of the drug—one-eighth of the ordinary standard dose.

Willcox produced several reasons for supposing that death was caused by septicaemia acquired from pyorrhoea, rather than agranulocytosis due to amidopyrin. First, blood tests had shown that the granulocyte cells were present to the extent of 28% of 600 total leucocytes per c.mm —far too high a level to account for death from agranulocytosis. There had been no sign of throat or mouth ulceration. The occurrence of parotid gland infection two weeks before death was inconsistent likewise, but was consistent with septicaemia from infection from the teeth; according to the husband's evidence Mrs. Julier had taken no Yeast-Vite within three weeks of death. And lastly, Dr. Lionel Whitby, in his book on Disorders of the Blood, had listed many causes of agranulocytosis, including bacterial infection and septicaemia.

The Manager of the Company said that their preparation had been launched on the market in 1924 after experimental work on rabbits and guinea pigs indicated its safety, and by 1935 the annual sale of tablets amounted to over 1,300 million. He had never heard of any previous example of its harmful effects. The tablets said to have been taken by deceased were of the type manufactured before the change of formula in May of that year.

The Jury agreed with the coroner that it was a case of three opinions against one, and recorded a verdict of natural death due to septicaemia.

The drug acquired such a bad reputation in the medical profession as a result of the Julier case that it almost ceased to be prescribed—and probably rightly so—for there were other equally effective drugs available as analgesics for rheumatic pains and headaches.

The second inquest at which Willcox supported the cause of the Company was held at Manchester in 1937. Again in this case the deceased, Mrs. Ada Gallimore, had tablets from a stock of the old formula which had come into her possession before 1935. The analysts confirmed the presence of amidopyrin in them, 5/8ths grain per tablet. According to her husband, a railway inspector, she had at times taken Yeast-Vite since 1931 whenever she felt ill. Following a minor wound of her hand she felt ill and took two tablets after each meal on June 3rd and 4th. The next day her doctor found her seriously ill, with a fever and a whitlow on a finger which he incised the following day. She was admitted to the Manchester Royal Infirmary seriously ill on June 6th and died on June 14th. The total consumption was $3\frac{3}{4}$ grains of amidopyrin, less than a single recognised dose.

Willcox made many red pencil marks on the post-mortem report of the Resident Surgical Officer, Dr. Griffiths. All the findings pointed to death from septicaemia, yet this relatively junior surgeon rashly concluded that the cause of death was, in his own words "toxaemia and haemorrhage into the adrenal gland due to agranulocytosis due to amidopyrin and not due to natural causes."

When the inquest opened on June 25th, Dr. Griffiths gave his opinion that death was "accelerated by a patent medicine, Yeast-Vite". The hearing was adjourned in order to allow the firm's representatives to be present.

Accordingly Willcox held a meeting at Welbeck Street on July 12th, attended by Professor C. S. Gibson, Professor of Chemistry at Guy's

Hospital, the Manager of the Company and their Counsel, Mr. G. D. Roberts K.C. and Mr. (now Mr. Justice) Eustace Roskill. Sir Eustace has recently discussed the way that he and his senior colleague were advised as to the wisest way to conduct their case and how the discussion was continued on the train journey the next day when they all travelled to Manchester together.

At the resumed inquest on July 14th, the deceased's doctor described how the illness was caused by septicaemia resulting from a wound of a finger due to a scratch from a fence. The city analyst, Harry Heap, considered that death was caused by amidopyrin to which deceased had an idiosyncrasy. But he suffered severe handling by Mr. Roberts, which must have had a strong effect on the Jury. "Do you agree that you are totally unqualified to express an opinion as to the cause of death?" —"I could not express an opinion by qualification." "You agree that a registered medical practitioner, who diagnosed septicaemia after seeing the patient, is in a much better position to judge than an unqualified man called in as an analyst after death?"—"Though not a Registered Practitioner I am a Master of Science, an F.I.C., and I have taken certain courses in Medicine."

Dr. Griffiths still persisted in court that he considered death was caused by amidopyrin and not septicaemia, in spite of one negative blood culture test. He had made the simple mistake of failing to repeat the test and to investigate the bacteriology of the wound infection. He had overlooked the fact that deceased's granulocyte blood cells had actually increased in number during the course of treatment. From being 5% of 400 leucocytes per cmm. they rose to 54% of 22,000 on the day before death.

Willcox pointed out that this finding was the opposite condition from agranulocytosis. He had not the slightest doubt that death was due to septicaemia arising from the infected wound of the finger. It was inconceivable that two doses of $4\frac{1}{2}$ grains of amidopyrin on two days could have caused such dramatically acute symptoms. "This person", he added, "had been taking the tablets for years. If she had had an idiosyncrasy it would have manifested itself a long time earlier."

Mr. Roberts told the jury that about 80 million tablets had been sold yearly for a long time and in only one case—that of Mrs. Julier in 1935— had it ever been suggested that Yeast-Vite had contributed to the cause of death—a case in which it had been shown that septicaemia had arisen from infected teeth.

The jury without hesitation returned an open verdict of "death due to septicaemia without sufficient proof to show how it came about".

Following the Julier inquest the drug amidopyrin had become more or less obsolete. Henceforth it was scarcely prescribed any more, so great was the publicity in the medical journals attached to its dangers as a result of intermittent reports of cases of agranulocytosis caused by it. Associated with Willcox in the planning of the new formula of Yeast-Vite was Professor C. S. Gibson who had carried out analyses of the tablets found in the house of Mrs. Julier. For the Yeast-Vite Company the Gallimore inquest was not the end of their anxiety. Many tablets of the old formula were still in the hands of consumers, and there remained the risk of further cases of a similar nature.

A thirty-six-year-old mechanic in Rhodesia died in 1938 following an illness lasting only three or four days. Because he had taken Yeast-Vite over a period of two weeks before the illness commenced his doctor, at the suggestion of a colleague who was not a practising doctor but the Director of the Public Health Laboratory at Salisbury, certified death as due to agranulocytosis contained in Yeast-Vite. The magistrate holding the inquest at Salisbury having recorded a verdict accordingly, the stage was set for a heavy compensation claim by the widow against the firm. Gibson and Willcox were again consulted by the solicitors for the firm to protect its interests. Their reports sent to Rhodesia successfully quashed a claim in a court case planned to be held before a judge in February 1939. The case was finally settled out of court by amicable agreement between both parties.

The case for a diagnosis of agranulocytosis was considered by Gibson and Willcox to have been utterly unfounded and the inquest verdict entirely at fault. "All the evidence I have seen", wrote Gibson, "points to there being in Salisbury a generally biased knowledge of the relationship between amidopyrin and agranulocytosis. Because the tablets contained small amounts of the drug it was assumed that the illness arose from it." This case had never been investigated by any laboratory tests, no blood count or swab was taken from the ulcer of the throat. The doctors seemed to have been under the misapprehension that the only cause of agranulocytosis was amidopyrin in spite of the fact that many other causes were listed in the current textbooks of the time. Willcox had even considered from the evidence submitted that Diphtheria was an equally likely cause of death.

Chapter 27

Doctor in Law and Practice—1937–1938

In the spring of 1937 Willcox twice appeared in court for the defence of persons charged for being under the influence of alcohol while in charge of cars, and in both cases helped to secure an acquittal. In the first of these, an accused doctor was defended at the London Sessions on the grounds that he was the victim of carbon monoxide poisoning due, as an expert mechanic testified, to a defective exhaust manifold whereby fumes were emitted into the closed car on a very cold morning. The medical man who examined him on arrest found no signs of alcoholism. In his evidence Willcox explained how easily the early stages of carbon monoxide poisoning could be mistaken for alcoholism. He laid special emphasis on the closed car and considered that the charge should never have been brought. This understandable mistake of the police was not the first of its kind. The difficulty encountered by police surgeons in differentiating the two conditions had been discussed by Professor J. S. Haldane at the Medico-Legal Society in 1929 and was reiterated by Willcox in an article in the *Practitioner* (September 1937) on the Medical Aspects of Motoring.

Medical evidence may play an important part in court in decisions concerning the testamentary capacity in disputed Wills. The testimony of Willcox and Dr. G. W. B. James, his colleague and psychiatrist of the St. Mary's staff, in the High Court in the Probate Division in April 1937 contributed to the success of the plaintiff, a married woman, contesting the Will of her late father Mr. Arthur Strutt, though the evidence of the nurse who had been in charge of deceased at the time of his illness was probably the major factor in winning the case in favour of the plaintiff whereby she benefited to the extent of £30,000, which would otherwise have been claimed by other relatives.

The medical evidence was specially interesting in that it illustrated the seriousness of typhoid fever in the days when the complications of the disease were commoner and more often fatal than is the case nowadays, before antibiotics were ever dreamed of. Several points on the legal side were extraordinary. The deceased, a young man of thirty-six, had died twenty-nine years before the case came to court, and it was unusual to find a woman contesting a Will against her mother and uncle instead of arriving at an amicable settlement without the need for litigation.

The case was heard in the King's Bench Division before Mr. Justice Langton and lasted three days. Willcox was sufficiently interested to attend the case throughout the hearing.

The Will contested by plaintiff's counsel, Mr. Roland Oliver, had been signed and executed on November 16th 1908 only two hours before the testator died. Arthur Strutt had been married in 1900 to his wife Maud (who became Mrs. Harley when she subsequently remarried). They had one son who died in the first year of marriage, another son born in 1907 and a daughter, the plaintiff, born in June 1908. A year earlier a Will had been drafted by the deceased's solicitor and sent to deceased for approval in June 1907—a highly technical document of nine pages of type—but it was never signed. In that the plaintiff was born a year later it was clear that no contemplation of provision for her was possible at the time the Will was drawn up.

It was perhaps unusually fortunate that the doctor who had attended deceased so long ago was still alive and able to give evidence though he did not materially help the plaintiff's cause in court.

The illness, at first thought to be influenza, was later correctly diagnosed as typhoid fever when the typical rash appeared. Several days later the patient collapsed, and the doctor diagnosed perforation of the colon. At a consultation with a surgeon it was decided that it was by then too late, and therefore too great a risk, to operate. The unsigned Will was produced by deceased's brother for the patient to sign only two hours before death while he was propped up in bed with abdominal pain and shock, too ill for the Will to be read to him.

The doctor, recalling to mind his patient after an interval of nearly thirty years, testified that at the material time he had considered the patient mentally capable of understanding the Will. For the other side, the nurse's evidence was that her patient was delirious and so ill that she had told his brother that he was incapable of signing the Will. But the doctor had overruled her with the words "It is merely a matter of form, nurse. It will save a lot of complications afterwards. I will hold his hand".

Willcox and James were emphatically for the plaintiff's cause. They testified that from the evidence submitted perforation of the bowel would have caused general peritonitis and that pain and shock would have been so great that any mental concentration must have been impossible.

Judgement was for the plaintiff. She was granted £30,000 in the form of a trust fund for herself and issue plus an additional sum of £3,000 for expenses.

The Croydon Typhoid Epidemic

After retiring from the staff of St. Mary's Hospital Willcox continued to serve the London Fever Hospital in Liverpool Road as Senior Physician. Though he was familiar with typhoid fever in the earlier part of his career when it was comparatively common, his experience of this group of diseases —typhoid and paratyphoid—on a grand scale commenced in the Great War at Mudros in 1915 and continued in Mesopotamia where the disease was more prevalent than in any other campaign. From then onwards he had seen cases in consulting practice and at the London Fever Hospital. Poor Arnold Bennett, the author, died from typhoid in 1931 under his care; his infection was contracted from a visit to the South of France.

A small epidemic occurred at Bournemouth in 1936 and was traced to milk infected at a dairy. Willcox was consulted in August and September to see four children in a family who had stayed at a hotel supplied with milk from that source.

The serious outbreak in Croydon in 1937 caused such public concern that the Minister of Health, under pressure from the local residents and the press, was forced to set up a special inquiry to investigate its source. There were in all 297 cases with 43 deaths, a mortality of nearly 15%. Fifteen of these cases were treated at the London Fever Hospital, nine under Willcox's care.

The Minister appointed Harold Murphy K.C. as Chairman, and Sir Humphry Rolleston, a past President of the Royal College of Physicians and H. J. Gourley, a civil engineer, as assessors of the Inquiry. Aware of Willcox's exceptional experience of typhoid and his long experience in the sphere of public health, Rolleston selected him as an expert witness to give evidence at the proceedings. The Inquiry, held at the Town Hall in Croydon, occupied sixteen days, from December 21st to January 12th, 1938. Verbatim reports appeared daily in the local papers. The story of the epidemic illustrated the urgent necessity of precautionary measures to prevent the spread of the disease at a time when the disease was a much greater menace and the fatality rate far higher than it is today.

The Medical Officer of Health was put off his guard by the fortuitous occurrence of a sporadic case of typhoid in a lady living in the affected area of Croydon who had quite clearly picked up her infection while on holiday in the South of France.

Between October 27th and 30th six cases had been notified and by November 8th the epidemic was well established, about six daily notifications being made. On October 31st a local resident, whose son died during the outbreak, called a meeting of local residents of the affected area. It was attended by the M.O.H. and the Borough Engineer. The former was disinclined to believe that water was the source of infection and the latter had been unaware that typhoid had been notified.

The source of the infection was traced within a few days to the chalk well at Addington which provided the high level water supply to the affected district. Investigation by the Ministry of Health showed heavy pollution of the well water though no typhoid bacteria were isolated by bacteriologists. The supply from the well was promptly cut off on November 4th but by that time the tanks in many houses must have been full of infected water.

Repair work had commenced at the well on September 24th and was completed on October 28th. All the cases of typhoid were notified within three weeks of this period—the maximum incubation period of the disease. The repairs, carried out by eighteen men, were directed to one of the adits to the well to control the inflow so as to enable repairs to the pumping plant to be carried out.

It was discovered during the course of the Inquiry and after Willcox had given evidence, that the water in this well, which supplied a catchment area for a population of 40,000 people, had been contaminated by the excreta of a workman proved to be a "carrier" of typhoid bacteria who had originally contracted the disease while serving in the army in the

Great War and had for many years remained a carrier of infection through no fault of his own.

But it was brought out at the Inquiry that a contributory cause of the epidemic was an extraordinary degree of misunderstanding and lack of communication between the responsible officers of the corporation in connection with the repairs. Not only was the M.O.H. unaware that the work in the well had been going on but he and the borough engineer were unaware that chlorination of the water had ceased. Chlorination was promptly started on November 1st but several cases were by then already notified, and nine by November 3rd.

As so often happens at public inquiries at times of crisis a scapegoat is sought. At Croydon the M.O.H. was the obvious choice. When Willcox gave evidence on January 6th he clearly showed his contempt for the tendency to attach all the blame to one person. There were clearly several links in the chain of responsibility.

"I do not criticise the Medical Officer of Health but I do criticise the lack of co-operation and liaison throughout the country between public health authorities and the general practitioners".

He considered that at the meeting of the residents and the M.O.H. the local doctors should have been invited. He congratulated the M.O.H. and the Ministry officials for the prompt way they had put a stop to the epidemic after diagnosing its cause. He went on to make further suggestions:

"There should be (throughout the country) an 'ad hoc' committee representing local doctors and the M.O.H. who could advise the M.O.H. and in turn be helped by him. It was easy to say that a general practitioner did not know much about public health. Perhaps not, but he was the first one to establish contact with the patient and the first one who could put in simple language to the public the dangers to which they were exposed and the precautions to take." Part of the difficulty, he explained, lay in the fact that typhoid fever had become so much rarer at that time than thirty years past that doctors were becoming less familiar with the diagnosis and the dangers of the disease.

The report of the Inquiry (February 1938) quoted Willcox's view that special condemnation of the Croydon corporation's medical services for their lack of co-operation was not justifiable but it emphasised that this lack of co-operation was nation-wide at that time. On the contrary, the epidemic had been dealt with promptly at a reasonably early stage directly the source had been discovered.

Six weeks later—on March 22nd—Willcox was again at Croydon to address the Croydon division of the B.M.A. on "The Clinical Aspects of Typhoid Fever". He recalled that the continued fevers of Britain were commonly called Typhus until Typhoid was clinically differentiated in 1849, though the typhoid bacillus was not discovered until 1880. He presented figures to show the effectiveness of public health measures, by reviewing the death rate per million of population from 101 in 1903, to 41 in 1913, 12 in 1923 and 6 in 1936. The public had become so accustomed to freedom from outbreaks which thirty years earlier had been extremely common that by 1937 they had become not unnaturally alarmed by the outbreak at Croydon; hence the Inquiry, which was forced on the Minister of Health by the request of a Croydon resident and press publicity. The public took the view that they had a right to expect to be guaranteed freedom from the disease. It was a reasonable and understandable attitude at a time when the mortality rate was 10% or more.

Turning to prophylactic inoculation he recalled the attention of the audience to the history of the triple vaccine which had been introduced in 1916 as a result of the work of Captain (later Sir Robert) Archibald and himself at Mudros in 1915. In the Dardanelles campaign it was found that paratyphoid fever was six times as common as typhoid. The troops were being inoculated with typhoid vaccine which had been introduced by Sir Almroth Wright so successfully in the South African War. Its lack of success in the Dardanelles campaign was due to the predominance of paratyphoid there. Acting on the advice of Willcox and Archibald in November 1915 to the War Office, the official vaccine was altered to include the two types of paratyphoid bacilli—the familiar T.A.B. vaccine which has been universally used since that time.

Some of the cases in which Willcox was consulted at this stage of his life were fascinating and mysterious tragedies. The death of a forty-year-old engineer, Herman Smith, from heatstroke in Baghdad in July 1937 was a cruel example both of the failure to take adequate precautions and of the dangers of air travel, not then fully recognised, by the elimination of the process of acclimatisation to heat consequent on the sudden arrival of a person in a very hot climate in the hot season. Willcox was consulted by the deceased's widow's legal advisers at the suggestion of Dr. Hamilton Fairley, the tropical medicine expert, in May 1938. Fairley was aware of Willcox's influence as an expert medical witness in all types of litigation and of his great experience gained among troops in Mesopotamia (1916–1918) of the effects of heat and that his colleague Sir Victor Horsley had died of heatstroke there through failure to take full precautions.

Herman Smith, employed by an important engineering works at Scunthorpe, had been ordered to proceed to Baghdad somewhat hurriedly to repair their plant at Beled, near Baghdad. He left England by air on July 11th and arrived on July 14th. For the next six days he worked at these two places and died unexpectedly on July 21st.

On the day of his death he worked on the plant from 5 to 7.30 a.m. ate a hearty breakfast and did his last spell of physical work from 8.30 to 11 a.m. After a frugal lunch he was seen on his bed smoking and reading but felling unwell. His german mechanic found him in great distress at 4.30 p.m. but before he could summon a doctor, he was dead. It seemed strange, that, though he had worked for six days in the trying climate, he should succumb on the seventh day while at rest in his bungalow. Nevertheless, Dr. (later Sir) Harry Sinderson (who later became Professor of Medicine at Baghdad) carried out the post-mortem and considered that death was due to heatstroke; he had found no other cause of death. On the day of the tragedy the maximum temperature in Baghdad was 119°F and it was estimated that at Beled it would have been about 115°F.

On June 7th 1938 Willcox gave some instructive comments in a report on the evidence. Experience in Iraq in the Great War (Address to Medical Society of London March, 1920) had shown that a temperature of 110°F in the shade appeared to be the danger threshold for heat. The incidence of illness due to heat among troops markedly increased *pari passu* with each degree above this level. To withstand such heat the necessary precautions are acclimatisation and advice concerning suitable clothing, an adequate intake of water and salt, and the need to avoid exposure to sunshine after 8 a.m. In the case of Smith, he had worked until 11 a.m. in the open. It was unfortunate that he had been sent at two days' notice without time to get expert medical advice before departure.

Two points of law were made by counsel for deceased's widow. Firstly, he considered that application of the Workmen's Compensation Acts would fail because the tragedy had occurred in a foreign country. Secondly, he considered that in law it is the duty of a person who employs another to do work under conditions he knows may be dangerous (a) to see that he is fit to run into the particular danger without undue risk and (b) to see that he is warned of the danger and of the need to take adequate precautions so that the employee has a chance of exercising his choice whether to go or not. In this case these precautions had not been adequately undertaken.

Fortunately the case never came to litigation in court, an adequate and amicable settlement of compensation to the widow being made.

Epidemic Arsenical Poisoning

The tragedy of chronic arsenical poisoning affecting a Norwegian family living on a ranch in the North Eastern Transvaal was the subject of litigation in August 1938 in the Supreme Court at Pretoria when compensation of £80,000 was awarded against the Union Government for the damage to health of a family, and to some hundreds of sheep and cattle on the ranch. At the end of June 1938 Willcox's opinion was sought by counsel acting for the family on the advice of a doctor in practice in Pretoria who was the father-in-law of the counsel concerned. According to the legal advisers there was no expert toxicologist available in South African with sufficient experience in the subject to be prepared to give expert advice.

H. A. Mordt, the manager of the Oslo Land Ranching Company, came with his family in November 1934 to live on the ranch. The tragedy that befell them is best explained in Willcox's report. In April the Union Government in combating a locust invasion used extensively on the ranch a fine powder and also an aqueous solution of Sodium Arsenite. Considerable quantities were sprayed by hand and from aircraft on the ranch, in April 1934. The veterinary inspector conclusively showed that the cattle on the ranch between April 1934 and 1936 suffered seriously from arsenical poisoning. Over 1100 were affected and in those that had to be destroyed analysis showed considerable amounts of arsenic in the bones. If the cattle suffered from arsenical poisoning, which was in no doubt whatever, it was clear that the milk must have contained arsenic. Many sheep also suffered and died. The ranch closed down in July 1936. Sheep's liver was a favourite meat dish in the Mordt family of eight children ranging from two to nineteen years of age at the time of litigation. It was estimated that the family consumed about four gallons of milk daily, each member imbibing an appreciable amount of arsenic, the younger members being most susceptible to poisoning.

Between March 1935 and July 1936, and within three months of exposure, all the children developed chronic diarrhoea, fever, headache, arthritis, pains in the feet and legs, loss of hair, pigmentation and scaling of the skin and flat feet. In one case typical ulcers of the feet and legs were seen. In the youngest child, breast fed at the time, similar symptoms appeared, and kidney damage was caused as a result of arsenical poisoning from her mother's milk. These symptoms of chronic arsenical poisoning almost exactly corresponded to those of the victims of the Manchester beer epidemic of 1901. The children improved in health when the poison was cut off, though it was a slow process. But far more serious was the deterioration in the intelligence and mental faculties which permanently affected all the children except the two elder ones. From being bright and intelligent they became dull-witted, unreceptive to education and unable to pass examinations, their educational prospects being far below those required for any skilled trade. In fact the mental deterioration reminded Willcox of Mrs. Armstrong who became temporarily so insane that institutional treatment was necessary.

Willcox had no hesitation in concluding that arsenical poisoning was the cause of ill health in all the children and cattle. He anticipated a slow but steady recovery of physical health but not of intellectual capacity. It seemed to him extraordinary that the South African doctors felt so unconversant with the subject that they were unwilling to give evidence in Court, though they had made a correct diagnosis; and that the Union Government should have been so ignorant of the dangers of chronic arsenical poisoning, a subject which was not only recorded in several current medical text books but had been the subject of Willcox's address to the Section of Industrial Diseases of the B.M.A. at Glasgow in 1922.

Two subjects were in the forefront of Willcox's mind in the last three years of his life—research in arthritis sponsored by the Empire Rheumatism Council and secondly, the impact on medical practice arising as a result of the introduction of new drugs.

The truism that every drug is a poison, if it is abused, was not always acted upon by the profession nor adequately understood by the public. Willcox's address to the Barnett Division of the B.M.A. in March 1938 was directed along two separate channels. He traced the history of legislation controlling the sale of drugs and poisons from the time of the Arsenic Act of 1851 which restricted the sale of arsenic to qualified chemists and druggists. Before that time there had been an increasing number of deaths from poisoning, about a third of which were due to arsenic. By the Pharmacy Act of 1868 the regulations were entrusted to the Pharmaceutical Society of Great Britain (founded in 1841) which came under the control of the Privy Council. At that time few substances were in the "Poisons List". Various amendments and additions to the list were made in the 1908 Act. Willcox himself had taken part in the amendments which followed in 1911, 1912, 1926 and 1933, and in the Dangerous Drugs Acts between 1920 and 1937. By the Pharmacy and Poisons Act of 1933 the Poisons Board (to which Willcox and Roche Lynch were appointed), took over the duties from the Pharmaceutical Society in 1935, its first statutory rules coming into force in 1936 whereby the regulations became the concern of the Home Office.

The Poisons Board was a widely representative body whose duty was to schedule in appropriate categories new drugs and poisons whose sale required restriction to qualified and approved vendors. Rules controlled the storage, transport, labelling, manufacture and dispensing of drugs.

The other part of his address was an account of certain cases of poisoning and of drug addiction in his own experience; he gave warning of the potential dangers of the drugs Benzedrine and Sulphanilamide, introduced in 1935. The former had already acquired a place in the treatment of narcolepsy and as a mental stimulant in certain cases of depression.

The discovery in Germany of the anti-bacterial power of Sulphanilamide was the most important and far-reaching advance in treatment in medical practice since Insulin, and ranked in importance with Ehrlich's discovery of the action of Arsenobenzol (salvarsan) in the treatment of syphilis and other spirochaetal diseases. In 1936 Leonard Colebrook and his colleagues had demonstrated the dramatic success of Sulphanilamide in cases of puerperal fever due to streptococcal infection at Queen Charlotte's Hospital. This success was enhanced by the discovery that this remedy also controlled infections due to the pneumococcus, gonococcus, and meningococcus.

When he opened a discussion on "The Rise and abuse of Sulphanilamide" at the Medical Society of London in October 1938 Willcox quoted some of his own successes in cases of pneumonia, erysipelas, cerebrospinal fever and the complications of scarlet fever. Already eight derivatives of Sulphanilamide were on the market and controlled in the poisons list. But the Ministry of Health in its annual report of 1937 gave warning of possible toxic effects. Several fatalities had already occurred in the U.S.A. as a result of the prescription of a sulphanilamide elixir, though the toxic effect was found to be due to contamination with Diethylene glycol. The derivatives of sulphanilamide, now termed sulphonamides, in current use are, relatively speaking, so safe that the early experience of those years has been almost forgotten except by doctors in practice at that time. But within two years or so of its introduction Willcox at the meeting warned the Medical Society of London of the potential danger to the liver, kidneys, to the blood forming cells in the bone marrow, of skin rashes, and of the less common cases of idiosyncrasy, drug fever and the abnormal blood pigments methaemoglobin and sulphaemoglobin.

It is interesting here to recall that when Professor Alexander Fleming followed Willcox in this discussion and described the bactericidal effect of sulphanilamide on the pneumonococcus he had already in his possession at St. Mary's Hospital small amounts of the substance penicillin which was to become the greatest medical discovery in the history of medicine and the source of the new era of antibiotic treatment. Though Willcox died before penicillin became available for practical use he had heard from Fleming himself the story of its discovery several years earlier.

Appropriately on the last occasion on which Willcox entertained the Clinical Club at Welbeck Street, on April 26th, 1938, the subject of drug toxicity was again discussed. The meeting resolved that the experimental work in connection with the introduction of new drugs should be entrusted to the Medical Research Council, a body which, it was hoped, might in the future give guidance and warning when new drugs were introduced on the market.

His experience in the art of putting across scientific knowledge in a simple way to ordinary educated people was the source of the popular illustrated 15th Cavendish lecture to the West London Medico-Chirurgical Society on June 1st, 1938 on "Toxicology with reference to Crime", a subject which drew a large crowd, as was to be expected, of medical men and the laity alike. It was a brief but interesting survey of poisoning from the times of ancient Egypt, Greece and Rome to the mediaeval Borgias, and thence to comments on famous trials from *Rex* v *Donellan* (prussic acid) of 1781 to more modern cases encountered by Sir Thomas Stevenson and himself. Among interesting exhibits were the Marsh apparatus and its modifications, and Armstrong's chocolates.

The subject of "Co-operation within the Profession" was taken up in a big way in two separate symposia at B.M.A. meetings on June 24th and July 22nd. The first occasion was a special meeting of the Kensington Division at B.M.A. House and the second a meeting of the section of medical sociology held at Plymouth. Regarded as an elder statesman of his profession, Willcox had acquired some reputation as an opener of discussions on subjects of special interest to pave the way for speakers who followed.

At the meeting at B.M.A. House he opened by recalling the comparatively recent history of public health legislation since the first Public Health Act of 1848.

> "Today, when one Act after another has reached the statute book we have become ultra health-conscious. The advances of the last few years have been so rapid that it is wise to pause, think and ruminate a little. The developments are so manifold, such a state of flux exists, that the public and the profession are bewildered by the problems that have arisen. Hasty advances which have not been considered in all their aspects, medical, economic and social, are to be deprecated. The process of evolution by carefully considered and well-thought-out advances will give the best results . . . In this country the State does not lead but it points the way. That is the reason why the Empire has been so great and successful."

A timely warning, it may be thought, of the dangerous consequences that might follow the commencement of political interference in the profession ten years later.

Before the Act of 1929, he recalled, the hospital services had comprised the Poor Law infirmaries on the one hand and the voluntary hospitals on the other, with little or no co-operation between them. By this Act the former, which had constituted the majority of hospitals in this country, became controlled by county councils and municipal authorities. The advantage gained was freedom from financial embarrassment. But the great step forward had been the formation of the Voluntary Hospitals Committee which had done remarkably good work by increasing the sense of co-operation in the tasks of hospital planning and construction. The committee was composed of an equal number of lay and medical members. The public health service in Britain was, he thought, one of the best in the world but the service covered such a wide field that it was impossible for medical officers of health to be expert in all branches; therefore the need was all the greater for co-operation with general practitioners in each locality concerned, as the Croydon epidemic had shown. He urged the important part which general practitioners could play in co-operation with the public health departments concerned with child welfare, the school medical service, immunisation, maternity and ante-natal services, tuberculosis, and venereal diseases.

This subject was elaborated by Dr. James Fenton, President of the Society of Medical Officers of Health, Dr. W. Allen Daley, Principal Medical Officer of the L.C.C., Dr. G. C. Anderson, secretary of the B.M.A. and by Lord Dawson of Penn, the leading medical statesman of his time, who was nearing the end of his Presidency of the Royal College of Physicians.

Lord Dawson, like Willcox, was an implicit believer in advancing the medical services of the nation by evolutionary, rather than by revolutionary, measures. "The exact form in which co-operation should take place", he explained, "might be safely left to be tried out in different districts. The important thing was to have in each district a professional authority representing the collective opinion of the profession. My ideal for the future was a medical faculty in each district, meeting periodically, in which the best men would become the leaders of medical opinion locally. The public would then have some authoritative voice to which to listen and would no longer be dependent on advice given in newspaper advertisements and the popular press".

One wonders how many of the three hundred people at the gathering guessed that within little more than a year hospital, and indeed all medical policy, would have to undergo radical changes to meet the outbreak of war, the terror of German bombs, and the struggle for survival.

Ten days after that meeting Willcox was summoned to an emergency conference at the Home Office by Sir Samuel Hoare, Home Secretary, to consider the arrangements to be made to assist Austrian refugee doctors fleeing from their country invaded by Hitler. In considering the proposed admittance of a quota of these unhappy people, at the request of the

Co-ordinating Committee of Refugees, Hoare pointed out that their duty was to meet the dire emergency in their best interests to fit in with the welfare of the British public and medical profession.

Willcox made several points at this meeting. The profession in Britain at that time was nearing saturation point; the standard of medical ethics and sense of responsibility to the patient was lower in most European countries and the period of clinical study considerably shorter. The meeting decided that no more than 50 doctors should be admitted to the British register provided they obtained a registrable qualification after two years' study, and that those so qualified should be allowed to stay permanently to practise here. A medical advisory committee was formed to co-operate with the Co-ordinating Committee dealing with refugees from Germany and Austria. The Home Office had by this time already sanctioned the admittance to Britain of 180 German doctors.

The Medical Advisory Committee consisted of Dr. (later Sir Robert) Hutchison, President of the Royal College of Physicians as Chairman, Sir Cuthbert Wallace, P.R.C.S., Sir Girling Ball, Dr. G. C. Anderson, secretary of the B.M.A. and Willcox, representing the Society of Apothecaries. The unenviable task of selecting 50 out of 1,000 applications from refugee doctors was completed by the end of September, the closest possible scrutiny being made of each application by the committee and co-opted assessors. Preference was given to applicants between the ages of 30 and 50, to male applicants married to British-born women with young children provided they had some form of financial security to support them for a period of two years' study at a medical school for a British qualification. About two foreign doctors were allotted to each medical school. Over and above the 13 specialists and 37 general practitioners selected, many distinguished research workers, some of international renown, were admitted with the proviso that they were not permitted to practise in Britain.

The same committee was reformed the following year to select 50 refugee doctors from Czechoslovakia from among 361 applicants and completed its work a month before the outbreak of war.

References

"Typhoid Fever: Clinical Aspects". Croydon B.M.A. Address. B.M.J. May 21st, 1938, p. 1085.

"The Nature, Prevention and Treatment of Heat Hyperpyrexia". Discussion at the Medical Society of London, March 8th, 1920. B.M.J. March 20th, 1920.

"Dangers to Health arising from the Use of Industrial Preparations of Arsenic". Paper read at B.M.A. Meeting at Glasgow, July 1922. B.M.J. August 26th, 1922.

"Toxicology with Reference to Its Criminal Aspects". The 55th Cavendish Lecture to the West London Medico-Chirurgical Society, June 1st, 1938. West London Med. J., July 1938.

Chapter 28

The Second World War—1939–1941

Lives of great men all remind us
We can make our lives sublime,
And departing, leave behind us
Footprints on the sands of time.

H. W. Longfellow.

When Willcox reached the age of sixty-nine in January 1939, his activities in no way diminished; his appointment book was still full enough to provide him with a reasonable income to cover his heavy expenses. Having no hobbies other than riding, hunting and shooting, he gave considerable time and effort to non-professional activities, some of them of a charitable kind.

He had been President of the Rutland Agricultural Society for a year in 1937, attending all the main meetings at Oakham, and in the same year supported the appeal in aid of the extension for the London Fever Hospital. As a member, and for a time on the Council, of the British Empire Cancer Campaign, he had been a regular attender at meetings ever since 1923 until his death. But more important, he remained until the end Chairman of the Research Advisory Committee of the Empire Rheumatism Council, and of the Medical Board of the Central Clinic of the British Red Cross Society. Of his activities as a Mason, one cannot say more than that he reached a high rank, having attended since 1910 meetings of the Sancta Maria and Misericordia Lodges at regular intervals.

He enjoyed visits to the theatre and became devoted to Ballet and the Opera mainly through his friendship with his patient Frank Isitt and his wife, Adeline Genée, the famous ballerina. As a member of the Advisory Committee of the Association of Operatic Dancing of Great Britain, he was one of the signatories to the appeal for the granting of the Royal Charter in 1935, whereby it became known as the Royal Academy of Dancing. News of the appeal's success had been cabled to him while he was in Australia. Later he helped to draw up the rules for the approval of the Privy Council and presented to the Academy the original design of the armorial bearings.

On May 4th, 1939, he was the guest-speaker of the Windsor and District Medical Society, his subject being Drug Toxicity and addiction, the last address he ever gave to a provincial medical society, and in July he commenced lecturing to the women students of the West London Hospital on Forensic Medicine and Toxicology, a duty which continued until 1941.

It was at this time that Willcox developed symptoms of diabetes and he must have realised that his life expectation was seriously restricted. Yet he enjoyed his customary summer holiday in the New Forest with his family and his two horses, "The Major" and "Whiskers".

When Chamberlain declared war on Germany in September, he at first seemed astonishingly unaware of the gravity and length of the struggle lying ahead, for he recorded in his diary a bet of half a crown (no mention with whom) against the war lasting more than three months. But as time passed on he became more and more depressed by regrets that age and ill health would prevent him rendering useful war service. Yet he had complete confidence in the courage of the British people. "We seem to be in for a tough time", he wrote to Philip on September 17th, "but courage and persistence should see us through. I have supreme confidence in that". Though his health had not yet obviously declined, save for slight loss of weight, his self confidence showed signs of wavering for the first time in his life. Invited to become President of the Section of Therapeutics and Pharmacology of the Royal Society of Medicine, he hesitated and took the unprecedented step of asking the youngest member of the family for his advice. "Do you think I am fit enough to accept?"—"I am sure you are. You are not ill now and no one would think you are. You are so used to presiding at meetings that the duties would to you be easy to carry out. At any rate you can resign later if you feel you cannot carry on during your term of office".

His Presidential Address to the Section on "Pharmacy and Pharmacology" was delivered on October 10th, thirty years—he reminded the audience—after he had succeeded Sir Thomas Stevenson as Visitor to the Examinations of the Pharmaceutical Society on behalf of the Privy Council, a post which meant paying twelve visits yearly to the examinations, an annual report and consultations about proposed changes in the curriculum caused by new advances in research. Thus he had been for all these years a bridge between the professions of Pharmacy and Medicine. It was therefore natural that the address should have been historical, for no one was more acquainted than he with history of Pharmacy, the rules and regulations controlling the sale and handling of drugs and poisons, and the part played by the Pharmaceutical Society in initiating research on biological standardisation and the control of the safety of new drugs.

He began his address by announcing the war-time policy of the Royal Society of Medicine and the Section of which he was President. "Business as usual. War calls for courage. Courage begets courage, just as fear begets fear", and ended with a quotation of James I: "Grocers are merchants, but the business of the Apothecary is a Mystery".

In March 1940 he was confined to bed for the first time in his life— with an attack of heart failure, the cumulative effect of years of overwork. He had had no previous illness except for the fracture of his leg in 1929, which incapacitated him for no more than a few days. Though this was not coronary thrombosis, he was by any standards seriously ill, yet in an astonishing way he rallied and put up such a good fight against the illness that he insisted on resuming his practice within two weeks in spite of the warnings of Hubert Broadbent, his past house physician, and medical adviser. Willcox was an obstinate patient. Unknown to Broadbent,

316

at the request of an Exeter doctor, he agreed to attend a consultation there exactly two weeks after the onset of his illness. Accompanied by Nancy and a nurse, he successfully carried out the task, going by train to Exeter. He returned straight to bed, where he was on Broadbent's next visit, and nothing was ever mentioned about the journey. He had been fortunate to have been ill during a lull in the air raids. He resumed work and carried on for another year.

In the three years 1938–1940 Willcox appeared in court in the King's Bench Division on four occasions, two cases of food poisoning and two of accident compensation claims. The last of these attracts attention, being the last occasion he appeared in court with Sir Bernard Spilsbury and the second time in which they fought on opposing sides.* The attributability of illness to accidents is a frequent cause of medico-legal disputes in which doctors beg to differ, as happened in an amicable way in this case of a rare and fatal illness with a complicated medical history.

No sooner had he become ambulant after his illness than Willcox was approached by the solicitor acting for the widow of a forty-six-year-old policeman who had died on June 14th, 1939, a year and four months after sustaining multiple injuries in an accident on the North Circular Road. On January 21st, 1938, when riding his bicycle he had caught his front wheel in a tram track and was thrown off his balance into an on-coming tramcar, sustaining concussion, a brain contusion, fractured collarbone and other minor injuries, for which he was treated at Whipps Cross Hospital and later at a police nursing home. After convalescence, he never regained his normal health enjoyed during twenty-six years' service, but suffered so much from post-concussion symptoms on resuming part-time work that he had to be discharged from the Service in March 1939. Sir Ambrose Woodall, Surgeon to Manor House Hospital and Medical Adviser to the Ministry of Pensions, who examined him twice, found some loss of memory, of his sense of smell and taste, depression, and loss of weight, and considered him unfit for any form of work. On June 11th, 1939, he became so acutely ill that his doctor admitted him to the London Hospital where he died three days later. At post-mortem he was found to have a brain contusion, chronic tuberculosis of the adrenal and lymphatic glands and other features of Addison's Disease. Though the pathologist considered there was no evidence that the accident had accelerated death every doctor who had treated the patient, including Woodall, agreed with the view of the patient's own doctor. "He was never the same after the accident", he reported "but his appetite failed and, though he forced himself to return to work, he did not feel fit for it. Probably the shock and asthenia reduced his vitality and caused the tuberculous process in the adrenals to flare into activity".

The inquest verdict was Accidental Death caused by brain laceration and tuberculosis of the adrenal glands accelerated by the injuries. The driver of the tramcar was exonerated from blame. The solicitors for the London Passenger Transport Board had admitted negligence on account

* Chapter 23, Richards v. Appenroots

of a defective condition of the tram track and had paid into court £200 to cover expenses incurred by the injury. Litigation arose through the refusal of the L.P.T. Board to admit liability for the policeman's death and the allegation that death was due to natural causes and was not in any way attributable to the accident. Willcox's opinion was required, in the light of all the evidence, on the views expressed in all the medical reports.

The case for the plaintiff, the widow, against the London Passenger Transport Board was heard before Mr. Justice Hallett on April 15th, 1940.

There was general agreement among all the medical witnesses on the facts of the case. The differences of medical opinion concerned the relative importance attached to the accident in causing death. Willcox strongly supported the view of the policeman's doctor and that of Woodall and others. He said that Addison's Disease was rare and that this dispute in court over an accident compensation claim was unprecedented in Britain. The disease in over 80% of cases was caused by tuberculosis of the adrenal glands. Calcification in various groups of lymphatic glands and in the adrenals, as occurred in this case, would develop slowly for many years so that it was probable that in this case the infection commenced in the early part of the policeman's service in the Force, or even before he joined. Having remained quiescent for so long, the tuberculous process could be reactivated by any form of shock such as a severe injury undermining the immunity of the body. He went on to say that the policeman's health declined soon after the accident; his failing appetite and loss of weight several months before death suggested that the adrenal glands were already damaged and Addison's disease was already established a long time before death. It was probable that, but for the accident, the disease would never have developed at all, certainly not at that time.

For the Defendants Dr. J. R. Gilmour, the pathologist, and Sir Bernard Spilsbury based their testimony almost entirely on the microscopical appearances of the adrenal glands. They described the typical appearances found in chronic adrenal failure seen in Addison's disease arising naturally, and expressed the opinion that sooner or later death would have occurred had there been no accident at all.

Accepting the medical evidence for the plaintiff, the judge awarded damages to the widow. In fairness to Spilsbury it must be admitted that at that time the sensitivity of the adrenal glands to damage by shock was not so generally recognised as it is to-day, though even then Willcox was able to quote from a well-known American textbook (Cecil and Loeb, 1927) that adrenal failure could be provoked by shock and injury.

While giving evidence Spilsbury was noticed to be looking strained and tired, beads of perspiration being visible on his face. Perhaps it was the strain of finding himself up against his old friend and colleague and of fighting for a cause he feared to be doomed to failure. No more than a month later, in mid-May, he was taken ill for the first time while doing a post-mortem. Fortunately a slight stroke incapacitated him for only two weeks, he returned to work and survived through the war whereas Willcox was destined to live for only one more year.

He remained on the Advisory Committee dealing with alien refugee doctors, and at no time would allow his name to be used as a "rubber stamp" in the proceedings. In May 1940 he took a firm stand against the suggested policy of allowing an unlimited number of doctors and medical students of German origin on qualifying in this country to engage in practice unless they became naturalised British subjects, or unless their parents or guardians were naturalised. This was for fear of them being German spies. He protested to the Chairman, Sir Robert Hutchison, about the incorrect reporting of the minutes of a committee meeting by a secretary who was no more than a junior Home Office official. On discovering that the same official was actually putting across to the committee his own personal views as representing those of the Home Office, Willcox protested to Sir John Anderson and persuaded his friend Sir Ernest Graham Little to raise a question in Parliament about the precautions being taken by the Home Office to prevent enemy agents being admitted to Britain alongside alien doctors.

During the first six months of the war, the so-called "phoney" war, certain deficiencies became apparent in planning for the expected air raid casualties and military casualties on a vast scale. Willcox took part (June 1st) in a lengthy correspondence in *The Times*, initiated by Sir Morton Smart, criticising the Ministry of Health for the lack of proper organisation for physiotherapy services, and urging the provision of equipment for the whole country and the full employment of all trained physiotherapists in readiness for the thousands of civilian and military casualties that would require treatment within a short time.

By a curious chance, the last occasion on which Willcox appeared to give evidence in a court of law was in the Divorce Court on June 12th, 1940. For him it was a unique experience, for he had never before given expert evidence in a case of divorce or of any matrimonial dispute.

The case was that of a young man, a wealthy and titled aristocrat, who petitioned for the annulment of his marriage. The circumstances surrounding the marriage in May 1939 were, at any rate to Willcox, unprecedented, interesting and amusing, though the consequences of the marriage were tragic enough.

The petitioner alleged that when he went through the marriage ceremony in London he was in such an acute state of alcoholism that he was unaware that he was being married. The wife contested the suit, and in a cross-petition sought a decree for the restitution of conjugal rights.

Sir Patrick Hastings had sought Willcox's opinion at a consultation, attended by the petitioner, held a month after the marriage, the case having therefore been *sub judice* for a year. To Hastings the case appeared, if not unique, an extremely difficult one in which the medical evidence was clearly of supreme importance. Could the mind and judgment of a man be so impaired by alcoholic intoxication that he was unaware of being married and, if so, would this be accepted in a court of law as an excuse for an annulment?

At this meeting the full story came out. The petitioner had had an unusually gay evening, a dinner party and ball, followed by visits to two night clubs in the company of a lady. During the course of the night and the following morning, after staying at the flat of the lady's married sister, he consumed a large amount of champagne and some brandy. He claimed, and the subsequent evidence tended to show, that he was under its influence at the time of the wedding held at an Anglican Church, he being a Roman Catholic; that he had been persuaded by the lady and her sister to enter a hastily arranged marriage without the knowledge of his relatives or friends; and that his volition was so impaired that he was unaware of what was going on at the time of the marriage.

To Hastings and Willcox there seemed no doubt that this easy-going and easily influenced young man had been in fact enticed into marriage hastily arranged, without the consent of his mother, by a lady ambitious to acquire wealth and position in society. The case seemed to them to be a challenge worth taking up in the cause of justice and truth.

In order that a marriage should be valid, Hastings argued, it was necessary that the parties should consent to marry one another, and a marriage brought about by fraudulent means over a person in a state of alcoholic intoxication or other poisoning, would be voidable as having been contracted without real consent. But the degree of intoxication required by the courts would need to be such as to have produced a state of mind where the person desiring to avoid the marriage had not been able to understand the nature of the contract of marriage to which he had become a party. It was in this context that the medical evidence carried weight.

Willcox's immediate answer was that a man could be so confused by alcohol that he became an easy prey to be enticed into a sudden marriage and could have a confused memory of what had taken place. Nevertheless, he was not prepared to say so in court without the support of an expert psychiatrist.

In due course a consultation was held at Welbeck Street, attended by the petitioner's doctor who had attended him since the age of ten, and Dr. G. W. B. James, the St. Mary's Hospital psychiatrist, and colleague of Willcox.

The petitioner had been a delicate asthmatic boy and had had three serious accidents causing concussion. The last one—two years previously— while serving as a guards officer had rendered him unfit for further military service.

The three experts concluded that there was evidence to show, both in this case and in others, that following head injuries causing concussion, susceptibility to the effects of alcohol is often enhanced, and that asthma may have a similar effect. The alcohol consumed by the petitioner on the morning of the marriage and on the previous night amounted to a total of four bottles of champagne, an unknown amount of brandy, and a glass of port. Their report went on to say that the absence of acute inebriation and the apparent normality of gait and speech at the time of the wedding was due to the lengthy period during which alcohol had been consumed— until noon on the wedding day. And at this time the petitioner's volition, judgment and memory of events was likely to have been seriously impaired.

From the legal standpoint, the weakness in the case for the petitioner lay in his behaviour after the marriage, his cohabitation with the wife and her subsequent pregnancy. Within two days the marriage was, from a practical point of view, terminated when the petitioner abandoned his wife and returned to his mother. Nevertheless, the case was fought for three days before the petition was dismissed.

During the last year of his life Willcox's activities became restricted both by the decline in his health, and by the increasingly serious and disturbing air raids. He and Mildred decided to remain at Welbeck Street, come what may. His sister Minnie, ex-Matron of King's College Hospital and now Deputy Matron-in-chief of the British Red Cross, was now living there. The only remaining domestic staff were Kate Compton, who had served the family for over thirty-five years, and Mrs. Honeyfield, the cook. They all shared the same indomitable courage and none sought the refuge of air raid shelters during those terrible nights of the London blitz. As far as possible "business as usual" still applied to the simplified life they led. Dick (R.R.) Willcox noted in his diary a visit to Welbeck Street with his wife Sadie (ex-Sister of Prince's Ward at St. Mary's) on the evening of December 3rd, 1940. "Tonight's blitz very noisy till 10 p.m. Dinner consisted of tomato soup, soused herrings, guinea fowl, apricots and custard, Stilton cheese, beer and port. O.K. for war-time".

A few nights later came one of the longest of London's raids—$13\frac{1}{2}$ hours. Several windows of 40, Welbeck Street were broken by the explosion of a land mine a mile away. Nevertheless, Willcox still continued to see patients in his own home. Neither the blitz nor ill health prevented him from wielding his pen.

When he heard of the plan of the Ministry of Food to supplement white flour in bread by adding Vitamin B1, he wrote to *The Lancet* (January 25th) urging the consumption of wholemeal flour in all bread by doing away with the white loaf and substituting a loaf containing at least 75% of whole meal flour—a step which would mean the incorporation of other vitamins (B2, B6, A and E) into bread consumed by the whole population. Recalling the outbreak of Beriberi among British troops on a restricted diet in Mesopotamia in 1917, he drew attention in his letter to its control by the introduction of Marmite in the diet and of wholemeal flour mixed with equal parts of white flour in bread supplied to the troops. Again, he tried to convert public opinion in another letter to the magazine "Food" (April 1941) by urging the necessity of his suggestion in view of "the stress of war and the difficulty of obtaining the usual articles of a peacetime diet as a result of which the composition of bread has become a subject of great national importance".

From another severe heart attack at the end of March—it was exactly a year since the first—he again survived, thanks to the care he received in the Lindo Wing of St. Mary's. But the drain on his strength was greater now. He lost weight and became more depressed by the course of the war. But his mental activity remained unimpaired and his courage undaunted. The April raids on Britain accounted for over six thousand killed, and more than that number injured and in hospital. He succeeded in dealing with an incendiary bomb on his house, which did little damage except to his secretary's room. The same night two other houses in the street were ruined, one bombed out, the other completely burnt down, while another nearby house in Queen Anne Street was in ruins. At least two of his colleagues, Graham Little and F. W. Price, the editor of the Text Book of Medicine, lost their homes nearby, though mercifully no one was injured.

In May and June he attended Committee meetings of the Empire Rheumatism Council and the Medical Sickness Assurance Society, the Apothecaries Society Court, and the Pharmaceutical Society examinations held at Brighton. On January 14th, Mildred drove him down to Taplow to enjoy once more, and for the last time, the kind hospitality of Professor and Mrs. Grey Turner at Huntercombe Manor.

The Last Report. Rex v. *Mareo*

To the end of his life Willcox's mental faculties remained unimpaired. His shrewd judgment was illustrated five days before he died, in his last medico-legal report on the New Zealand poisoning case, *Rex* v *Mareo*. It was strangely appropriate that it concerned a case of homicidal poisoning by veronal, where expert knowledge of toxicology was destined to play a part.

If Willcox had lived a year or two longer the fate of poor Mareo might have been less tragic and cruel than it turned out to be. At the time of his death he was most interested in the outcome of the case; no doubt he would have regarded it as a great challenge to struggle hard for this unfortunate man in whose innocence he firmly believed.

Eric Mareo, the conductor of an orchestra in a theatrical company, went to Australia in 1931. In the course of his work he met his future second wife Thelma—an actress. In 1933 they were married in New Zealand. His daughter and son joined them there in 1934. Both Eric and Thelma were addicted to alcohol, no doubt as a result of the irregular life they led—late hours, irregular meals and uncertainty of employment. Thelma was said to have homosexual tendencies, and from the evidence was certainly a barbiturate addict, while Eric had made purchases of veronal in the spring of 1935. Thelma died from barbiturate poisoning on April 15th, 1935. Eric was charged with the murder of his wife in 1936, convicted and sentenced to death, but at a retrial the same year the sentence was altered to life imprisonment. The result of the trial excited a great wave of criticism and concern in influential circles in New Zealand for several years.

Willcox was consulted on May 20th, 1941, by Mr. Maurice Smith, the solicitor instructed by Mareo's sympathisers in New Zealand, with the request to review the medical evidence and make an affidavit if, to use Smith's own words, "it happens that your views should be helpful to the prisoner". The history of the case having been discussed, Willcox was supplied with depositions and evidence of the two trials. He somewhat vaguely remembered having been consulted about the case two years earlier.

We must now go back to August 1939 when Sir James Elliott, the noted New Zealand surgeon, visited England carrying instructions from Mareo's counsel, Mr. Humphrey O'Leary, K.C., to spare time to consult Willcox and seek his help to obtain a reprisal of the trial. He saw Willcox at Welbeck Street on August 25th. Elliott and O'Leary firmly believed, as did many others, that Mrs. Mareo's death had been caused by misadventure or suicide, and that there had been a miscarriage of justice. It was known that Thelma had threatened suicide fearing she was pregnant. They considered that the evidence of the doctor in attendance, Dr. Gilmour, had received inadequate attention at the first trial. A crucial part of his opinion was that "once a person wakens after having taken a dose of veronal he will not again relapse into coma without a further dose. This view was that of the noted authority Sir William Willcox".

Willcox told Elliott that Gilmour had been perfectly correct in his testimony and he entirely agreed with it. A large dose of 100 grains of veronal would produce coma without return to consciousness, and a 30–50 grain dose would produce coma followed by a confused state of mind in which the patient might take further fatal doses without remembering having done so.

Willcox reported to Maurice Smith on July 4th, 1941—four days before he died—that he had not the slightest doubt about his opinion and would willingly sign an affidavit as soon as it was prepared—a step which was never fulfilled.

His survey and assessment of the evidence would have done credit to the summing up of any judge. It is too lengthy to quote in detail but certain points merit attention.

A doctor who had examined Thelma in March 1935, found her "shaking and trembling, likely to commit suicide", in a severe psychoneurotic breakdown due to alcoholic excess which would make the taking of a powerful sedative, such as a barbiturate, almost a necessity. The veronal habit would follow at once, the drug being taken to counteract the depression and to promote sleep, leading to the state of automatism first described by Willcox and Purves Stewart in 1934 (*Lancet*, March 10th, 1934). In this case there was evidence of access and purchase of the drug. Thelma had been continuously under the influence of veronal for the last three days of her life and no treatment to eliminate the poison had been given. About forty hours before death a friend (who was staying in the house at the time) had given sal volatile which would unwittingly have hastened the absorption of the drug. The clinical and post-mortem findings of hypostatic pneumonia were entirely consistent with self-administration of a fatal dose at about 8 a.m. on the Saturday morning, and that at least 100 grains had been taken during the last three days to account for her death at 5.30 p.m. on Monday, April 15th.

It was not until 1946, when sufficient funds became available through the kindness of Mareo's supporters, that his case was heard before the Court of Appeal at Wellington, but his appeal was dismissed. After spending twelve years in prison he was released in 1948 and subsequently died of natural causes.

Mr. Maurice Smith has recently (May, 1969) recalled Willcox's opinion that there had been a miscarriage of justice and the importance he attached to the administration of sal volatile which would have tended to hasten the solution and absorption of any veronal present in the stomach at the time it was given. Roche Lynch, who was consulted by Smith shortly after Willcox's death, agreed with this view, adding that Willcox was the leading toxicologist in this country and one of the three most eminent in the world.

It is certain that had he survived a year or two longer, Willcox would have struggled hard to rectify on Mareo's behalf what he felt sure had been a sad miscarriage of justice. It is interesting to speculate on the steps he would have taken. Perhaps, by using his influence with the Privy Council or through the Court of Criminal Appeal, he might have succeeded in shortening Mareo's term of imprisonment by five years or more. Who can say?

Willcox died in harness. On July 1st, he went to Brighton for the Pharmaceutical Society examinations and was due to go to Cardiff on July 10th for the same duties. He attended an Empire Rheumatism Council meeting on July 3rd, and two days later discussed research projects with Will Copeman, Fortescue Fox and Mervyn Gordon over lunch at the Athenaeum.

Mildred, on whom he had come to rely more and more during the last few months whereas formerly he had been the dominant partner all through their married life, noted in her diary the warm fine weather and the peace and quiet in the air over London of those last four days. In the evening she drove him to Queen Mary's Gardens, where they sat together in the cool of the evening till 11 p.m., he quietly reading a book on Persia. Then he returned to his desk for the last time. In the middle of the Sunday night of July 7th, he had a sudden stroke and never regained consciousness. On his desk was his partially written article promised for "The Medical Press and Circular" on the History of St. Mary's Hospital. On the early afternoon of July 8th, to use a phrase of his friend Marshall Hall, that little spark of life went out.

At the funeral service the large Parish Church of St. Marylebone, which he had supported for so many years and attended the previous Sunday morning, was packed with relatives, doctors, nurses, and friends in the Church and the Law, together with representatives of many organisations and hospitals. Of the family, only John, the engineer, was absent, still working in Ecuador before he joined the Army. Fourteen years before, Sir Edward Marshall Hall's funeral was held in the same church and had been equally well attended.

The death of any popular man of integrity and good will is attended by generous tributes. In this case they came from far and wide and from almost every walk of life. He had never been a favourite of the Press, as the good looking Spilsbury had been for so long, perhaps because for obvious reasons he had been intentionally cold and aloof, or because, considering himself unphotogenic, he had been shocked by some press photographs of the distant past. But the *Daily Mirror* paid a glowing tribute, referring to years long past before the Great War, in its obituary headed "The King's Poisoner is dead" which revealed for the first time the nickname he had earned among reporters because, they said, he probably knew more about poisons than any other man and gave evidence in so many trials.

"No more will sealed glass jars be brought to his laboratory, holding grim relics which were shown by him to speak their tale of a man's burst of insane anger or a woman's jealousy. No more will defending counsel vainly seek to break down that patient composure, to shatter the cold record of scientific fact by a more theatrical unscientific attack. And never again will a guilty man, steeling himself to show confidence before a hundred critical eyes, hear with a shudder the quiet dispassionate sentences which have so often brought an edifice of pitiable lies crashing to ruin".

But those who had known only of the part he played in criminal cases to bring culprits to their trials and convictions gained an entirely false impression of his character. In these pages are recorded some of his efforts to see justice done for those unjustly treated. In law he always stood up for the truth, and justice tempered with mercy. "In court", he said at a meeting of the West London Medico-chirurgical Society in 1935, "the medical man should give evidence on the side of justice and truth. The doctor was in court to speak the truth, the lawyer to conduct his case".

Willcox once quoted at the Medico-legal Society what his patient and friend, Sir Richard Muir, had told him shortly before his death in 1924. Muir was considered the greatest criminal lawyer of his time. "I have been at the law for many years and in all kinds of cases. But what has impressed itself upon me all my life has been that, though in court you hear all sorts of lies told, in the end truth always prevails". But both would have agreed from their experience that, though truth always prevailed, justice had not always been done. Nevertheless, it was the duty of the law to reconcile justice with truth.

Roche Lynch in "The Analyst" wrote of his thoroughness and steadfast convictions, his loyalty, generosity and kindness to so many people; of his help to young doctors and chemists in their careers and to his colleagues in their practices. Willcox considered each individual of supreme importance in the community. Dr. Cecil Rutherford recently recalled his association with Willcox at Mudros when he served as a young R.A.M.C. officer in 1915, the thoroughness and unassuming humility with which he discussed every patient brought to his notice. Similar tributes were paid by nurses and patients.

Among his records were found tributes received several years before he died. Here are two examples. A patient who had served in Mesopotamia, Major George Pirie, wrote in 1933 to thank him for the benefits of his consultation: "Since I saw you I have been feeling very fit. The C-in-C, General Sir William Marshall, once told me that you were one of the kindest men he had ever met and I heartily endorse that". And the

Homeopathy-Physician, George Burford, in thanking him for a Christmas card wrote in more prosaic style: "Such a life as your own no biographer could fitly evaluate, for its influence extends the world over. The uplift you have given to personalities and to causes from time to time only those can adequately appreciate who have received it. Of the former I am proud to reckon myself one and of the latter, an admiring constituent. O Si Sic Omnes".

Though he never visited the United States except on the world tour in 1935, his name was widely known there. One of the most glowing tributes came from Dr. Richard Miller of Boston, and appeared in the Journal of the American Medical Association of December 27th, 1941. He had never met Willcox, though he had served in the American forces in the Great War. His outline of the part that Willcox had played in Mesopotamia ended thus: "The story of the devastating war in Meso-potamia is now seldom thought of, but in all the firmament of military medicine the star of Sir William Willcox will shine as brightly as any other".

Willcox was a generous and big-minded man. A year or two before he died he had a disagreement with one of his colleagues, and struggled successfully to obtain a generous enough pension for the retiring paid secretary of a learned society. It was an example of his view that a labourer is worthy of his hire if he has done his life's work well. And again, writing to Philip on his 29th birthday: "The great thing in professional work is to know your job well and to be above all these pettifogging jealousies and gossiping. I hate humbug as you know". One knew exactly what he meant. It cost him five pounds to say this and he enclosed a note in his letter.

What imprint did he leave on the sands of time? His name is not perpetuated in any disease he discovered or instrument he devised, but is recorded in the annals of the law; as the author of articles in encyclo-pedias, medical journals, transactions of societies, and chapters of books of his time; and for his encouragement and help to younger members of his profession in their careers. Few in his profession exerted an influence so powerful, in so many spheres for so long a period. Neither he nor Mildred was a believer in memorials. They were sometimes amused by epitaphs on tombstones which fade with the lapse of time.

Index